Exploring maths

Class Book

PEARSON
Longman

Anita Straker, Tony Fisher, Rosalyn Hyde, Sue Jennings and Jonathan Longstaffe

5

Contents

Powers and roots

This unit will help you to:

◉ calculate whole-number powers of numbers;

◉ estimate square roots;

◉ write a number as the product of its prime factors;

◉ find the highest common factor (the HCF) of two numbers;

◉ find the lowest common multiple (the LCM) of two numbers.

1 Integer powers of numbers

This lesson will help you to work out integer powers of numbers and use the power keys of a calculator.

Exercise 1

The short way to write $2 \times 2 \times 2 \times 2 \times 2$ is as 2^5, or '2 to the power 5'.

The small number 5 is called the **index**.
An index can be negative as well as positive. For example:

$$9^{-2} = \frac{1}{9 \times 9} = \frac{1}{81}$$

The calculator key to find powers of numbers looks like this: $\boxed{x^y}$.

Example 1   Find the value of 6^4.

Key in $\boxed{6}\boxed{x^y}\boxed{4}\boxed{=}$. The display shows the answer: `1296`

To multiply two numbers in index form, add the indices, so $a^m \times a^n = a^{m+n}$.

Example 2   Simplify $3^4 \times 3^2$.

$3^4 \times 3^2 = 3^{4+2} = 3^6$

To divide two numbers in index form, subtract the indices, so $a^m \div a^n = a^{m-n}$.

Example 3   Simplify $5^3 \div 5^2$.

$5^3 \div 5^2 = 5^{3-2} = 5^1 = 5$

1 Write each expression in index form.

   a $2 \times 2 \times 2$ **b** $4 \times 4 \times 4 \times 4 \times 4$

   c $3 \times 3 \times 3 \times 3 \times 3 \times 3 \times 3 \times 3$ **d** $(-1) \times (-1) \times (-1) \times (-1)$

   e $\dfrac{1}{5 \times 5}$ **f** $\dfrac{1}{6}$

2 Work out each value **without using your calculator**. Show your working.

   a 2^6 **b** $(-3)^5$ **c** 4^4 **d** $(-2)^7$

   e 12^0 **f** $(-1)^{17}$ **g** 4^{-2} **h** 5^{-3}

3 **Use your calculator** to work out each value.

   Where appropriate, give your answer correct to two decimal places.

   a 7^4 **b** 5^6 **c** 11^3 **d** 3^9

   e $(-2)^{10}$ **f** 1.5^6 **g** 31.8^3 **h** $1.78^5 + 10.3^4$

4 Simplify these.

   a $2^5 \times 2^3$ **b** $3^4 \times 3$ **c** $10^2 \times 10^2$ **d** $a^5 \times a^3$

   e $5^6 \div 5^2$ **f** $12^5 \div 12$ **g** $8^4 \div 8^4$ **h** $b^5 \div b^2$

5 A palindromic number reads the same forwards and backwards.
Copy and complete this cross-number puzzle.

Across	**Down**
1 A square number	1 23×5
3 A square palindromic number	2 A multiple of 13
4 A cube number	

6 Some numbers can be written as the sum of three square numbers.
For example:

$$35 = 5^2 + 3^2 + 1^2$$

Write each of these numbers as the sum of three square numbers.

   a 19   **b** 41   **c** 50

   d 65   **e** 75   **f** 94

7 Rachel is 3 years older than her sister Hannah.
The sum of the squares of their ages in years is 317.
How old are Rachel and Hannah?

Extension problem

 8 Find the two smallest whole numbers where the difference of their squares is a cube, and the difference of their cubes is a square.

Points to remember

⊙ The number 2 raised to the power 4 is 2^4 or $2 \times 2 \times 2 \times 2$.
4 is called the **index** or **power**, and 2^4 is written in **index form**.

⊙ To multiply numbers in index form, add the indices, so $a^m \times a^n = a^{m+n}$.

⊙ To divide numbers in index form, subtract the indices, so $a^m \div a^n = a^{m-n}$.

⊙ A negative number raised to an even power is positive.
A negative number raised to an odd power is negative.

2 Estimating square roots

This lesson will help you to estimate square roots and to use the root keys of a calculator.

Exercise 2

$\sqrt{n}$ is the **square root** of n. For example, $\sqrt{81} = \pm 9$.

You can find positive square roots on a calculator.

Example 1

To find $\sqrt{81}$, press $\boxed{8}\,\boxed{1}\,\boxed{\sqrt{}}$.   The display shows the answer: $\boxed{\qquad\qquad 9}$

On some calculators you press the square-root key first: $\boxed{\sqrt{}}\,\boxed{8}\,\boxed{1}$

Some calculators have a **cube-root** key $\boxed{\sqrt[3]{}}$.

Example 2

To find $\sqrt[3]{64}$, press $\boxed{8}\,\boxed{1}\,\boxed{\sqrt[3]{}}$.   The display shows the answer: $\boxed{\qquad\qquad 4}$

You can **estimate** the positive square root of a number that is not a perfect square.

Example 3

Estimate the value of $\sqrt{70}$.

$\sqrt{70}$ must lie between $\sqrt{64}$ and $\sqrt{81}$, so $8 < \sqrt{70} < 9$.
Since 70 is closer to 64 than to 81, we expect $\sqrt{70}$ to be closer to 8 than to 9.

An estimate is 8.4.

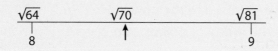

You can **estimate** the value of a square root more accurately using **trial and improvement**.

Example 4

Solve $a^2 = 135$.

Value of a	Value of a^2		
11	121	too small	
12	144	too big	a is between 11 and 12.
11.5	132.25	too small	a is between 11.5 and 12.
11.6	134.56	too small	a is between 11.6 and 12.
11.7	136.89	too big	a is between 11.6 and 11.7.
11.65	135.7225	too big	a is between 11.6 and 11.65.

So a must lie on the number line between 11.6 and 11.65.

Numbers between 11.6 and 11.65 round down to 11.6 to 1 d.p, so $a = 11.6$ to 1 d.p.

(1) Write two solutions to each of these equations.

    a $x^2 = 9$ **b** $x^2 = 49$ **c** $x^2 = 144$ **d** $x^2 = 1$

(2) Write the value of each of these expressions. **Use a calculator** to help you.
    Where appropriate, give your answer correct to two decimal places.

    a $\sqrt{2}$ **b** $\sqrt[3]{10}$ **c** $\sqrt[3]{(-64)}$ **d** $\sqrt{0.04}$

    e $\sqrt[3]{(-125)}$ **f** $\sqrt{1.5}$ **g** $\sqrt{3}$ **h** $\sqrt[3]{(-1)}$

3 Estimate the integer that is closest to the positive value of each of these.

   a $\sqrt{6}$ **b** $\sqrt{45}$ **c** $\sqrt{115}$ **d** $\sqrt{70}$

4 **Use your calculator** to find the positive value of each of the square roots in question **3**. Give your answers correct to one decimal place.

5 A square patio is to be paved with square paving slabs. Only whole slabs will be used.

The paving slabs come in packs of 50. 15 packs of slabs are needed to make sure that there are enough slabs.

How many slabs are used?

6 Solve these equations by using trial and improvement. Make a table to help you. Give your answers to one decimal place.

   a $a^2 = 95$ **b** $a^2 = 152$ **c** $a^2 = 415$

7 The area of this square rug is 15 m². Use trial and improvement to find the length of a side correct to two decimal places.

Extension problem

8 What is the smallest square number that begins with three 8s?

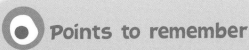

Points to remember

⊙ $\sqrt{n}$ is the square root of n, for example $\sqrt{81} = \pm 9$.

⊙ $\sqrt[3]{n}$ is the cube root of n, for example $\sqrt[3]{125} = 5$, $\sqrt[3]{-27} = -3$.

3 Prime factor decomposition

This lesson will help you to:

- write a number as the product of its prime factors;
- find the highest common factor (the HCF) of two numbers;
- find the lowest common multiple (the LCM) of two numbers.

 Did you know that...?

The Greek mathematician **Euclid** proved in about 300 BC what is called the Fundamental Theorem of Arithmetic.

This shows that every integer can be written as a product of prime factors in only one way.

Exercise 3

You can use a **division or ladder method** to find the **prime factors** of a number.

Example 1   The prime factors of 75 are $5 \times 5 \times 3 = 5^2 \times 3$.

The prime factors of 24 are $3 \times 2 \times 2 \times 2 = 3 \times 2^3$.

```
3 | 75        3 | 24
5 | 25        2 | 8
5 |  5        2 | 4
      1       2 | 2
                  1
```

You can also use a **tree method** to find the **prime factors** of a number.

Example 2

The prime factors of 48 are $2 \times 2 \times 2 \times 2 \times 3 = 2^4 \times 3$.

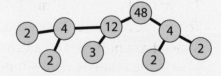

You can use prime factors to find the **highest common factor** (HCF) and the **lowest common multiple** (LCM) of two numbers.

Example 3

The prime factors of 72 are $2 \times 2 \times 2 \times 3 \times 3$.
The prime factors of 60 are $5 \times 3 \times 2 \times 2$.
These are shown on the Venn diagram.
The overlapping or common prime factors give the **HCF**:

$2 \times 2 \times 3 = 2^2 \times 3 = 12$

All the prime factors give the **LCM**:

$2 \times 2 \times 2 \times 3 \times 3 \times 5 = 2^3 \times 3^2 \times 5 = 360$

1. The number 18 can be written as the product of prime factors.

$$18 = 2 \times 3 \times 3 = 2 \times 3^2$$

Write each of these numbers as the product of prime factors.

a 12   b 15   c 21   d 24   e 27   f 54

2. a List all the factors of 50.

b Write 50 as the product of prime factors.

3. a List all the factors of 45.

b Write 45 as the product of prime factors.

4. Find a number bigger than 50 that has the same number of factors as 50.

5. Using the Venn diagrams below, work out the HCF and LCM of:

a 72 and 30   b 50 and 80   c 48 and 84

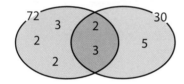 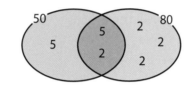 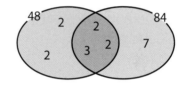

6. The prime factors of 120 are 2, 2, 2, 3 and 5.
The prime factors of 75 are 3, 5 and 5.
Show these numbers on a Venn diagram.
Use the diagram to work out the HCF and LCM of 120 and 75.

7. The prime factors of 40 are 2, 2, 2 and 5.
The prime factors of 90 are 2, 3, 3 and 5.
Show these numbers on a Venn diagram.
Use the diagram to work out the HCF and LCM of 40 and 90.

8. a Which prime numbers are factors of both 42 and 54?

b What is the biggest number that is a factor of both 42 and 54?

c What is the smallest number that is a multiple of both 42 and 54?

9. Find the HCF and LCM of:

a 28 and 40   b 200 and 175   c 36 and 64

10. A four-digit number is a multiple of 21 and a multiple of 35.
What is the smallest number that it could be?

Extension problems

 11 **a** What is the smallest number with exactly 3 factors?

b What is the smallest number with exactly 5 factors?

c What is the smallest number with exactly 7 factors? Exactly 9 factors? 11 factors? 13 factors?

12 Seven friends are having lunch at the same café.

The first one eats there every day,
the second every other day,
the third every third day,
the fourth every fourth day,
the fifth every fifth day,
the sixth every sixth day,
and the seventh once a week on the same day.

The next time they all meet at the café they are planning to have a lunch party.
In how many days from now will the lunch party be?

⊙ Points to remember

- Writing a number as the product of its prime factors is its **prime factor decomposition.**

  For example, $24 = 2 \times 2 \times 2 \times 3$ or $2^3 \times 3$.

- The **highest common factor** (HCF) of a pair of numbers is the largest number that is a factor of each number.

  For example, $8 = 2 \times 2 \times 2$ and $12 = 2 \times 2 \times 3$.
  The highest common factor is 2×2.

- The **lowest common multiple** (LCM) of a pair of numbers is the smallest number that is a multiple of each number.

  For example, $8 = 2 \times 2 \times 2$ and $12 = 2 \times 2 \times 3$.
  The lowest common multiple of 8 and 12 is $2 \times 2 \times 2 \times 3 = 24$.

How well are you doing?

Can you:

- work out whole-number powers of numbers?
- estimate square roots?
- write a number as the product of its prime factors?
- find the highest common factor (the HCF) of two numbers?
- find the lowest common multiple (the LCM) of two numbers?

Powers and roots (no calculator)

1 *2006 level 6*

a Put these values in order of size with the smallest first.

$$5^2 \qquad 3^2 \qquad 3^3 \qquad 2^4$$

b Look at this information.

5^5 is 3125

What is 5^7?

2 *2001 level 6*

a Look at these numbers.

| 1^6 | 2^5 | 3^4 | 4^3 | 5^2 | 6^1 |

Which is the largest?

Which is equal to 9^2?

b Which two of the numbers below are not square numbers?

| 2^4 | 2^5 | 2^6 | 2^7 | 2^8 |

3 Work out the value of each expression.

a $3^7 \div 3^5$　　　　　　b $2^4 \times 2^3$　　　　　　c $\dfrac{3^4 \times 2^5}{3^2 \times 2^4}$

4 Look at these equations.

a $24 = 3 \times 2^a$

What is the value of a?

b $28 = 7 \times 2^b$

What is the value of b?

5 a Find the highest common factor of 84 and 60.

b Find the lowest common multiple of 16 and 36.

Powers and roots (calculator allowed)

6 Suzy thinks of a number.

She uses her calculator to square the number and then adds 5.

Her answer is 29.01.

What is Suzy's number?

7 The three numbers missing from the boxes are different prime numbers bigger than 3.

$$\square \times \square \times \square = 1045$$

What are the missing prime numbers?

Sequences and graphs

This unit will help you to:

- generate sequences from rules;
- find the nth term of a linear sequence;
- explore linear sequences using a spreadsheet;
- sketch, draw and interpret graphs of linear equations;
- explore linear graphs of real-life contexts.

1 Generating sequences

This lesson will help you to use rules to generate sequences.

Exercise 1

A **sequence** of numbers follows a rule.

You can generate a sequence if you know its **term-to-term rule**.

For example, if the first term is 3 and the term-to-term rule is 'add 7', then the sequence is 3, 10, 17, 24, …

You can also generate a sequence if you know the formula for the nth term.
This is called its **position-to-term rule**.

For example, if the formula is $T_n = 2n + 1$, then the sequence is 3, 5, 7, 9, …

You can use the formula for the nth term to calculate any given term.

For example, if the formula for the nth term is $T_n = 4n - 3$, the 25th term is 97.

You can use a calculator or computer to generate a sequence.

1 Write the term-to-term rule for each sequence.
Then write the next five terms.

a 2, 9, 16, 23, ...

b 55, 50, 45, 40, ...

c 3, 1, −1, −3, ...

d 2.0, 1.7, 1.4, 1.1, ...

e 64, 32, 16, 8, ...

f $\frac{1}{3}$ 1, 3, 9, ...

2 Write down the first five terms of each sequence.

	1st term	Term-to-term rule
a	5	add 12
b	0	subtract 3
c	100	multiply by 2
d	15	add 0.9
e	1	multiply by 3 and subtract 2
f	−5	add 4 and multiply by 2
g	0.5	multiply by 4 and subtract 2
h	4096	divide by 8

3 In each of these sequences, the difference between consecutive terms is always the same.
Copy each sequence. Replace each box by the term of the sequence.

a 3, ☐, ☐, 12, 15, ☐, ☐

b ☐, ☐, ☐, 52, 59, ☐, 73

c −18, ☐, ☐, −3, ☐, 7

d 78, ☐, ☐, ☐, 50, ☐, 36

e 0.3, ☐, ☐, 3.0, ☐, ☐, 5.7

f ☐, −9, ☐, ☐, ☐, −3, ☐

g −20, ☐, ☐, ☐, −18, ☐, ☐

4 Each expression is the *n*th term of a sequence.
Use it to generate the first five terms for the sequence.

a 9*n*

b 4*n* + 3

c 2*n* − 1

d 5*n* + 2

e 3*n* + 5

f 6*n* − 3

g 0.5*n* + 2

h 0.5*n* − 1

i 0.1*n* + 0.5

j 200 − 3*n*

5 Use the formula for the *n*th term of a sequence to work out the given term.

	*n*th term	Find this term
a	5*n*	80th
b	3*n* + 7	36th
c	6*n* − 1	23rd
d	14*n* + 9	84th
e	500 − 3*n*	150th
f	156 − 7*n*	30th
g	0.25*n* + 0.3	16th
h	10*n* + 4	9th
i	7*n* − 5	4th
j	0.5*n* − 0.1	25th

6 Here are three arrangements of bathroom tiles.
For each pattern work out how many grey tiles are needed for 100 green tiles.

a

b

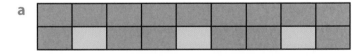

c

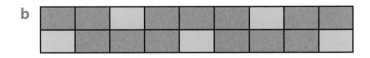

7 Write whether each of these sequences is finite or infinite.

    a The sequence of multiples of 11

    b The sequence of even numbers between 0 and 100

    c The sequence of multiples of 8 greater than 48

    d The sequence of square numbers less than 25

Extension problems

 8 Work out the term-to-term rules for each sequence.
Write the next three terms.

    a 0, 1, 5, 21, ...   **b** 1, 2, 5, 14, ...

    c 2, −2, 2, −2, ...   **d** 1, 0, −5, −30, ...

    e 5, 14, 32, 68, ...   **f** 36, 20, 12, 8, ...

9 Use the formula for the nth term of a sequence to work out the given term.

	nth term	Find this term
a	n^2	9th
b	$2n^2 + n$	7th
c	$n^2 - n$	10th
d	n^3	3rd
e	$n^3 + 4$	2nd
f	$n^3 + n^2$	5th
g	$n^3 - n$	7th
h	$n + n^2 + n^3$	1st

⦿ Points to remember

⊙ A sequence of numbers follows a rule.

⊙ You can generate a sequence if you know the first term and the **term-to-term rule**.

⊙ You can also generate a sequence if you know the formula for the nth term. This is called the **position-to-term rule**.

⊙ A **linear sequence** has the same difference between consecutive terms.

2 Making generalisations

This lesson will help you to find a formula for the nth term of a linear sequence.

Exercise 2

In a **linear sequence**, the difference between consecutive terms is always the same.

You can work out the formula for the nth term of a linear sequence if you know the difference between consecutive terms.

Example

Find the nth term in the sequence 3, 7, 11, 15, 19, …

Term	1	2	3	4	5	…
Sequence	3	7	11	15	19	…
Difference		4	4	4	4	…

The sequence is increasing so the coefficient of n in the nth term is 4.
The formula for the nth term is $4n - 1$.

Check your formula using substitution.
For example, when $n = 5$, the 5th term is $4 \times 5 - 1 = 19$.

1. Work out the difference between each term of these sequences.
   Use it to work out the formula for the nth term.
   In each case, check that your answer is correct.

   a 1, 3, 5, 7, 9, …   b 2, 7, 12, 17, 22, …

   c 5, 9, 13, 17, 21, …   d 10, 16, 22, 28, 34, …

   e 2, 12, 22, 32, 42, …   f −3, 0, 3, 6, 9, …

   g −4, −2, 0, 2, 4, …   h 0.5, 4.5, 8.5, 12.5, 16.5, …

   i 5, 14, 23, 32, 41, …   j 9, 11, 13, 15, 17, …

2. Work out the difference between each term of these sequences.
   Use it to work out the formula for the nth term.
   In each case, check that your answer is correct.

   a 1.5, 2, 2.5, 3, 3.5, …   b 0.5, 0.7, 0.9, 1.1, 1.3, …

   c $\frac{4}{5}$, $\frac{5}{5}$, $\frac{6}{5}$, $\frac{7}{5}$, $\frac{8}{5}$ …   d $\frac{2}{3}$, $\frac{3}{3}$, $\frac{4}{3}$, $\frac{5}{3}$, $\frac{6}{3}$ …

(3) Work out the formula for the nth term of these sequences.
Use the formula to find the given term.

Find this term

a 3, 5, 7, 9, 11, …   25th

b 1, 5, 9, 13, 17, …   46th

c 9, 14, 19, 24, 29, …   100th

d 10, 13, 16, 19, 22, …   43rd

e 5, 11, 17, 23, 29, …   22nd

f 9, 16, 23, 30, 37, …   95th

g 2, 5, 8, 11, 14, …   36th

h 9, 13, 17, 21, 25, …   72nd

(4) a S & M make cakes for special occasions.
They put a decorative wrapping around each cake.

One of their cakes is made in the shape of a regular octagon with side x cm.
They need an extra 1 cm to fix the wrapping around the cake.

Work out a formula for the length of wrapping needed for each cake.

b If x is 6 cm, how much wrapping do they need for each cake?

c How much wrapping do they need to order for 250 cakes?

(5) a Carrie makes shirts for the Straw Factory.
She earns a basic wage of £150 a week plus
£2.20 for every shirt that she makes.

Write a formula for the amount she earns
when she makes n shirts a week.

b One week Carrie makes 105 shirts.
How much does she earn that week?

c The company decide to change the way they
pay Carrie.
They do not give her a basic wage but pay
£3.60 for every shirt that she makes.

How many shirts does Carrie need to make
in order to earn more with this payment
method?

Extension problems

6 Calculate the difference between each term of these decreasing sequences.
Use it to work out the formula for the nth term.
In each case, check that your answer is correct.

a 57, 54, 51, 48, 45, …   b 43, 41, 39, 37, 35, …

c 9, 8, 7, 6, 5, …   d 9, 6, 3, 0, −3, …

e 15, 10, 5, 0, −5, …   f 32, 28, 24, 20, 16, …

g 190, 180, 170, 160, …   h 33, 26, 19, 12, 5, …

i 24, 23, 22, 21, 20, …   j 89, 78, 67, 56, 45, …

7 a Boris works as a waiter.

His earnings each week are the sum of his basic pay of £240 and 10% of the takings for his tables.

Write a formula for his earnings when the takings are £n.

b Work out how much his pay will be when his takings are £3500.

Points to remember

- A **linear sequence** is one with a constant difference between consecutive terms.
- To find the formula for the nth term of a linear sequence, first work out the difference between consecutive terms.
The constant difference gives you the coefficient of n.

3 Using computers

This lesson will help you use a computer to explore linear sequences.

Exercise 3

A spreadsheet on a computer can speed up the work of generating sequences.

It also makes it easy to find specific terms of a sequence.

Each cell on a spreadsheet is given a name using the column and row headings.

For example, cell B5 is in column B and row 5.

1. a Use a computer spreadsheet to generate this sequence.

   b The first term is in cell A2. What cell is the 150th term in?

   c Use the spreadsheet to find the 150th term.

	A
1	Sequence
2	7
3	12
4	17
5	22
6	27
7	32
8	37
9	42
10	47
11	52
12	57

2. a Use a computer spreadsheet to generate this sequence.

   b Use the spreadsheet to find the 320th term.

	A
1	Sequence
2	3
3	9
4	15
5	21
6	27
7	33
8	39
9	45
10	51
11	57
12	63

3 **a** Work out the formula for the nth term of this sequence.
   Use the formula to generate the sequence on a spreadsheet.

	A	B
	Position	**Term**
1	Position	Term
2	1	1
3	2	4
4	3	7
5	4	10
6	5	13
7	6	16
8	7	19
9	8	22
10	9	25
11	10	28

b Use the spreadsheet to work out the 180th term.

c Draw the graph showing the relationship between the position and the term.

4 **a** Work out the formula for the nth term of this sequence.
   Use the formula to generate the sequence on a spreadsheet.

	A	B
1	**Position**	**Term**
2	1	12
3	2	17
4	3	22
5	4	27
6	5	32
7	6	37
8	7	42
9	8	47
10	9	52
11	10	57

b Use the spreadsheet to work out the 146th term.

c Draw the graph showing the relationship between the position and the term.

5 **a** Draw a table with columns for 'Position' and 'Term'.
   Use it to record the coordinates of the points on this graph.

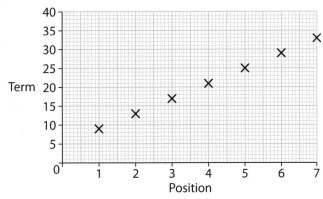

b Use the table to work out the formula for the nth term of the sequence.

Extension problem

 6 **a** Draw a table with columns for 'Position' and 'Term'.
Use it to record the coordinates of the points on this graph.

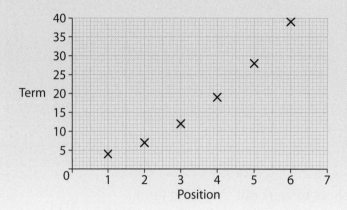

b Use the table to work out the formula for the nth term of the sequence.

4 Sketching linear graphs

This lesson will help you to sketch, draw and interpret linear graphs.

 Did you know that…?

It wasn't until the 14th century that mathematicians were able to show relationships as graphs on coordinate axes.

Nicole Oresme (1323–1382) invented a coordinate system.

However, **René Descartes** (1596–1650) took the credit. He had his name used to describe the Cartesian coordinate system

Nicole Oresme (1323–1382)

A **sketch** of a linear graph is a neat drawing using a pencil and ruler.

For example, the graph of $y = 2x - 1$ is a straight line with gradient 2 going through the point $(0, -1)$.

Example

Sketch the graph of $y = 4x + 5$.

Inspect the equation $y = 4x + 5$.

This equation is in the form $y = ax + b$.

The coefficient of x is 4.
This tells you that the gradient of the graph is 4.

The number b is 5.
This tells you that the graph cuts the y-axis at $(0, 5)$.

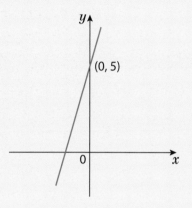

(1) Look at these linear graphs.

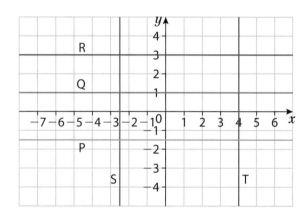

a Write down the equation of the x-axis.

b Write down the equation of the y-axis.

c Write down the equations of the lines marked P to T in the diagram above.

d Write down the equation of a line parallel to the x-axis passing through $(2, -3)$.

e Write down the equation of a line parallel to the y-axis passing through $(5, 2)$.

2 Look at this graph.

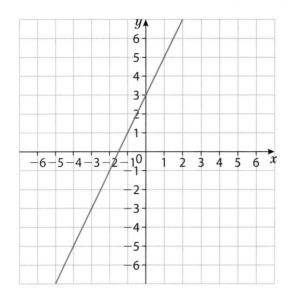

a What is the gradient of the graph?

b At what point does the graph intercept the y-axis?

c Write down the equation of the graph.

d Which of these points lie on the line?

A $(2, 7)$ B $(-4, -11)$ C $(8, 20)$ D $(-6, -9)$

e Which of these equations have graphs parallel to the graph above?

P $y = 3x - 2$ Q $y = 2x - 19$ R $y = 2x - 3$ S $y = -2x + 7$

f A graph is parallel to the graph above and passes through the origin.
What is its equation?

g A graph is parallel to the graph above and passes through $(0, -9)$.
What is its equation?

h A graph is parallel to the graph above and passes through $(3, 11)$.
What is its equation?

3 Write the equations of these linear graphs.

a Gradient 5, intercept $(0, 3)$ **b** Gradient 2, intercept $(0, -1)$

c Gradient -6, intercept $(0, 9)$ **d** Gradient -1, intercept $(0, -5)$

e Gradient 4, intercept $(0, 7)$ **f** Gradient 0.5, intercept $(0, 4)$

g Gradient -2, intercept $(0, 0.5)$ **h** Gradient 3, intercept $(0, -11)$

i Gradient 1, intercept $(0, 9)$ **j** Gradient -5, intercept $(0, -6)$

4 Sketch each of these graphs.

Label the origin and the axes, and the point where the graph crosses the y-axis.

Write the gradient of the graph.

a $y = 2x - 3$
b $y = x - 8$

c $y = 3x + 6$
d $y = -x - 2$

e $y = 4x - 1$
f $y = 0.5x + 1$

g $y = 5x + 4$
h $y = 6x - 4$

i $y = 2x - 1.5$
j $y = 0.25x + 3$

Extension problem

5 This is the graph of $y = 2x + 1$.

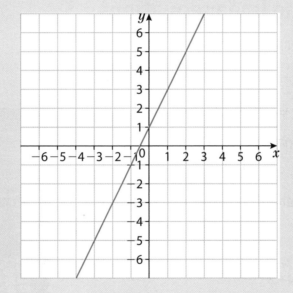

a Imagine reflecting the graph in the y-axis.
What is the equation of the reflected line?

b Imagine rotating the graph clockwise 90° about the point (0, 1).
What is the equation of this line?

c Imagine translating the graph 4 units up.
What is the equation of this line?

d Imagine translating the graph 4 units right.
What is the equation of this line?

Points to remember

⊙ The equation $y = ax + b$ is a **linear equation**.
The coefficient of x is a.
This gives the gradient of the graph of the equation.
The number b gives the point $(0, b)$ where the line intercepts the y-axis.

⊙ The equation $y = 5x - 4$ is in the form $y = ax + b$.
The gradient of its straight-line graph is 5 and the intercept on the y-axis is $(0, -4)$.

⊙ A sketch of a graph is a neat drawing showing some of the features that can be seen from its equation. Label the axes and mark the origin and the point where the line crosses the y-axis.

5 Rearranging linear equations

This lesson will help you to rearrange a linear equation in the form $y = ax + b$.

 Did you know that...?

Linear equations are not always in the form $y = ax + b$.

Rearranging an equation into this form helps you to draw or sketch its graph.

For example, you may have to put the equation in this form to enter it into a graphing program or a calculator.

Casio produced **the world's first graphing calculator** in 1985.

Exercise 5

The equals sign in an equation is like a balance.

When you rearrange an equation you must keep it in balance. What you do to one side of an equation you must do to the other side.

Example 1

Rearrange the equation $y - 3x = 6$ in the form $y = ax + b$.
Write down the gradient of the graph and the intercept.

Add $3x$ to both sides: $y = 3x + 6$.

The gradient of the graph is 3 and the intercept is $(0, 6)$.

1 a Which of these equations are the same as $5 + 8 = 13$?

    P $5 = 13 - 8$ Q $5 = 8 + 13$ R $13 - 5 = 8$ S $5 = -8 + 13$

b Which of these equations are the same as $10 - 6 = 4$?

    P $10 = 6 - 4$ Q $10 = 6 + 4$ R $6 - 4 = 10$ S $10 - 4 = 6$

c Which of these equations are the same as $x - y = 5$?

    P $x = y + 5$ Q $x = 5 - y$ R $x - 5 = y$ S $x = 5 + y$

d Which of these equations are the same as $y = 4x + 7$?

    P $y - 4x = 7$ Q $y - 7 = 4x$ R $4x - y = 7$ S $y + 4x = 7$

e Which of these equations are the same as $y = 5x - 2$?

    P $y - 5x = 2$ Q $y - 5x + 2 = 0$ R $5x - y = 2$ S $5x - y = -2$

2 Rearrange these equations in the form $y = ax + b$.

a $y - 5x = 0$ **b** $y - 7x = 6$

c $y - 4x = 9$ **d** $y + 2x = 3$

e $y + x = -5$ **f** $y - 3x = -7$

g $6x + y = 9$ **h** $5x + y = 11$

i $13 = y - x$ **j** $3 = y + 4x$

3 Write down the gradient of the graph and the intercept for these equations.

a $y - 4x = 0$ **b** $y - 3x = 1$

c $y - 2x = -3$ **d** $y - x = 5$

e $y + 7x = -8$ **f** $y - 9x = -2$

g $5x + y = -7$ **h** $2x + y = 14$

i $1 = y - x$ **j** $y + 5x - 3 = 0$

4 Which of these points lie on the graph of $y - 5x + 4 = 0$?

    A $(2, 14)$ B $(-2, -14)$ C $(1, 1)$ D $(-3, -19)$

5 Which of these equations has a graph parallel to the graph of $y + 2x = 5$?

    P $y - 2x + 9 = 0$ Q $y = -2x - 3$ R $y = 2x + 7$ S $y + 2x + 16 = 0$

6 For each of these equations write down the gradient of the graph and the intercept on the y-axis.

Sketch the graph.

a $y - x = 0$

b $y - 3x = 4$

c $y - 2x + 5 = 0$

d $y + x = 0$

e $y + 2x = 7$

f $y + 3x + 5 = 0$

g $4x + y - 6 = 0$

h $5x - y = 8$

i $2x + y + 7 = 0$

j $y - 9 - 6x = 0$

Extension problem

The coefficient of y in the equation $y = ax + b$ is 1.

If the coefficient of y is not 1, then divide every term in the equation by that number.

Example 2

Rearrange the equation $2y = 6x + 10$ in the form $y = ax + b$.

Divide every term by 2:

$y = 3x + 5$.

7 Put these equations in the form $y = ax + b$.

a $2y - 6x = 0$

b $3y - 3x = 12$

c $5y - 10x + 5 = 0$

d $7y + 14x = 0$

e $4y + 12x = 20$

f $3y + 9x + 15 = 0$

g $12x + 2y - 4 = 0$

h $2x - 0.5y = 3$

i $0.3x + 0.1y + 0.5 = 0$

j $13y - 39 - 26x = 0$

⊙ Points to remember

⊙ The equation of a straight line is normally given in the form $y = ax + b$.

⊙ The number a, the coefficient of x, gives the gradient of the straight-line graph of the equation, and the number b gives the intercept on the y-axis.

⊙ If a linear equation is in a different form, you can rearrange it to the normal form.

6 Graphs using real-life contexts

This lesson will help you to explore linear graphs of real-life contexts.

Exercise 6

When you read information from a graph of a real-life context, first look at the axes and decide what the scales represent.

Try to make sense of the graph before you answer any questions.

1   This graph shows the conversion of pounds sterling to Indian rupees.

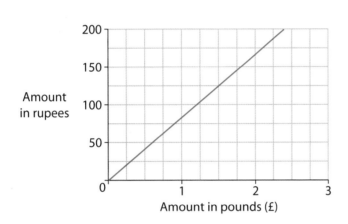

Indian bank notes

a   Estimate the number of rupees you get for £1.

b   Estimate the number of pounds you get for 200 rupees.

c   Peter is going to India on a business trip.
    He wants to take £300 with him.
    Estimate how many rupees he will get.

d   Peter's Indian colleague Radhesh returns to London with him.
    He books a hotel room for two nights at a cost of £180.
    Estimate how many rupees this is.

e   Radhesh's manager Rafiq asks him to buy his son a present.
    He gives Rafiq 4000 rupees.
    About how much is this in pounds?

f   Let x represent pounds and y represent rupees.
    Write an equation for the conversion graph.

2 Carl likes to keep fit by training in his local gym.
The graph shows one of his workouts on the running machine.

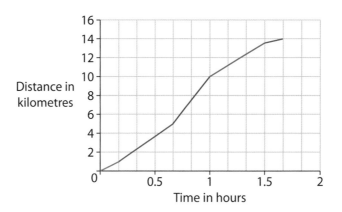

a What time does each mark represent along the horizontal axis?

b What distance does each mark represent along the vertical axis?

c How long does Carl spend warming up by walking?

d Estimate how far Carl walks during his warm-up.

e About how far has Carl walked and run after one hour?

f How long does Carl spend altogether on the running machine?

g Carl does the same workout on the running machine three times a week.
About how far does he walk and run in a week?

h If Carl repeats his exercise every week of the year, roughly how far will he run and walk altogether?

3 This graph shows the charges in pounds made by an estate agent for selling a house.

Charge (£)

Sale price (£)

a A house owner paid £7000 to the estate agent.
Estimate the price of the house.

b Estimate the percentage of the sale price paid by the house owner.

c Estimate how much an owner would pay for selling a flat for £125 000.

d If x is the sale price and y the charge, write an equation for the cost of selling a house.

e A different estate agent charges a fixed fee of £2500 plus 1.5% of the sale price.
Write this as an equation in y and x.

> **⦿ Points to remember**
> ⊙ When you read information from a graph representing a real-life context, first check the scales and units on the axes.

How well are you doing?

You will need squared paper, pencil and ruler for these questions.

Sequences and graphs

1 Calculate the difference between each term of this sequence.
Use it to work out the formula for the nth term.

$$5, \quad 7, \quad 9, \quad 11, \quad 13, \quad 15, \quad \ldots$$

2 *2006 level 6*

Look at these pairs of number sequences.

The second sequence is formed from the first sequence
by adding a number or multiplying by a number.

Work out the missing nth terms. Write them in your book.

a 5, 9, 13, 17, ... nth term is $4n + 1$

   6, 10, 14, 18, ... nth term is   ....

b 12, 18, 24, 30, ... nth term is $6n + 6$

   6, 9, 12, 15, ... nth term is   ....

c 2, 7, 12, 17, ... nth term is $5n - 3$

   4, 14, 24, 34, ... nth term is   ....

3 *1998 level 6*

This sequence of patterns is made from blue and white tiles.

It continues by adding 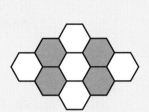 each time.

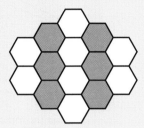

Pattern number 1   Pattern number 2   Pattern number 3

Write an expression to show the total number of tiles in pattern number n.
Show your working and simplify your expression.

4 *2004 level 6*

The graph shows a straight line.

a Write an equation of the straight line.

b On squared paper, draw the straight line
that has the equation $x + y = 6$.

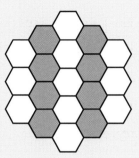

5 *1998 level 6*

a The line through points A and F
has the equation $y = 11$.
What is the equation of the line
through points A and B?

b The line through points A and D
has the equation $y = x + 3$.
What is the equation of the line
through points F and E?

c What is the equation of the line
through points B and C?

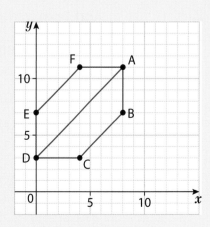

The graph shows the average heights of young children.

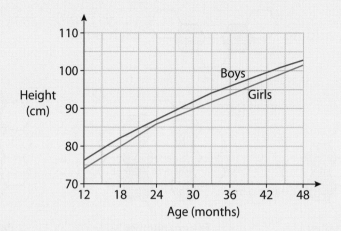

a   The table shows approximately how much an average girl grows each year between the ages of 12 and 48 months.

Copy this table. Use the graph to complete it.

Age (months)	Approximate height at start (cm)	Approximate height at end (cm)	Approximate growth (cm)
12 to 24	74	86	12
24 to 36	86		
36 to 48			

b   This formula tells you how tall a boy is likely to be when he grows up.

> Add the mother's and father's heights.
> Divide by 2.
> Add 7 cm to the result.
>
> The boy is likely to be this height, plus or minus 10 cm.

Marc's mother is 168 cm tall. His father is 194 cm tall.

What is the greatest height Marc is likely to be when he grows up?
Show your working.

Measures and mensuration

This unit will help you to:

- estimate, measure, calculate and solve problems involving measures;
- convert between measures in the same system;
- know and use the formulae for the circumference and area of a circle;
- use the π key of a calculator;
- calculate the surface area and volume of prisms.

1 Perimeter and area

This lesson will help you to find the perimeter and area of 2D shapes.

Exercise 1

Perimeter of a rectangle $= 2 \times$ (length + width) $= 2 \times$ (base + height)

Area of a rectangle $=$ length $\times$ width $=$ base $\times$ height

Example 1

An L-shape is made from rectangles A and B.

Find its perimeter and area.

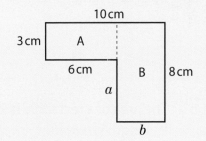

First find the two unknown lengths a and b:

$a = 8 - 3 = 5$ cm and $b = 10 - 6 = 4$ cm

Perimeter $= 10 + 8 + 4 + 5 + 6 + 3 = 36$ cm

Total area $=$ area of A + area of B $= 6 \times 3 + 8 \times 4 = 18 + 32 = 50$ cm^2

Area of triangle $= \frac{1}{2} \times$ base $\times$ perpendicular height

Example 2

Calculate the area of this triangle.

Area $= \frac{1}{2} \times 24 \times 20 = 240$ mm

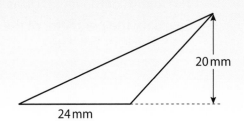

Area of a parallelogram = base × perpendicular height

Example 3

Calculate the area of this parallelogram.

Area = 10 × 4 = 40 cm²

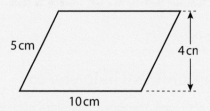

5 cm

4 cm

10 cm

Area of a trapezium = $\frac{1}{2}$ × sum of the parallel sides × perpendicular height

Example 4

Calculate the area of this trapezium.

Area = $\frac{1}{2}$ × (11 + 3) × 6 = 42 cm²

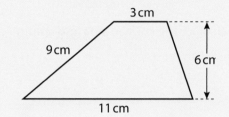

3 cm

9 cm

6 cm

11 cm

① Estimate the area of this shape.

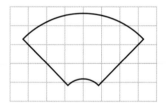

② A netball pitch is approximately 15.3 m wide by 30.5 m long.

   a Calculate its perimeter.

   b Calculate its area.

③ The area of a rectangle is 24 mm².
Its length is 0.6 cm.
What is the width of the rectangle?

④ A rectangle has an area of 144 mm².
The length of the rectangle is 16 mm.
Calculate the perimeter of the rectangle.

5 These shapes are made from rectangles.
Calculate the perimeter and area of each shape.

a
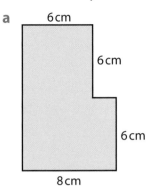
6 cm

6 cm

6 cm

8 cm

b
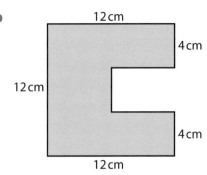
12 cm

4 cm

12 cm

4 cm

12 cm

6 A triangle has a base of 23.5 m and a perpendicular height of 15.6 m.
Calculate its area.

7 A triangle has a base of 650 mm and a perpendicular height of 0.5 m.
Calculate its area.

8 Three of the triangles below have the same area.
The fourth has a different area.
Which triangle is it, A, B, C or D?

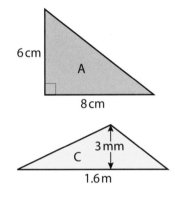
6 cm

A

8 cm

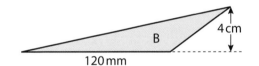
B

4 cm

120 mm

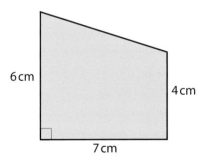
3 mm

C

1.6 m

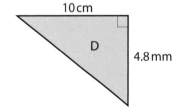
10 cm

D

4.8 mm

9 Calculate the area of each shape.

a
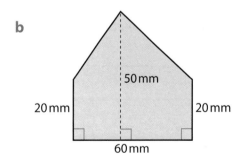
6 cm

4 cm

7 cm

b
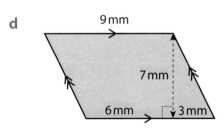
50 mm

20 mm

20 mm

60 mm

c
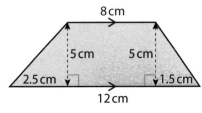
8 cm

5 cm

5 cm

2.5 cm

1.5 cm

12 cm

d
9 mm

7 mm

6 mm

3 mm

10 Calculate the areas of these trapezia and parallelograms.
Give each answer correct to the nearest whole number.

a
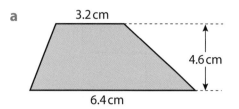
3.2 cm
4.6 cm
6.4 cm

b
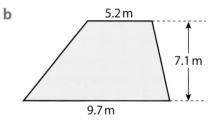
5.2 m
7.1 m
9.7 m

c
6.7 cm
10.7 cm

d
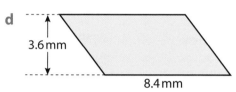
3.6 mm
8.4 mm

Extension problems

11 A small patio is a 300 cm by 250 cm rectangle.
Tiles, which are squares of side 50 cm, are used to tile the patio.
Work out how many tiles are needed.

12 Ajit wants to make a rectangular lawn in his garden.
He wants the lawn to be 25 m by 8 m.

Ajit buys rectangular strips of turf 5 m long and 1 m wide.
How many strips of turf does Ajit needs to buy?

13 Jade's bedroom floor is a rectangle 5 m long and 3.5 m wide.
She wants to cover the floor completely with carpet tiles.
Each carpet tile is square with sides of length 50 cm.
One tile costs £3.75.
Work out the cost of covering Jade's floor completely with carpet tiles.

⊙ Points to remember

- **Area of a rectangle** = base × height
- **Area of a triangle** = $\frac{1}{2}$ × base × perpendicular height
- **Area of a parallelogram** = base × perpendicular height
- **Area of a trapezium** = $\frac{1}{2}$ × sum of parallel sides × perpendicular height
- Area is measured in square units.
- When you work out the perimeter or area of a shape, make sure that the sides are in the same units.

2 Finding π

This lesson will help you calculate the circumference and diameter of any circle.

Did you know that...?

People have known that if you divide the circumference of any circle by its diameter the answer is the same for all circles for at least 4000 years.

A circular Roman amphitheatre

- In 1650 BC, the Egyptians thought the value of π was 3.16.

- The Romans knew that $3\frac{1}{7}$ was a good approximation but used $3\frac{1}{8}$ in their buildings.

- In 1489 the Arabic mathematician **Al-Kashi** calculated π to 16 decimal places.

- In 1610 the German **Ludolph van Ceulen** calculated π to 35 decimal places. He had it engraved on his tombstone.

- Since the 1940s, the value of π has been worked out by computers. It has now been calculated to over a thousand billion digits. So far no repeating pattern has been found.

It is useful to know the first few digits of π, such as 3.14 or 3.142.

If you need to know more digits there are mnemonics to help you:

See, I have a rhyme assisting my feeble brain.

If you count the letters in each word you get 3.141 592 65, the first nine digits of π.

In 2005 **Kate Bush** recorded a song called Pi, on her CD *Aerial*. She sang the first 137 digits of π although for some reason she missed out the 79th to 100th decimal places.

Kate Bush

Exercise 2

The circumference C of a circle is just over three times the length of its diameter d.

This diagram can help you with calculations involving $C = \pi d$.

When the required term is covered up, what remains is an expression for that term. So:

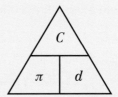

- ⊙ π = circumference ÷ diameter
- ⊙ circumference = π × diameter
- ⊙ diameter = circumference ÷ π

Example 1

Find the circumference of this circle.

Circumference = πd = π × 8

Key in $\boxed{\pi}$ $\boxed{\times}$ $\boxed{8}$.

You should get $\boxed{25.132741}$.

So the circumference is 25.1 cm to 1 d.p.

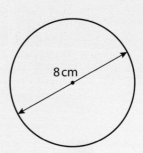

8 cm

Example 2

Calculate the circumference of this circle.
Give your answer to one decimal place.

The diameter d is 2 × radius = 2 × 2.7 = 5.4 m.

Circumference = πd = π × 5.4 = 17.0 m to 1 d.p.

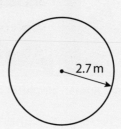

2.7 m

Use a calculator for these questions. Give your answers to questions **1** to **3** to one decimal place.

①　Find the circumference of circles with these diameters.

   a 7 mm　　　　**b** 9.1 m　　　　**c** 2.4 km　　　　**d** 6.3 cm

②　Find the diameter of circles with these circumferences.

   a 31.4 cm　　　　**b** 60 m　　　　**c** 7.85 km　　　　**d** 568 mm

③　**a** The radius of a semicircle is 2.7 m. Work out its perimeter.

   b The diameter of a semicircle is 8.2 cm. Work out its perimeter.

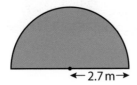

←2.7 m→

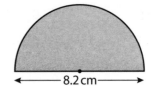

←——8.2 cm——→

(4) The radius of a bicycle wheel is 35 cm.

a Calculate the circumference of the wheel.
Give your answer to the nearest centimetre.

b How many times does the wheel turn when the
bicycle is ridden for 4 km?
Give your answer to the nearest turn.

(5) A roundabout has a circumference of 220 metres.
What is the diameter of the roundabout?
Give your answer to the nearest metre.

(6) The Earth has a diameter of 12 756 km.
Calculate the distance round the Equator.
Give your answer to the nearest 100 kilometres.

(7) The London Eye is the largest Ferris wheel in the world.
From the top, you can see 25 miles on a clear day.

The Eye has a diameter of 135 metres.

32 capsules are equally spaced round its circumference.

What is the distance between two adjacent capsules?

(8) *2005 level 6*

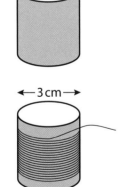

←3 cm→

←3 cm→

a The cross-section of a cylindrical cotton reel is a circle.

The diameter of this circle is 3 cm.

What is the circumference of this circle?

Give your answer to the nearest millimetre.

b 91 metres of cotton goes round the cotton reel.

About how many times does the cotton go round the reel?

Show your working, and give your answer to the nearest ten.

Extension problems

(9) The Earth is about 149 600 000 km from the Sun. It orbits around the Sun.

Assuming that its orbit is a circle, about how far does the Earth travel in one year?

10 The pink shape is made using semicircles.

One semicircle has a diameter of 24 cm.
The other has a diameter of 36 cm.

Calculate the perimeter of the pink shape.

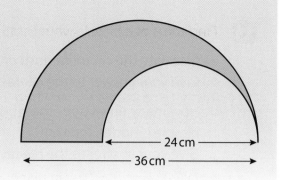

Points to remember

⊙ The circumference of a circle is $\pi \times$ diameter.

⊙ The diameter of a circle is circumference $\div \pi$.

⊙ π is a little bit more than 3.
Approximations for π are $\frac{22}{7}$ and 3.14.

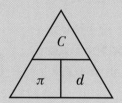

3 Area of a circle

This lesson will help you calculate the area of a circle.

Exercise 3

Area of a circle $= \pi \times$ radius $\times$ radius $= \pi \times (\text{radius})^2 = \pi r^2$

If you are given the diameter of the circle, divide it by 2 to find the radius before you use the formula πr^2 for the area of a circle.

Example

Calculate the area of this circle to one decimal place.

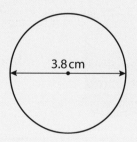

The radius r is diameter $\div 2 = 3.8 \div 2 = 1.9$ cm.

Area $= \pi r^2 = \pi \times 1.9 \times 1.9 = 11.3$ cm^2 to 1 d.p.

Give your answers to one decimal place, unless stated otherwise.

1 Find the area of circles with these radii.

     a 3 mm   **b** 7.1 mm   **c** 21 m   **d** 5.9 km

(2) Find the area of circles with these diameters.

    a 4 cm   **b** 1.2 m   **c** 6.72 mm   **d** 4.72 km

(3) The catchment area for a school has a radius of 25 km.
Calculate the size of the catchment area.

(4) A cylindrical poster holder has a diameter of 67 mm.
What is the area of the circular end?

(5) Olympus Mons on Mars is the largest
known volcano in the Solar System.
It is 27 km high and has a crater with a
diameter of 72 km.

    a Assuming that the top of the crater
is circular, what area does it occupy?

    b The diameter of the base of the
Olympus Mons volcano is 600 km.

       Assuming that it is circular,
what area does it occupy?

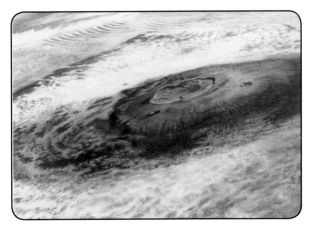

Olympus Mons on Mars

(6) The distance round a circular running track is 400 m.

    a Find the diameter of the track.

    b Find the area enclosed by the track.

(7) **a** The radius of a semicircle is 2.7 m.
        Work out its area.
                b The diameter of a semicircle is 8.2 cm.
                           Work out its area.

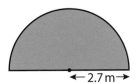

←2.7 m→

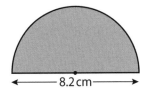

←8.2 cm→

(8) The goal area on an ice hockey rink
is a semicircle.
The diameter is 3.6 m.
What is its area?

(9) A farmer has 280 m of chain-link fence to make a pen for his pigs.
What area can he enclose:

    a if the pen is square?   **b** if the pen is circular?

(10) The centre circle of a football pitch has a radius of 9.15 m.
What is the area of the centre circle?

(11) The marking at each corner of a football pitch is a quarter circle with radius 1 m.
What is the area of this quarter circle?

Extension problem

(12) The diagram shows a 8 cm by 6 cm rectangle
inside a circle of diameter 10 cm.

Work out the area of the shaded part of the
diagram.

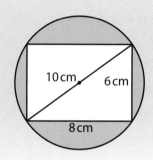

10 cm   6 cm

8 cm

Points to remember

- Area of a circle = $\pi \times$ radius $\times$ radius = $\pi \times$ (radius)^2 = πr^2
- The area of a circle is measured in square units.

4 Solving circle problems and using π

This lesson will help you solve problems involving π.

Exercise 4

You can often work out the area of an irregular shape by adding or subtracting
one area to or from another.

Example

Find the shaded area.

Area of square = $9 \times 9 = 81$ cm^2

Radius of circle = 4.5 cm

Area of circle = $\pi \times 4.5 \times 4.5 = 63.6$ cm^2 to 1 d.p.

Shaded area = area of square − area of circle

           = $81 - 63.6 = 17.4$ cm^2 to 1 d.p.

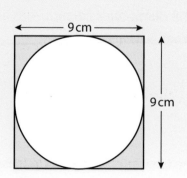

9 cm

9 cm

Write your answers correct to one decimal place.

1 A window is made from a rectangle and a semicircle.

Calculate the area of the window.

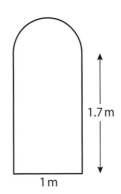

1.7 m

1 m

2 Find each shaded area.

a
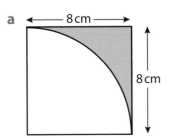
8 cm

8 cm

b

4 cm

2 cm

c
10 cm

10 cm

3 This shape is made from semicircles.

Find the shaded area.

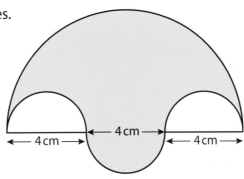

4 cm

4 cm   4 cm

4 a A semicircle is drawn with a diameter of 12 cm.

Another semicircle is drawn as shown that has a diameter of 6 cm.

Calculate the shaded area.

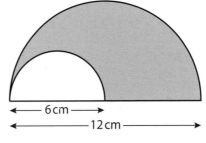

6 cm

12 cm

b A semicircle is drawn with a diameter of 10 cm.

Two semicircles are drawn as shown, each with a diameter of 5 cm.

Calculate the shaded area.

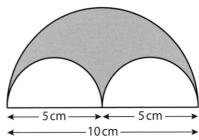

5 cm   5 cm

10 cm

5 The circumference of a circle is 27 mm. Find the area of the circle.

6 The diagram shows a running track.
The ends are semicircles of diameter 57.3 m
and the straights are 110 m long.
Work out the area enclosed by the track.

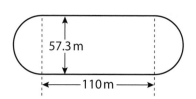

Extension problems

7 **a** Identical cylindrical pots of marmalade are packed into a rectangular box.
Each pot of marmalade has a diameter of 6 cm.

The box is 24 cm by 36 cm and is packed like this.

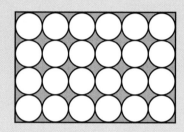

The shaded part of the diagram shows wasted space.
How much wasted space is there?

b Cylindrical pots of honey with a diameter of 4 cm are packed in an identical box.
How much wasted space will there be this time?

c Cylindrical pots of herbs with a diameter of 2 cm are packed in an identical box.
How much wasted space is there now?

⦿ Points to remember

⦿ The circumference of a circle is $\pi \times$ diameter.

⦿ The diameter of a circle is circumference $\div \pi$.

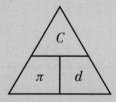

⦿ π is a little bit more than 3. Approximations for π are $\frac{22}{7}$ and 3.14.

⦿ Area of a circle $= \pi \times$ radius $\times$ radius $= \pi \times$ (radius)$^2 = \pi r^2$

⦿ The area of a circle is measured in square units.

5 Volume of prisms

This lesson will help you find the volume of prisms.

Exercise 5

A **prism** is a solid which has two parallel end faces of the same size and shape, and side faces which are rectangles.

If you cut a prism across anywhere at right angles to its length, you will see the same 2D shape as an end face.

This is the **cross-section** of the prism.

The cross-section is the same throughout the prism's length.

The formula for the **volume of a prism** is:

Volume of a prism $=$ area of cross-section $\times$ length $= A \times l$

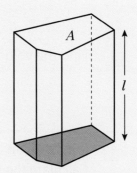

Example

Find the volume of this triangular prism.

The cross-section A is a right-angled triangle with base 3 cm and height 4 cm.

Its area is:

$\frac{1}{2} \times 3 \times 4 = 6 \text{ cm}^2$.

The length l of the prism is 10 cm.

So the volume of the prism is $A \times l = 6 \times 10 \text{ cm}^3$.

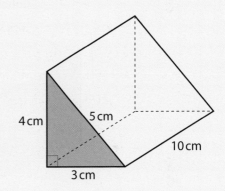

---

① Calculate the volume of each of these cuboids.

a
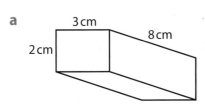
3 cm
8 cm
2 cm

b
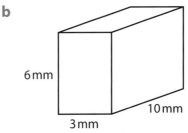
6 mm
3 mm
10 mm

c
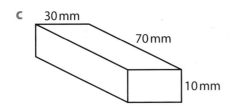
30 mm
70 mm
10 mm

d
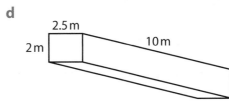
2.5 m
2 m
10 m

2 Calculate the volume of each prism.

a
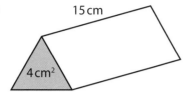
15 cm

4 cm²

b
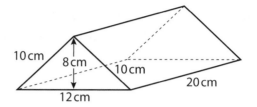
20 cm

16 cm²

3 Find the volume of this triangular prism.

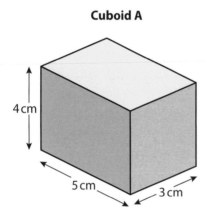

10 cm
8 cm
10 cm
12 cm
20 cm

4 A cuboid has a volume of 144 cm³ and a cross-section area of 36 cm².
Calculate the length of the cuboid.

5 These two cuboids have the same volume. Work out the length marked x in centimetres.

Cuboid A

4 cm

5 cm   3 cm

Cuboid B

2 cm

5 cm x cm

6 In 2003, the world record for the number of people who can fit in a telephone box was broken.

14 teenagers in Edinburgh managed to do it.

The previous record was 12 people in Germany in 1997.

A telephone box is 2.54 m tall, with a square base with side 91 cm.

Assuming it is a cuboid, what is its volume?

On average, how much space did each of the 14 teenagers occupy?

(7) The volume of a cuboid is 120 m³. Its length is 8 m and its width is 6 m.
Work out its height.

(8) A packet of butter measures 11 cm by 6.5 cm by 4 cm.
A box measures 55 cm by 26 cm by 24 cm.
How many packets of butter are needed to fill the box?

(9) A box of chocolates measures 20 cm by 20 cm by 5 cm.
A container is a cuboid which measures 80 cm by 60 cm by 30 cm.
Work out the greatest number of boxes which can be packed in the container.

Extension problem

(10) *1998 level 6*
A box for coffee is in the shape of a hexagonal prism.
One end of the box is shown below.

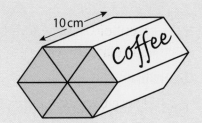

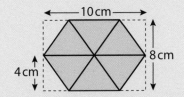

Each of the six triangles in the hexagon has the same dimensions.

a Calculate the total area of the hexagon.

b The box is 10 cm long.
Calculate the volume of the hexagonal prism.

c After packing, the coffee fills 80% of the box.
How many grams of coffee are in the box?
(The mass of 1 cm³ of coffee is 0.5 grams.)

d A 227 g packet of the same coffee costs £2.19.
How much per 100 g of coffee is this?

  Points to remember

⊙ A **prism** is a solid with two parallel end faces of the same size and shape, and rectangular side faces.
It has the same cross-section throughout its length.

⊙ The formula for the **volume of a prism** is:
Volume = area of cross-section × length = $A \times l$

⊙ Volume is measured in cubic units.

6 Surface area of prisms

This lesson will help you to find the surface area of prisms.

The **surface area** of a prism is the sum of the areas of all the faces. The surface area of this triangular prism is A + B + C + D + E.

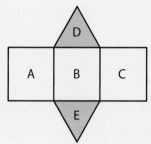

Example

Find the surface area of this triangular prism.

The two end faces are right-angled triangles with base 3 cm and height 4 cm.

The area of one of these triangles is:

$\frac{1}{2} \times 3 \times 4 = 6\,cm^2$.

The side faces are rectangles, each of length 10 cm.

One rectangle has area $10 \times 3 = 30\,cm^2$.
The second rectangle has area $10 \times 5 = 50\,cm^2$.
The third rectangle has area $10 \times 4 = 40\,cm^2$.

The total surface area of all five faces is: $6 + 6 + 30 + 50 + 40 = 132\,cm^2$.

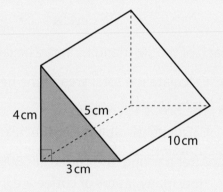

① Work out the surface area of each cuboid.

a

3 cm
8 cm
2 cm

b
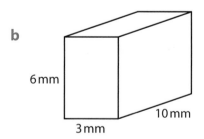

6 mm
3 mm
10 mm

c
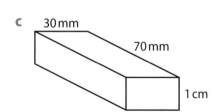

30 mm
70 mm
1 cm

d
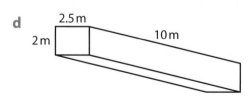

2.5 m
2 m
10 m

2 Work out the surface area of:

a a cube of side 5 cm;

b a cuboid which is 4 cm by 4 cm by 8 cm;

c a cuboid which is 7 cm by 3 cm by 10 cm.

3 Work out the surface area of each triangular prism.

a A prism with a right-angled triangle as its cross-section.

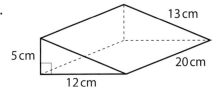

b A prism with an isosceles triangle as its cross-section.

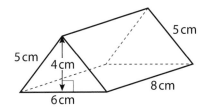

c Another prism with a right-angled triangle as its cross-section.

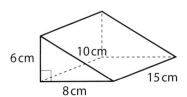

4 Work out the surface area of each prism.

a A prism of length 30 cm with this trapezium as its cross-section.

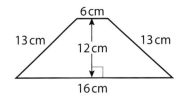

b A prism of length 15 cm with this trapezium as its cross-section.

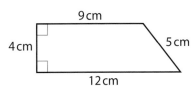

c A prism of length 12 cm with this parallelogram as its cross-section.

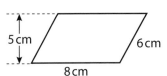

5 A cuboid is 8 cm wide, 4 cm high and 11 cm long. Work out its surface area.

6 A cuboid has a volume of 72 cm³. It is 4 cm wide and 9 cm high. Work out its surface area.

7 This prism has a volume of 288 cm³.

Work out its surface area.

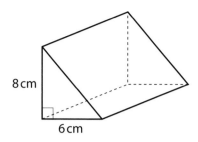
8 cm

6 cm

Extension problems

8 Work out the surface area of this hexagonal prism.

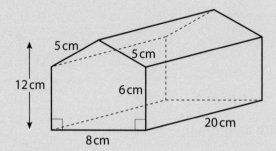
5 cm

5 cm

12 cm

6 cm

8 cm

20 cm

9 A large tank is in the shape of a cuboid.
It does not have a top.

The width of the tank is 2.8 metres.
The length of the tank is 3.2 metres.
The height of the tank is 4.5 metres.

The outside of the tank is going to be painted.
1 litre of paint will cover 2.5 m² of the tank.
The cost of paint is £2.99 per litre.

Calculate the cost of paint needed to paint the outside of the tank.

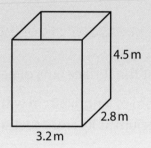
4.5 m

2.8 m

3.2 m

Points to remember

⊙ Surface area is measured in square units.

⊙ The **surface area of a prism** is the sum of the areas of all the faces.

⊙ The formula for the **volume of a prism** is:

Volume = area of cross-section × length = $A \times l$

⊙ Volume is measured in cubic units.

How well are you doing?

1 *1999 level 6*

Each shape in this question has an area of 10 cm².

a Calculate the height of the parallelogram.

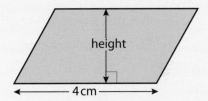

b Calculate the length of the base of
   the triangle.

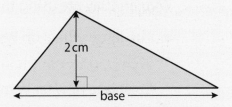

c What might be the values of h, a and b in this
   trapezium? (a is greater than b)

   What else might the values of h, a and b be?

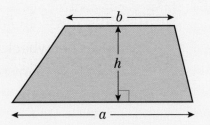

2 *1999 level 6*

a A circle has a radius of 15 cm.
   Calculate the area of the circle.
   Show your working.

b A different circle has a circumference of 120 cm.
   What is the radius of the circle?
   Show your working.

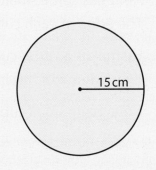

2000 level 6

The diagram shows a circle and a square.

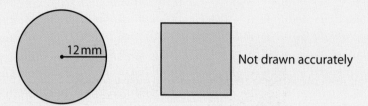

Not drawn accurately

a The radius of the circle is 12 mm.
What is the area of the circle to the nearest mm²?
Show your working.

b The ratio of the area of the circle to the area of the square is 2 : 1.
What is the area of the square to the nearest mm²?

c What is the side length of the square?
Show your working.

4 *1996 level 6*

Wyn and Jay are using their wheelchairs to measure distances.

a The large wheel on Wyn's wheelchair has a diameter of 60 cm.

Wyn pushes the wheel round exactly once.
Calculate how far Wyn has moved.
Show your working.

b The large wheel on Jay's wheelchair has a diameter of 52 cm.

Jay moves her wheelchair forward 950 cm.
Calculate how many times the large wheel goes round.
Show your working.

5 *2000 level 6*

Amit has some small cubes.
The edge of each cube is **1.5 centimetres.**

He makes a larger cube out of the small cubes.
The **volume** of this larger cube is **216 cm³.**

How many small cubes does he use?

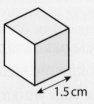

1.5 cm

6 *2003 level 6*

The squared paper shows the nets of cuboid A and cuboid B.

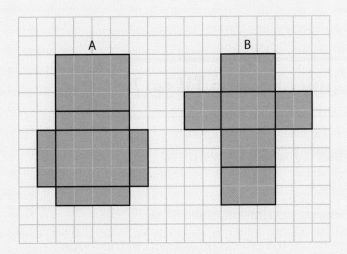

a   Do the cuboids have the same surface area?
    Show calculations to explain how you know.

b   Do the cuboids have the same volume?
    Show calculations to explain how you know.

Functional skills 1

Should you buy or rent a TV set?

This group activity will help you to:

- ⊙ model a situation;
- ⊙ select the mathematical information to use;
- ⊙ change values to see the effects on answers in the model;
- ⊙ interpret results and draw conclusions.

Background

Let's say your family wants a new high-definition TV set with a big screen.

Some of the factors that you will need to consider are:

- ⊙ what the HDTV set costs to buy;
- ⊙ monthly rental charges;
- ⊙ loss of interest on the money you spend;
- ⊙ the depreciation of the value of the TV set;
- ⊙ the cost of repairs;
- ⊙ how long you will keep the TV set before you get a better model.

General information

If you buy a TV set, you can ignore the cost of any repairs in the first year, since the main guarantee covers them.

Many people buy an extended guarantee to cover, say, 3 years.

Rental charges always include the cost of repairs.

Some costs are the same regardless of whether you buy or rent, so you can ignore them, e.g.

- ⊙ the cost of electricity to run the set;
- ⊙ the cost of a TV licence.

Problems

To rent or buy?

Suppose the high-definition TV you want costs £1200 to buy or £50 per month to rent.

The rental charge covers the cost of any repairs needed.

Should you buy the TV or rent it?

Make some assumptions about:

- ⊙ how many years you will keep the TV set;
- ⊙ the loss of annual interest on money in a savings account;
- ⊙ the annual depreciation rate on a TV set;
- ⊙ if you buy, the cost of an extended guarantee after the first year.

Work out the annual costs for a suitable number of years and come to a conclusion.

Which way would you be better off, if you buy or if you rent?

How much better off would you be?

Be prepared to justify your assumptions and conclusions to other groups.

Proportional reasoning

This unit will help you to:

○ add, subtract, multiply and divide fractions;

○ solve problems involving percentage changes, ratios and direct proportion.

1 Adding and subtracting fractions

This lesson will help you to add and subtract fractions.

 Did you know that...?

The **Ancient Egyptians** used fractions as early as 1700 BC.

They used the fractions when they were planning irrigation systems, or when they were dividing up the land.

The ancient Egyptians used only unit fractions, which have 1 as a numerator.

Other fractions were expressed as the sum of unit fractions. For example:

$$\frac{4}{9} = \frac{1}{3} + \frac{1}{9}$$

$$\frac{2}{5} = \frac{1}{5} + \frac{1}{6} + \frac{1}{30}$$

Exercise 1

When you add or subtract fractions, deal with whole numbers first.

Example 1

Work out $2\frac{5}{8} + 3\frac{7}{12}$.

$2\frac{5}{8} + 3\frac{7}{12} = 5\frac{5}{8} + \frac{7}{12}$ First add the whole numbers.

$= 5\frac{15}{24} + \frac{14}{24}$ Change the fractions to a common denominator.

$= 5\frac{29}{24}$ Add the two fractions. If the result is an improper fraction

$= 6\frac{5}{24}$ change the improper fraction to a mixed number.

Example 2

Work out $4\frac{5}{12} - 2\frac{3}{4}$.

$4\frac{5}{12} - 2\frac{3}{4} = 2\frac{5}{12} - \frac{3}{4}$ First subtract the whole numbers.

$= 2\frac{5}{12} - \frac{9}{12}$ Change the fractions to a common denominator.

$= 1\frac{17}{12} - \frac{9}{12}$ As you can't take 9 from 5, change 1 whole to 12 twelfths.

$= 1\frac{8}{12}$ Subtract the fractions.

$= 1\frac{2}{3}$ Simplify the fraction by cancelling.

Example 3

Work out $1\frac{3}{4} + 2\frac{4}{5}$ using your calculator.

Enter  .

The display should show something like .

Do question **1 without using a calculator**. Show your working.

(1)

   a $\frac{3}{5} + \frac{2}{9}$ **b** $\frac{7}{12} - \frac{3}{8}$

   c $\frac{4}{5} + \frac{6}{15}$ **d** $\frac{5}{6} - \frac{3}{4}$

   e $1\frac{2}{5} + 2\frac{1}{2}$ **f** $3\frac{4}{9} - 1\frac{1}{3}$

   g $2\frac{5}{8} + 4\frac{1}{2}$ **h** $6\frac{1}{3} - 1\frac{3}{5}$

You may **use your calculator** to answer questions **2** to **8**.

(2)   Unit fractions have a numerator of 1 and an integer denominator greater than 1.

     $\frac{9}{20}$ is written as the sum of two unit fractions.
     One of them is one quarter. What is the other one?

(3)   Two fractions lie between 0 and 1.
     They have a difference of $\frac{7}{8}$.
     What could the two fractions be?

4 One third of a fruit salad is melon and three eighths are bananas.

What fraction of the whole fruit salad are the melon and bananas combined?

5 How much more is three fifths of a mile than one eighth of a mile?

6 Three eighths of the passengers on a train are going to Reading.
Two fifths are going to Bath.
The rest are going to Bristol.
What fraction of the passengers are going to Bristol?

7 A bag has coloured cubes in it.
One sixth of the cubes are green, one twelfth are yellow,
one half are white and one fifth are blue.
What fraction of the cubes are other colours?

8 Make these fractions by adding two unit fractions.

a $\frac{1}{3}$　　　　b $\frac{1}{4}$　　　　c $\frac{1}{5}$　　　　d $\frac{1}{6}$

Write these fractions as the difference of two unit fractions.

e $\frac{1}{12}$　　　　f $\frac{1}{56}$　　　　g $\frac{1}{90}$　　　　h $\frac{1}{110}$

Extension problem

9 Find, **without a calculator**, the sum of these fractions.

$$\frac{1}{7} + \frac{1}{8} + \frac{1}{9} + \frac{1}{10} + \frac{1}{12} + \frac{1}{14} + \frac{1}{15} + \frac{1}{18} + \frac{1}{24} + \frac{1}{28}$$

● Points to remember

- ⊙ To find a fraction equivalent to a given fraction, multiply or divide the numerator and denominator by the same number.
- ⊙ To add and subtract fractions, they must have the same denominator.
- ⊙ When you add or subtract mixed numbers, it is usually best to deal with the whole numbers first.
- ⊙ You can use your calculator to add and subtract fractions.

2 Multiplying fractions

This lesson will help you to multiply and divide fractions.

Exercise 2

This diagram shows that $\frac{2}{3}$ of $\frac{4}{5}$ is $\frac{8}{15}$, or $\frac{2}{3} \times \frac{4}{5} = \frac{8}{15}$.

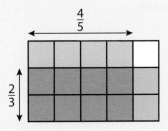

Example 1

$$\frac{5}{8} \times \frac{7}{12} = \frac{5 \times 7}{8 \times 12}$$

$$= \frac{35}{96}$$ Multiply the numerators and multiply the denominators.

Example 2

$$\frac{21}{40} \times \frac{15}{28} = \frac{^3\cancel{21}}{^8\cancel{40}} \times \frac{\cancel{15}^3}{\cancel{28}^4}$$

$$= \frac{3 \times 3}{8 \times 4}$$ Cancel first, then multiply the numerators and multiply the denominators.

$$= \frac{9}{32}$$

Do this exercise **without a calculator**.
Give each answer in its simplest form. Show your working.

1 **a** $\frac{3}{5} \times \frac{2}{15}$ **b** $\frac{6}{7} \times \frac{5}{12}$ **c** $\frac{4}{5} \times \frac{15}{16}$ **d** $\frac{3}{22} \times \frac{11}{12}$

     e $\frac{3}{5} \times \frac{20}{27}$ **f** $\frac{5}{11} \times \frac{33}{15}$ **g** $\frac{15}{28} \times \frac{42}{75}$ **h** $\frac{35}{39} \times \frac{52}{84}$

2 Four fifths of the people in a café are male.
Three quarters of these males are over 20 years old.
What fraction of the people in the café are males over 20 years old?

3 A hotel's oil tank is two thirds full.
The hotel uses four fifths of the remaining oil.
How full is the oil tank now?

4 There are $2\frac{3}{4}$ pints of milk in a large jug.

Meg uses two thirds of the milk.
How much milk does she use?

5 A lawn measures $4\frac{2}{3}$ yards by $6\frac{1}{3}$ yards. What is its area?

6 Two fifths of the pupils in a class go home by car.
Two thirds of those who are left go home by bus.
The remaining six pupils walk home.
How many pupils are in the class?

Points to remember

⊙ To multiply fractions, cancel first, then multiply the numerators and multiply the denominators.

⊙ To multiply mixed numbers, convert them to improper fractions.

3 Dividing fractions

This lesson will help you to divide fractions.

Exercise 3

Four fifths of this rectangle is shaded.

The shaded area is divided into three equal parts by the horizontal lines.

So four fifths divided into three equal parts, is the same as finding one third of four fifths,

or $\frac{4}{5} \div \frac{3}{1} = \frac{4}{5} \times \frac{1}{3} = \frac{4}{15}$.

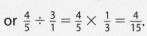

In general, to divide by a fraction, turn it upside down and multiply.

Example

$\frac{5}{14} \div \frac{10}{21} = \frac{5}{14} \times \frac{21}{10}$ Turn the dividing fraction upside down and multiply.

$= \frac{\overset{1}{5}}{\underset{2}{14}} \times \frac{\overset{3}{21}}{\underset{2}{10}}$ Cancel the 21 and 14 by 7, and the 5 and 10 by 5.

$= \frac{1 \times 3}{2 \times 2}$ Multiply the numerators and multiply the denominators.

$= \frac{3}{4}$

Do this exercise **without a calculator**.

Give each answer in its simplest form. Show your working.

(1)   **a** $\frac{3}{5} \div \frac{2}{15}$ **b** $\frac{3}{5} \div \frac{18}{25}$ **c** $\frac{4}{5} \div \frac{2}{3}$ **d** $\frac{3}{22} \div \frac{9}{11}$

     e $\frac{6}{7} \div \frac{3}{14}$ **f** $\frac{5}{11} \div \frac{5}{22}$ **g** $\frac{5}{8} \div \frac{25}{32}$ **h** $\frac{9}{14} \div \frac{18}{21}$

(2)   Two thirds of the sweets in a jar are shared equally among 5 children.

     What fraction of the sweets in the jar does each child get?

(3)   Angela has a bar of chocolate.
She keeps half for herself and shares the rest equally between 3 friends.

     What fraction of the full bar does each friend get?

(4) $2\frac{2}{3}$ pints of milk are poured into 4 glasses.
Each glass has the same amount of milk in it.
How much milk is there in each glass?

(5)   The perimeter of an octagonal garden pond is $14\frac{2}{3}$ yards long.
What is the length of each side of the pond?

(6)   What fraction is exactly halfway between $\frac{1}{3}$ and $\frac{3}{4}$?

Extension problems

7   One lap of a running track is two thirds of a mile long.
Callum runs $7\frac{1}{3}$ miles.
How many laps does he run?

8   A jar of sugar has $3\frac{3}{5}$ cupfuls of sugar in it.
A recipe for a cake uses $\frac{3}{10}$ of a cupful of sugar.
How many cakes can be made from the sugar in the jar?

⊙ Points to remember

- ⊙ To divide by a fraction, multiply by its reciprocal.
- ⊙ You can use a calculator to multiply and divide fractions.

4 Percentage change

This lesson will help you to solve problems involving percentage changes, recognising which numbers to take as 100%, or as a whole.

Exercise 4

Example 1

Sam scored 21 out of 35 marks in a test. What was his percentage score?

In this calculation, we know the whole (35) and the part (21).

35	100%
21	?

We calculate the percentage that is equivalent to the fraction $\frac{21}{35}$:

$\frac{21}{35} \times 100 = \frac{3}{5} \times 100 = 3 \times 20 = 60$ **Answer** 60%

Example 2

A suit cost £50. It is reduced by 15% in a sale.
What is its sale price?

In this calculation, you know the whole (£50) and the percentage (15%).

£50	100%
?	85%

You need to find 85% or $\frac{85}{100}$ of £50.

$\frac{85}{100} \times 50 = \frac{85}{2} \times 1 = 42.5$ **Answer** £42.50

Example 3

Ros spent 7% of her savings on a camera costing £84.
How much did Ros have in savings?

Here you know the part (£84) and the percentage (7%).

?	100%
£84	7%

You can think of this calculation as first finding 1% by dividing 84 by 7, then finding 100% by multiplying by 100.

The calculation is:

$\frac{84}{7} \times 100 = \frac{12}{1} \times 100 = 1200$ **Answer** £1200

---

(1) Roger cracked 26 of the 65 nuts in a bowl.
What percentage of the nuts did he crack?

(2) A bottle of shower gel contains 320 ml.
A special-offer bottle contains 8% more.
How much shower gel is in the special-offer bottle?

(3) A high street store has reduced its prices by 15% for its summer sale.
The sale price of a video game is £47.60.
What did it cost before the sale?

(4) The cost for a child of a camping holiday
is 70% of the adult price.
The child's price is £336.
What is the cost for an adult?

(5) David went on a diet before his holiday.
He reduced his weight from 80 kg to 68 kg.
What percentage of his original weight
did he lose?

(6) VAT stands for Value Added Tax.
You pay VAT of 17.5% on most things that you buy.
Daisy buys a stereo system that costs £290 without VAT.
How much VAT does she have to pay?

7 Parveen's savings account earned 5% interest last year.
She now has £294 in her savings account.
How much did Parveen have in her account before the interest was added?

8 Ryan bought a new car.
Its value went down by 25% in its first year.
The car is now worth £12 600.
What did the car cost when it was new?

9 Sienna has had a pay rise of 4%.
She now gets paid £12 168 per year.
What was she paid before the pay rise?

10 Harry's bill for his mobile phone was £59.86.
This was 18% less than his previous bill.
How much was Harry's previous phone bill?

11 Rashida took a taxi home after the disco.
She worked out that the fare plus a 10% tip would be £5.28.
What was the cost of the fare?

12 A shoe shop had a sale.
Each day the prices of shoes were reduced by 15% of the prices on the day before.
Find the selling price of each of these on the second day of the sale.

a Some calf-length boots costing £40 before the sale

b Some sandals costing £32 before the sale

13 Play the **Percentage game** with a partner.

You need **N5.2 Resource sheet 4.1**,
counters in two colours and a calculator.

Rules

◉ Take turns.

◉ The first player chooses a percentage, works out that percentage of 450, and points to
the answer square. The other player checks with the calculator.

◉ If the first player is right, they can cover the answer with one of their counters.
If not, they miss that turn.

◉ The winner is the first to get four counters in a straight line in any direction.

14 Carole carried out a survey.
She asked people if they liked lemonade.
She worked out the percentage using her calculator.

73.1707317% of the people Carole asked said 'yes'.

There were fewer than 50 people in Carole's survey.
How many of them liked lemonade?

Points to remember

⊙ To find 20%, find 10% by dividing by 10, then multiply by 2.

⊙ You can find 30%, 40%, 50%, … in a similar way.

⊙ If there is no quick way to find a percentage, first find 1%,
then multiply by the percentage.

⊙ Think carefully about which number to take as a whole.

⊙ Always include any units in the answer.

5 Ratio

This lesson will help you to solve problems involving ratios, including unitary ratios.

 Did you know that…?

Ratio and proportion were discussed by the Greek
mathematician **Euclid** about 300 BC.

One of his definitions was: 'Let magnitudes that have
the same ratio be called proportional.'

The ratio symbol **:** was first used in England in 1633.
It appeared in **John Johnson's** *Arithmetick in Two
Bookes* for the fraction three quarters, which was
written as 3 : 4.

In 1684, the German mathematician **Gottfried von
Leibniz**, the inventor of one of the first calculating
machines, used the symbol **:** for both ratio and
division.

**17th century computing machine by
G. W. Leibniz**

Ratios are simplified like fractions. If necessary, change different units to the same unit.

The ratio of 2 m to 50 cm, or 200 cm to 50 cm, is written as 200 : 50, or 4 : 1.

A **unitary ratio** is in the form $1 : m$.

To change a ratio such as 5 : 9 to a unitary ratio, divide both sides by 5.
5 : 9 is equivalent to the ratio $\frac{5}{5} : \frac{9}{5}$, or 1 : 1.8

Example

Paula has mixed two fruit drinks.
Drink A has 6 parts of orange juice to 9 parts of mango juice.
Drink B has 5 parts of orange juice to 8 parts of mango juice.
Which drink has the higher proportion of mango juice?

In drink A, the ratio of orange to mango juice is 6 : 9 or $\frac{6}{6} : \frac{9}{6} = 1 : 1.5$.

In drink B, the ratio of orange to mango juice is 5 : 8 or $\frac{5}{5} : \frac{8}{5} = 1 : 1.6$.

There is a higher proportion of mango juice in drink B.

Given a ratio and the size of one part, you can find the other part.

1. Simplify these ratios.

   a 18 : 24   b 25 : 10 : 50   c 2 days : 16 hours

   d 75p : £6.25   e 3.5 kg : 1250 g   f 750 mm : 50 cm : 1.5 m

2. A sack of nuts contains 1.25 kg of hazelnuts, 3 kg of walnuts and 750 g of pecans.
   What is the ratio of hazelnuts to walnuts to pecans?

3. Fruit drink A is made from 2 parts orange juice and 7 parts apple juice.
   Fruit drink B is made from 5 parts orange juice and 17 parts apple juice.

   Which has more apple juice, 1 litre of drink A or 1 litre of drink B?
   Explain how you know.

4. Andrew does not like to eat too much fat.

   Cake mix A uses 5 parts flour to 3 parts of fat.
   Cake mix B uses 8 parts of flour to 5 parts of fat.

   Which cake mix should Andrew choose? Explain why.

5 Which of each of these is the best value for money?

a 250 ml of orange juice for 39p
400 ml of orange juice for 58p
1 litre of orange juice for £1.50

b 15 postcards for £7.80
28 postcards for £14.70
40 postcards for £21.20

Exercise 5B

Example 1

Three boys divide £92 in the ratio 1:3:4.
How much money does each boy get?

There are 1 + 3 + 4 = 8 shares.

One share is $\frac{1}{8}$ of £92, or £11.50.

Three shares are $\frac{3}{8}$ of £92, or £34.50.

Four shares are $\frac{4}{8}$ of £92, or £46.

So the boys get £11.50, £34.50 and £46.

Example 2

A line segment is divided in the ratio 5:7.
The shorter part of the line is 15 cm long.
What is the length of the longer part?

There are 5 + 7 = 12 shares.

$\frac{5}{12}$ of the line is 15 cm.

For $\frac{1}{12}$ calculate 15 cm ÷ 5 = 3 cm.

For $\frac{7}{12}$ calculate 3 cm × 7 = 21 cm.

So the longer part of the line is 21 cm.

1 The instructions for a fruit drink say:

> Mix one part cranberry juice with three
> parts raspberry juice and six parts water.

I want to make 3 litres of this fruit drink.
How many millilitres of each of these should I use?

a cranberry juice   **b** raspberry juice   **c** water

2 The audience of 360 people at a circus consisted of men, women and children in the ratio 4:5:9.

a How many of the people were men?

b How many were women?

c How many were children?

3 Pete and Dave share the cost of some circus tickets in the ratio 3:8.
Pete's share is £45.
How much is Dave's share?

(4) A gym's members are men and women in the ratio 8 : 5.
There are 65 women.
How many members of the gym are there?

(5) Brass is made from copper and zinc
in the ratio 5 : 3 by weight.

  a A brass fender has 6 kg of zinc.
  What is the weight of the copper in the fender?

  b A brass statue has 25 kg of copper.
  What is the weight of the zinc in the statue?

(6) A recipe requires 50 g of sugar for every 125 g of flour.

  a How much flour is needed for 400 g of sugar?

  b How much sugar is needed for 400 g of flour?

(7) Halim, Malik and Asmat share some money in ratio of 2 : 5 : 9.
Halim's share is £28.50.

  a How much money is Malik's share?

  b How much money is Asmat's share?

(8) An alloy is made from iron, copper and zinc in the ratio 7 : 3 : 4.
92 kg of zinc is used to make the alloy.

  a How much iron is used?

  b How much copper is used?

(9) A type of plaster is made by mixing $2\frac{1}{4}$ parts cement to 3 parts of sand.
How much cement needs to be mixed with 27 kg of sand to make the plaster?

⊙ Points to remember

- ⊙ Ratios are simplified like fractions.
- ⊙ A **unitary ratio** is written in the form 1 : m.
- ⊙ To change 2 : 15 to a unitary ratio, divide both sides by 2 to get 1 : 7.5.
- ⊙ When you divide a quantity in the ratio 3 : 7, the smaller part is $\frac{3}{10}$ and the larger part is $\frac{7}{10}$ of the whole quantity.

6 Direct proportion

This lesson will help you to recognise when two sets of numbers are in proportion and solve problems involving direct proportion.

Exercise 6A

When we convert miles to kilometres, the ratio of miles : kilometres is always the same.

We say the number of kilometres is **directly proportional** to the number of miles.

miles : kilometres = 25 : 40
= 5 : 8

miles : kilometres = 100 : 160
= 5 : 8

miles : kilometres = 2.5 : 4
= 5 : 8

Miles	Kilometres
5	8
25	40
100	160
2.5	4

Some problems involving direct proportion can be solved using **scaling**.

Example 1

Paté costs £1.80 for 75 g.
Susan pays £9 for some paté.

How many grams of paté does she buy?

Susan buys 75 g × 5 = 375 g of paté.

	Cost (p)	Paté (g)
	180	75
× 5	900	?

Harder problems involving direct proportion can be solved using the **unitary method** and a calculator if necessary.

Example 2

The mass of 60 ml of olive oil is 45 g.
What is the mass of 108 ml of olive oil?

108 ml of olive oil has a mass of 81 g.

	Oil (ml)	Mass (g)
	60	45
÷ 60	1	0.75
× 108	108	81

Do these questions **without using a calculator**. Show your working.

① 5 buns cost £1.50.

    a What do 16 buns cost?

    b How many buns can you buy for £12?

② 3 biros cost 96p.

    a Work out the cost of 5 of the biros.

    b How many biros can you buy for £16?

③ Kate is paid £48 for 6 hours' work.

    a How much is she paid for 4 hours' work?

    b Kate is paid £144. How many hours' work did she do?

④

Chickpea curry
for 4 people

      2 large onions

      200 g sweet potato

      400 g chickpeas

      1 teaspoon curry paste

This recipe is for chickpea curry for 4 people.

    a Work out the amounts needed to make chickpea curry for 10 people.

    b Raj makes chickpea curry using 350 g sweet potato. How many people will his curry feed?

⑤ 1 metre of ribbon costs £1.35.
What does a 40 cm piece of ribbon cost?

⑥ The weight of card is directly proportional to its area.

A piece of card has an area of 36 cm^2 and a weight of 15 g.
A larger piece of the same card has an area of 48 cm^2.

Calculate the weight of the larger piece of card.

 Did you know that...?

The exchange rate between two currencies tells how much one is worth in terms of the other. For example, an exchange rate of 120 Japanese yen (¥) to the United States dollar ($) means that 120 yen are worth the same as 1 US dollar.

The foreign exchange market is one of the largest markets in the world. Some people estimate that about 2 trillion United States dollars change hands every day.

Exchange rates vary from day to day, depending on supply and demand.

You may **use a calculator**. Show your method.

1. Adam went to the USA.
   The exchange rate was £1 = 1.8 US dollars.

   a Adam changed £450 into dollars.
   How many dollars did he get?

   b When Adam returned home, he had 54 dollars left.
   He changed them back to pounds.
   How many pounds did Adam get?

2. a Janet went to Spain.
   She changed £200 into euros.

   The exchange rate was £1 = 1.62 euros.
   How much did Janet get in euros?

   b Janet came home. She had 62 euros left.
   She changed them back to pounds.

   The new exchange rate was £1 = 1.55 euros.
   How many pounds did Janet get?

3. Bader bought 15 tablets of guest soap for £9.75 in the duty-free shop.
   Work out the cost of 9 tablets of the guest soap.

4. Louise went to Switzerland.
   She hired a car for 5 days for 470 Swiss francs.

   The exchange rate was £1 = 2.35 Swiss francs.
   How much did Louise pay in pounds to hire the car?

5 John flew from Sydney to London.
His return flight cost him 1875 Australian dollars.

One Australian dollar is worth 40p.
What was the cost of his flight in pounds?

6 Assume that £1 is worth 1.75 US dollars.
In London, a pair of designer jeans costs £45.
In San Francisco, an identical pair of jeans costs 75 US dollars.
In which city are the jeans cheaper, London or San Francisco?

Extension problem

7 5 miles are approximately 8 kilometres.
What could be wrong with this Californian road sign?

Points to remember

⊙ If the ratio of two quantities stays the same as they get bigger or smaller, they are in **direct proportion**.

⊙ When you solve direct proportion problems:
  – use the **unitary method** to make the value of one of the variables to 1;
  – make sure that related quantities are in the same units.

How well are you doing?

Can you:

- add, subtract, multiply and divide fractions?
- solve problems involving percentage changes, ratios and direct proportion?

Proportional reasoning (no calculator)

1 Julie makes a fruit salad using mangoes, oranges and apples.
For every 2 mangoes, she uses 3 oranges and 7 apples.
Julie uses 36 fruits altogether.
How many oranges does she use?

2 **a** Pine nuts cost 70p for 100 grams.
What is the cost of 350 grams of pine nuts?

b Walnuts cost 80p for 120 grams.
Mohamed pays £4 for a packet of walnuts.
How many grams of walnuts does he get?

3 *1999 level 6*
In a magazine there are three adverts on the same page.

> Advert 1 uses $\frac{1}{4}$ of the page.
>
> Advert 2 uses $\frac{1}{8}$ of the page.
>
> Advert 3 uses $\frac{1}{16}$ of the page.

In total, what fraction of the page do the three adverts use?
Show your working.

4 *2005 level 6*

a How many eighths are there in one quarter?

b Now work out $\frac{3}{4} \div \frac{1}{8}$.

Proportional reasoning (calculator allowed)

(5) It is 8831 kilometres to Tokyo from Cape Reinga in New Zealand.

5 miles is approximately 8 kilometres.

What is the approximate distance in miles from Cape Reinga to Tokyo?

AA road sign at Cape Reinga, NZ

(6) *Year 8 Optional Test level 6*

The average mass of a female heart is 265 grams.
The average mass of a female heart is 19% greater than the average mass of a male heart.

What is the average mass of a male heart?
Show your working, and write your answer to the nearest gram.

(7) *2001 level 6*

The labels on yoghurt A and yoghurt B show this information.

Yoghurt A	125 g
Each 125 g provides	
Energy	430 kJ
Protein	4.5 g
Carbohydrate	11.1 g
Fat	4.5 g

Yoghurt B	150 g
Each 150 g provides	
Energy	339 kJ
Protein	6.6 g
Carbohydrate	13.1 g
Fat	0.2 g

a How many grams of protein does 100 g of yoghurt A provide?
Show your working.

b A boy eats the same amount of yoghurt A and yoghurt B.
Which yoghurt provides him with more carbohydrate?
Show your working.

Enquiry 1

This unit will help you to:

- use the data-handling cycle to carry out a statistical investigation;
- represent and interpret data in grouped frequency diagrams;
- use stem-and-leaf diagrams to help work out statistics and compare sets of data.

1 Stem-and-leaf diagrams

This lesson will help you to draw and interpret stem-and-leaf diagrams.

Exercise 1

The **range** measures the spread of a set of data.
It is the difference between the largest and smallest values.

Smallest number = 8   Largest number = 37   Range = 37 − 8 = 29 people

The **mode**, **median** and **mean** all measure the **average** of a set of data.

- The mode is the value that appears most often.
- The median is the middle value when the values are listed in order.
- The mean is the sum of all the values divided by the number of values.

A **stem-and-leaf diagram** shows each item of data in a data set.

This stem-and-leaf diagram shows the number of people waiting at 15 bus stops.
The stem represents 'tens digits' and the leaves represent 'units digits'.

```
0 | 8 9
1 | 1 5 5 8
2 | 0 2 4 4 4 8
3 | 1 3 7
```

Key: 2 | 4 means 24 people.

You can use a stem-and-leaf diagram to work out statistics. For the diagram above:

Mode = 24   Median = 22   Mean = 21.3

The mean is calculated from

(8 + 9 + 11 + 15 + 15 + 18 + 20 + 22 + 24 + 24 + 24 + 28 + 31 + 33 + 37) ÷ 15.

A stem-and-leaf diagram can be used to draw a **grouped frequency diagram**.

Example

Here are the ages in years of 25 members of a sports club.

15	23	36	18	42	27	17	24	31
35	19	23	26	28	34	40	30	29
19	20	31	32	23	26	32		

a   Draw a stem-and-leaf diagram to show this data.

Write the ages in order from lowest to highest.

15	17	18	19	19	20	23	23	23
24	26	26	27	28	29	30	31	31
32	32	34	35	36	40	42		

Draw the stem-and-leaf diagram.

```
1 | 5 7 8 9 9
2 | 0 3 3 3 4 6 6 7 8 9
3 | 0 1 1 2 2 4 5 6
4 | 0 2
```

Key: 2 | 4 means 24 members

b   Represent the data on a grouped frequency diagram.

Make a grouped frequency table for the data.

Draw the frequency diagram.

Age	Frequency
10−19	5
20−29	10
30−39	8
40−49	2

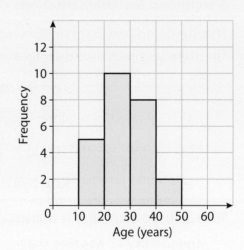

A grouped frequency diagram does not show the original data.

1   This stem-and-leaf diagram shows scores
    out of 50 in a maths test.

    a   How many people took the test?

    b   What is the range of the scores?

    c   What score is the mode?

    d   What is the median score?

0	8	9	9					
1	1	3	4	5	5	8		
2	0	6	6	6	6	7	8	9
3	1	3	3	5	8	8		
4	0	1	3	3	8			

Key: 3 | 5 means 35 marks

2   This stem-and-leaf diagram shows the
    times, in seconds, of tracks on a CD.

20	8			
21	4	8		
22	5	6	7	8
23	0	3	5	
24	2	6	8	8
25	7			

Key: 21 | 5 means 215 seconds

a   How many tracks are on the CD?   b   What is the range of the times?

c   What time is the mode?   d   What is the median time?

3   17 athletes tried the long jump. They jumped these lengths in metres.

    4.2   5.5   3.8   6.2   4.4   4.5   6.4   5.3   5.5

    4.5   5.8   4.1   6.2   3.4   5.5   6.8   5.1

    a   Copy and complete this stem-and-leaf diagram.

    b   How many jumps were more than 6 m?

    c   Calculate the range of the jumps.

    d   Find the median and mode of the lengths jumped.

    e   In a second jump, the shortest length jumped was 3.2 m.
        The range was the same as in the first jump.
        The median was 0.2 m less than in the first jump.
        The mode was equal to the median.

        Draw a possible stem-and-leaf diagram for the lengths jumped on the second jump.

3	4
4	
5	
6	

Key: 3 | 8 means
       3.8 metres

4 30 pupils solved a puzzle.
The stem-and-leaf diagram shows the times, in seconds, that they took.

a Copy and complete this table.

Time (t seconds)	Frequency
$90 \leqslant t < 100$	
$100 \leqslant t < 110$	
...	

9	0	8				
10	3	3	7	9	9	
11	0	6	6	8	9	
12	2	2	2	4	6	8	9
13	3	4	5	5	6	6
14	2	7	8			
15	4	8				

Key: 11 | 6 means 116 seconds

b Draw a grouped frequency diagram for the data.

c Show that the median and the mode are in the same group.

Extension problem

5 Here are the hours of sunshine recorded at 65 UK weather stations on 10 May 2000.

0.6 0.9 1.6 1.9 2.2 2.2 2.5 2.6 2.6 2.7

2.9 3.0 3.0 3.0 3.0 3.1 3.2 3.2 3.5 3.5

3.5 3.7 3.8 3.9 4.0 4.1 4.5 4.5 4.6 4.6

4.6 4.7 4.9 5.0 5.1 5.5 5.5 5.6 5.8 5.9

5.9 6.1 6.2 6.2 6.2 6.3 6.6 6.6 6.7 6.8

6.8 6.9 6.9 6.9 6.9 6.9 7.0 7.0 7.1 7.6

7.7 7.8 7.8 8.0 8.0

a Draw a stem-and-leaf diagram to show this information.

b Work out the median, the mode and the range

c Copy and complete this grouped frequency table for the data.

Hours of sunshine (h)	Frequency
$0 \leqslant h < 1.0$	
$1.0 \leqslant h < 2.0$	
...	

d Draw a grouped frequency diagram for the data.

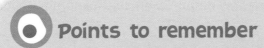
2 Starting a statistical investigation 1

This lesson will help you to learn how to start a statistical investigation.

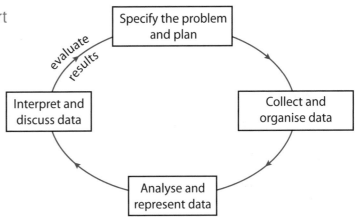

Exercise 2

Example

This table shows how Adele started an investigation on young people's memories.

Steps	What Adele did
1 Specify the problem and plan	Adele suggested: **'Girls have better memories than boys.'** She decided to test this hypothesis by asking pupils in her class to do a memory test. In the test each pupil looked at 40 items for 30 seconds. They then had one minute to list the items that they could remember.
2 Collect and organise data	Adele recorded the number of items remembered by each pupil and their gender.
3 Analyse and represent data	Adele presented the data in two stem-and-leaf diagrams, one for boys and one for girls.

These sheets were used to investigate how well people estimate the number of dots on a page.

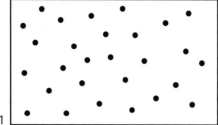
Sheet 1

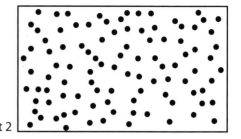
Sheet 2

1 Yonah thinks that it is easier to estimate when there are fewer dots on a page.

  a Write a statement as a hypothesis for Yonah to base an investigation on.

  b Yonah showed the sheets to each pupil in his class for 10 seconds.
     He asked them to estimate the number of dots.
     Their estimates are shown below.

Sheet 1

22	18	31	32	19	24	27
25	27	28	34	27	27	28
17	33	32	29	19	26	40
23	30	25	34	17	17	

Sheet 2

82	95	91	112	119	124	72
85	95	95	104	125	127	130
77	93	84	75	84	123	105
128	88	92	100	109	126	

     Draw a stem-and-leaf diagram for each set of data.

2 Ayla asked 30 pupils in Years 7, 9 and 11 to estimate the number of dots on sheet 2.
   The table shows the data she collected.

Year 7														
70	100	55	115	98	105	90	80	95	120	60	105	70	98	88
115	90	98	87	75	95	135	60	115	85	100	88	95	70	105

Year 9														
65	88	108	95	100	83	105	108	75	90	86	110	80	90	118
105	95	80	110	70	125	110	88	95	125	108	78	95	95	110

Year 11														
95	110	80	110	125	80	95	100	115	70	105	125	80	115	90
108	80	128	115	70	108	60	128	90	118	135	115	75	105	105

  a Write a statement that Ayla could test.

  b Draw a stem-and-leaf diagram for each set of data.

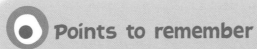

Points to remember

⊙ Make a **hypothesis** about what the results of the investigation might be.

⊙ To decide if your hypothesis is true, **collect and analyse** appropriate data.

⊙ You could order the data and draw a stem-and-leaf diagram.

3 Completing a statistical investigation 1

This lesson will help you to complete a statistical investigation.

Exercise 3

Example

This table shows the steps Adele took to complete her investigation on memory.

Steps	What Adele did
1 Analyse and represent data	Adele used the stem-and-leaf diagrams showing how many items boys and girls remembered to work out averages (mode and median) and the spread (the range).
2 Interpret and discuss data	Adele compared the averages and spread for boys and girls. She summarised any other differences or similarities she noted.
3 Draw a conclusion and evaluate results	Adele looked at the original hypothesis: **'Girls have better memories than boys.'** She used her evidence from the stem-and-leaf diagrams to decide whether the hypothesis was true or false.

① **a** Use your stem-and-leaf diagrams from Exercise 2 to copy and complete this table.

		Sheet 1	Sheet 2
Average	Median		
	Mode		
Spread	Range		

b The actual number of dots on sheet 1 is 28.
The actual number of dots on sheet 2 is 99.

Copy and complete these statements.

> The estimates for sheet … are more varied than those for sheet …
>
> The average estimate for sheet … is closer to the actual number of dots than for sheet …
>
> More estimates were close to the actual number of dots on sheet …
>
> For both sheets, more pupils underestimated the number of dots but more pupils did this on sheet …

c Is the statement you wrote in Exercise 2 question **1a** true or false?
Explain your answer.

2 Look at the statement you wrote in Exercise 2 question **2a**
and the stem-and-leaf diagrams that you drew in question **2b**.

a Use the stem-and-leaf diagrams to copy and complete this table.

		Year 7	Year 9	Year 11
Average	Median			
	Mode			
Spread	Range			

b The actual number of dots on sheet 2 is 99.

Write sentences comparing the average and spread for each of the sets of estimates.

3 **a** Write sentences describing other similarities or differences between the data sets.

b Is the statement you wrote in Exercise 2 question **2a** true or false?
Write a paragraph stating and justifying your conclusion.

Points to remember

- **Interpret** the data by comparing the spread (range) and average values (median, mode or mean) of the data sets.
- Look for other **similarities or differences** between the sets of data.
- **Draw a conclusion**. Decide if your original hypothesis is true or not.
- **Evaluate** results. Decide whether there are further questions to explore.

4 Data collection sheets

This lesson will help you to design a data collection sheet, including one for grouped continuous data.

Exercise 4A

Example 1

Rhona designed a data collection sheet to help her collect the data needed to test these statements:

☺ 'Most people travel to an out-of-town shopping centre by car.'

☺ 'A car is more likely to be used the longer the distance travelled.'

For each person asked, she completed a column by ticking appropriate boxes.

	1	2	3	4	5	6	7	8	9	10	11	12	13	14	15
Age															
15−24															
25−34	✓														
35−44		✓	✓												
45−54				✓	✓										
55+															
Distance travelled (*m* miles)															
$m < 5$															
$5 \leqslant m < 10$	✓				✓										
$10 \leqslant m < 20$		✓	✓												
$20 \leqslant m < 30$				✓											
$m \geqslant 30$															
Method of travel															
Bus	✓														
Train				✓											
Car		✓	✓		✓										
Walk															
Other															

Large sets of data are often collected in groups called **class intervals**.

Class intervals should have no gaps or overlaps. They should span the range of the data.

Choose class intervals so that there are not too many or too few groups.
Between 5 and 7 groups are usually best.

Example 2

This grouped frequency table show how the population of the UK was distributed in 1999.

Age	Population
0–14	5 917 365
15–29	6 234 857
30–44	7 608 956
45–59	5 705 792
60–74	3 364 102
75–89	1 533 287
90+	126 935

Work in a group of four.

① This chart shows how people travelled from the UK in 1988.

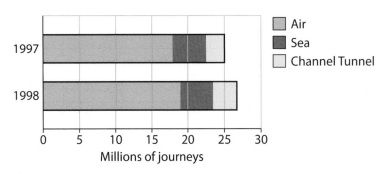

Results of a 1998 survey on the method of travel from the UK

Now look at the two data collection sheets on the next page.

a Discuss which data collection sheet could have generated the chart.

b What statement is the chart helping to investigate?

c What problems might be met when using sheets 1 or 2?

Data collection sheet 1

Circle or write in the appropriate answer

Age   16–25   26–35   36–45   46–55   over 55

Gender   M   F

Number of people travelling in group   ....

Method of travel   Air   Sea   Channel Tunnel

Destination ....

Accommodation at destination   Hotel
Self-catering (apartment or house)
Tent
Other

Data collection sheet 2

Circle or write in the appropriate answer

Age   16–25   26–35   36–45   46–55   over 55

Gender   M   F

Number of people travelling in group   ....

Method of travel this year   Air   Sea   Channel Tunnel

Method of travel last year   Air   Sea   Channel Tunnel

Destination ....

(2) Here is an alternative way of collecting information about travel from the UK.
Discuss and write sentences to explain how the sheet could be used.

Age range	M or F	Method of travel last year	Destination last year	Method of travel this year	Destination this year
16–25	M	Air	San Francisco	Air	New York
36–45	M	Channel Tunnel	Paris	Channel Tunnel	Paris
26–35	F	Sea	Calais	Sea	Amsterdam
16–25	M	Sea	Oslo	Air	Sydney

(3) What statement could be investigated using the sheets in question **1** that could not be investigated using the alternative sheet in question **2**?

① Sandit wants to test the statement:

'Most Year 8 pupils are more than 150 cm tall.'

He collects these heights of 50 Year 8 pupils to the nearest centimetre.

149	162	150	157	166	159	151	145	160	153
140	157	156	157	158	156	154	154	150	163
161	152	172	153	159	153	158	168	153	152
152	164	155	146	157	188	180	153	160	170
148	129	154	157	155	128	168	154	150	167

Copy and complete the table for this data.

Height (h cm)	Tally	Frequency
$h < 140$		
$140 \leqslant h < 150$		
...		

② The bleep test is a fitness test.

You do continuous 20-metre runs in time with recorded bleeps.
The time between the bleeps gets less as the test goes on.

You are given a fitness level from 0 to 23 depending on how many runs you can do before you can no longer keep up with the bleeps.

Only the very top sports people score levels above 20.

a Design a data collection sheet that records bleep test scores for males and females of different ages.

b Record these bleep test scores on your data collection sheet.

Tanya	F	aged 24	bleep level 7.2		Sue	F	aged 18	bleep level 7.4
Dipak	M	aged 37	bleep level 8.4		Lee	M	aged 27	bleep level 9.2
Terry	M	aged 53	bleep level 6.6		Kym	F	aged 43	bleep level 5.4

(3) Work in a group of four.

Your teacher will give your group one of these statements.

'More goals in football matches are scored towards the end of the game.'

'You can't rely on a bus turning up on time.'

'Young people watch more television than adults.'

'Most people shop at shopping centres closer to their homes.'

Answer the questions below for your group's statement.

a Decide on the data you need to collect in order to test if the statement is true or not.

b Design a data collection sheet.

c Decide how you would represent the data.

d Suggest how you could extend your investigation.

⦿ Points to remember

⊙ Make sure that the data you collect is relevant to your hypothesis.

⊙ Collect continuous data in groups that span the range of the data. These groups are called **class intervals**.

⊙ Choose class intervals so that the number of groups is neither too small nor too large. It is usually best to aim for 5 to 7 groups.

5 Starting a statistical investigation 2

This lesson will extend your skills in planning and carrying out a statistical investigation.

Exercise 5

A statistical investigation can involve collecting discrete or continuous data.

The data is often collected in **grouped frequency tables** and represented in **grouped frequency diagrams**.

Example

The table shows how Tim started an investigation on how good people's memories are.

Steps	What Tim did
1 Specify the problem and plan	Tim suggested: **'Boys have better memories than girls.'** He decided to test this statement by asking pupils in his class to do a memory test. In the test each pupil looked at 40 items for 30 seconds. Tim timed how long it took them to remember 25 of the items.
2 Collect and organise data	Tim recorded the gender and time for each pupil in two grouped frequency tables, one for boys and one for girls.
3 Analyse and represent data	Tim represented the data in two grouped frequency diagrams.

Work with a partner.

In this lesson and the next you will carry out a statistical investigation based on the data in the tables below.

These show estimates in metres of the height of an oak tree in a local park made by 50 boys and 50 girls in Year 7 and 50 boys and 50 girls in Year 10.

Estimates by Year 7 boys		Estimates by Year 7 girls		Estimates by Year 10 boys		Estimates by Year 10 girls	
18	36	28	36	28	40	45	32
29	25	26	28	30	47	30	30
32	50	43	29	52	55	20	35
40	43	40	31	48	35	34	50
36	35	28	42	54	22	39	24
26	39	42	29	45	35	55	36
19	23	27	34	38	46	35	40
42	17	32	31	50	50	48	30
31	44	31	27	44	45	20	25
26	29	41	39	54	45	42	40
52	32	29	44	34	26	35	46
38	37	37	23	42	55	25	36
56	41	49	50	46	34	35	29
27	25	24	35	32	55	45	35
29	34	24	28	45	42	20	35
47	51	37	39	29	52	34	40
37	47	29	28	48	36	30	20
41	36	40	40	40	49	35	38
35	26	33	31	35	45	25	32
42	29	22	19	47	50	30	28
21	34	31	28	50	36	43	55
28	43	29	33	38	49	35	32
34	52	19	49	42	37	36	25
37	38	32	29	39	58	47	40
41	44	37	41	60	40	28	34

1   **a**   Is the data discrete or continuous? Explain your answer.

      b   Winston decides to test the statement:

         '**Boys estimate more accurately than girls.**'

        Write another statement that could be investigated using this data.

      c   Using appropriate class intervals, record each set of data in an appropriate grouped frequency table.

      d   Represent each set of data on a grouped frequency diagram.

Points to remember

⊙ Base your investigation on a hypothesis about what the results might be.

⊙ Collect continuous data in **grouped frequency tables**.

⊙ Continuous data can be represented in a **grouped frequency diagram**.

6 Completing a statistical investigation 2

This lesson will extend your skills in interpreting data and drawing conclusions.

Exercise 6

Example

This table shows how Tim completed his investigation on memory.

Steps	What Tim did
3 Analyse and represent data	Tim used the grouped frequency diagrams (showing the time it takes to remember 25 items) to work out the modal class and the group in which the median lies.
	He also worked out which data set – boys or girls – has a bigger spread.
4 Interpret and discuss data	Tim compared the averages and ranges of the times for the boys and girls.
	He also summarised any other differences or similarities between the data sets.
5 Evaluate results	Tim looked at the original statement: '**Boys have better memories than girls.**' He used the evidence from the grouped frequency diagrams to decide whether it is true or false.

1 In this question you will complete the statistical investigation you started in the previous lesson.

a Use the data and diagrams from Exercise 5 to copy and complete this table.

		Year 7		Year 10	
		Boys	**Girls**	**Boys**	**Girls**
Average	**Group in which median lies**				
	Modal class				
Spread	**Range**				

b The oak tree is 37 m high to the nearest metre.

Compare the spread of the estimates for boys and girls for both year groups.

Look at how close the average estimates are to the accurate value.

c Write a statement about other differences or similarities between the data sets.

d Look at the statement 'Boys estimate more accurately than girls.'

Is the statement is true or false? Explain your answer.

e Repeat parts **a** to **d** for the other statement you wrote in question **1** part **b** of Exercise 5.

Extension problem

2 Five friends are investigating who can estimate lengths the best.

They each estimate nine different lengths of increasing size.

They work out their estimate as a percentage of the actual length to the nearest whole number.

A result of 100% means an accurate estimate.

A result greater than 100% means an overestimate.

A result less than 100% means an underestimate.

The results are shown in the table (page 92) together with the level that each pupil obtained in a practice test.

Length to be estimated	Estimates (%)				
	Amy	Ben	Cyd	Den	Eli
35 mm	86	91	100	129	109
145 mm	83	97	110	93	97
250 mm	88	80	120	104	100
75 cm	93	100	93	107	93
4.55 m	88	110	99	105	99
10.45 m	96	115	120	100	105
22.5 m	111	107	133	98	89
44 m	91	102	91	114	91
83 m	108	84	92	90	102
143 m	84	87	105	112	87
385 m	78	104	90	83	117
KS3 level	5	6	8	6	7

a Write some statements that could be tested using this table of data.

b Use the data to test the truth of the statements you wrote in part **a**.
Explain your answers.

Points to remember

⊙ To carry out a statistical investigation, follow the steps in the data-handling cycle.

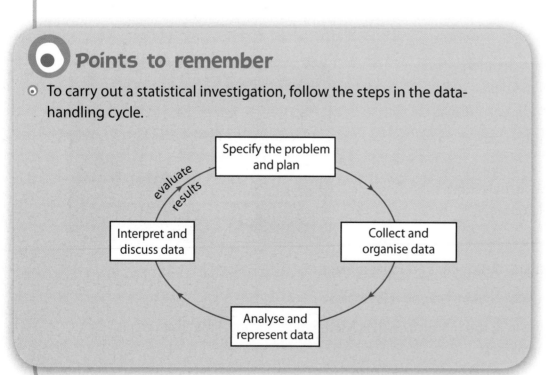

How well are you doing?

1. *2005 level 6*

   Bumps are built on a road to slow cars down. The stem-and-leaf diagrams show the speed of 15 cars before and after the bumps were built.

Before						After					
2						2	3	4	4		
2	7	8				2	6	6	7	8	8	9
3	0	2	4			3	0	0	0	1	2
3	5	6	8	9		3	5				
4	1	3	4	4	4	4					
4	6					4					

   Key: 2 | 3 means 23 mph.

   a Use the diagrams to copy and complete these sentences.

   Before the bumps, the maximum speed was …… mph, and …… cars went at more than 30 mph.

   After the bumps, the maximum speed was …… mph, and …… cars went at more than 30 mph.

   b Show that the median speed fell by 10 mph.

2. Look at the stem-and-leaf diagrams in question 1.

   a Suggest a statement that could be tested using the data in the stem-and-leaf diagrams.

   b Compare the average speeds before and after the bumps were built.

   c Compare the spread of the speeds before and after the bumps were built.

   d Is the statement you suggested in part a true or false?
   Give reasons for your answer.

The two diagrams show the heights of some girls and boys.

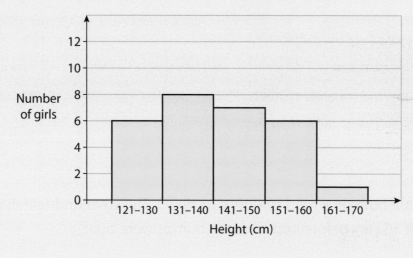

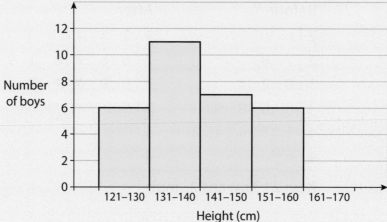

a Use the diagrams to decide whether these statements are true or false.

> There are more girls than boys.

Write True or False. Show calculations to explain how you know.

> The modal class for girls is the same as the modal class for boys.

Write True or False. Explain how you know.

b The height of the shortest girl is the same as the height of the shortest boy.

Is the range of girls' heights greater than the range of boys' heights?

Write Yes or No. Explain how you know.

Equations and formulae

This unit will help you to:

- simplify expressions;
- substitute numbers into formulae;
- change the subject of a formula;
- solve equations.

1 Multiplying out brackets

This lesson will help you to multiply out brackets and simplify expressions.

Exercise 1

When you **multiply out** a bracket, remember to multiply across all terms in the bracket.

Example 1

$5(2x + 4) = 10x + 20$

Example 2

$-3(7x - 2) = -21x + 6$

Multiplying out brackets and factorising are opposite actions to each other.

You can **simplify** an expression by multiplying out the brackets and collecting like terms.

Example 3

Simplify $2(7x - 4) - 5(2x + 3)$

$2(7x - 4) - 5(2x + 3) = 14x - 8 - 10x - 15$ Multiply out the brackets.

$= 4x - 23$ Collect like terms.

① Multiply out the brackets in these expressions.

a $2(x + 6)$

b $4(y - 3)$

c $9(x + 4)$

d $3(x + 7)$

e $12(4x - 1)$

f $11(3a + 5)$

g $6(9 + 3t)$

h $25(8x - 2)$

i $5(7a + 3b)$

j $8(2p - 6q + r)$

② Multiply out the brackets and simplify these expressions.

    a $8(x + 1) + 3(x + 5)$ **b** $2(y + 1) + 4(y + 3)$

    c $5(s + 3) + 7(s + 6)$ **d** $6(p + 9) + 7(p + 7)$

    e $3(8a + 7) + 5(a - 3)$ **f** $4(10x - 5) + 12(3x + 7)$

    g $9(8t - 3) + 4(7t - 6)$ **h** $9(7b + 5) + 8(5b - 9)$

③ Find pairs of matching cards.

on cards

$28x + 63$	$18x + 36$	$8(3x + 6)$	$12(2x + 5)$
$30x + 48$	$40x + 15$	$24x + 48$	$5(8x + 3)$
$24x + 60$	$6(5x + 8)$	$7(4x + 9)$	$9(2x + 4)$

④ Multiply out the brackets in these expressions.

    a $-2(x - 5)$ **b** $-3(y + 7)$

    c $-8(x + 4)$ **d** $-6(2x - 6)$

    e $-9(4x - 1)$ **f** $-11(3a + 5)$

    g $-5(7s + 2t)$ **h** $-10(14x - 9y)$

    i $-100(7a + 3b - 6c)$ **j** $-4(15p - 11q + 10r)$

⑤ Multiply out the brackets and simplify these expressions.

    a $8(x + 3) - 3(x + 4)$ **b** $7(y + 8) - 3(y + 1)$

    c $9(s + 5) + 4(s - 3)$ **d** $5(p + 3) - (p - 8)$

    e $10(7a - 2) + 9(a - 2)$ **f** $8(5x - 2) - 4(3x + 10)$

    g $7(5t - 4) - 6(2t - 8)$ **h** $12(8b - 6) - 7(8b - 9)$

    i $4(5x - 7) - 3(6x - 9)$ **j** $4(15y - 5) - 2(10y - 14)$

⑥ Find the matching pairs.

on cards

$4(x + 5) + 3(7x + 4)$	$3(6x + 8) - 5(2x + 3)$
$2(7x + 3) - 3(4x + 1)$	$7(4x + 5) + 2(3x - 9)$
$6(4x + 2) + 5(x - 3)$	$5(9x + 4) - 4(5x - 3)$
$9(6x + 1) - 4(5x - 2)$	$5(2x + 3) - 4(2x + 3)$
$7(4x + 7) - 4(5x + 10)$	$6(5x + 1) - (x + 9)$

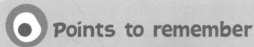

Points to remember

⊙ When you multiply out a bracket, remember to multiply each term in the bracket.

   Example $6(3x - 5) = 18x - 30$

⊙ Multiplying a bracket by a negative number changes the sign of each term in the bracket.

   Example $-4(2x - 3) = -8x + 12$

⊙ You can simplify an expression by multiplying out the brackets and collecting like terms.

2 Factorising expressions

This lesson will help you to factorise expressions.

Exercise 2

Numbers, letters or combinations of numbers and letters that divide exactly into an algebraic term are **factors** of that term. The factors of $5x$ are 1, 5, x and $5x$.

The **common factors** of $5x$ and $15x$ (excluding 1) are 5, x and $5x$.
The **highest common factor (HCF)** of $5x$ and $15x$ is $5x$.

You can **factorise** an expression by removing the HCF.

Example 1

$5x + 15 = 5(x + 3)$

Example 2

$12x - 20 = 4(3x - 5)$

Simplify expressions by multiplying out the brackets, collecting like terms and factorising.

Example 3

Simplify $2(7x - 4) - 5(2x + 4)$

$$2(7x - 4) - 5(2x + 4) = 14x - 8 - 10x - 20 \quad \text{Multiply out the brackets.}$$
$$= 4x - 28 \quad \text{Collect like terms.}$$
$$= 4(x - 7) \quad \text{Factorise.}$$

1   Write all the factors of these terms.

   a $5x$ **b** $3p$ **c** $6y$

   d xy **e** $3ab$ **f** $11c$

2. Write the common factors, excluding 1, of each set of terms.

   a $9x$ and $4x$

   b $12p$ and 15

   c $8x$ and $20y$

   d $18s$ and $45s$

   e $22s$, $55s$ and $99s$

   f $29m$, $32m$ and $24m$

3. Write the highest common factor of each set of terms.

   a $7x$ and 49

   b $3x$ and $7x$

   c $12p$ and $42p$

   d $55q$ and 10

   e $24m$ and $36m$

   f $48t$, $80t$ and 16

4. Factorise these expressions.

   a $26x + 18y$

   b $20a - 12$

   c $30m - 45n$

   d $49x - 63y$

   e $24ax + 72ay$

   f $44bp - 77bq$

   g $36xyz + 87wxy$

   h $56ab + 63abx$

5. Simplify these expressions. Factorise your answer.

   a $3(4x + 5) + 2(5x + 9)$

   b $4(2x + 5) + 5(4x + 3)$

   c $6(x - 3) - 2(2x - 7)$

   d $7(3x - 4) + 5(3x + 2)$

   e $8(3x - 7) - 7(2x - 3)$

   f $4(9x + 11) - 7(3x + 5)$

   g $10(6x + 5) - 4(3x + 5)$

   h $15(5x - 3) - 8(3x + 5)$

Extension problem

6. Factorise these expressions.

   a $4x^2 + 3xy$

   b $2ax - 6bx + 8x^3$

   c $ax^2 + bx^3$

   d $x^2y + xy^2$

   e $12x^3y^2 - 20x^2y^3$

   f $10x^2yz - 15xy^2z$

◉ Points to remember

⊙ You can factorise an expression by removing the **highest common factor**.

Example $16x + 28 = 4(4x + 7)$

⊙ You can simplify an expression by multiplying out the brackets, collecting like terms and factorising if possible.

⊙ Multiplying out brackets and factorising are opposite actions.

3 Substituting into formulae

This lesson will help you to substitute numbers into formulae.

Exercise 3

Remember to check the units before you substitute values into a formula.

Example

Callum walks for 45 minutes at 5 mph.
How far does he walk?

Use the formula $d = st$ to find the distance
when $s = 5$ mph and $t = 45$ minutes.

First convert 45 minutes to hours:

$t = 0.75$ hours

Distance $d = 5 \times 0.75 = 3.75$ miles

① The formula $m = \dfrac{y - c}{x}$ can be used to work out the gradient of a straight line.

Use this formula to work out the value of m when:

  a $x = 2, y = 13$ and $c = 6$ **b** $x = 3, y = 1$ and $c = 7$

② Work out the distance travelled using the formula $d = st$,
where d is the distance, s is the constant speed and t the time.

  a $s = 50$ mph, $t = 3$ hours   **b** $s = 62$ mph, $t = 30$ minutes

  c $s = 3$ m/s, $t = 2$ minutes   **d** $s = 4$ km/h, $t = 12$ minutes

③ Find the area of these triangles using
the formula $A = \frac{1}{2}bh$.

  a $b = 8$ cm, $h = 3$ cm

  b $b = 7$ cm, $h = 60$ mm

  c $b = 15$ m, $h = 750$ cm

  d $b = 80$ mm, $h = 9$ cm

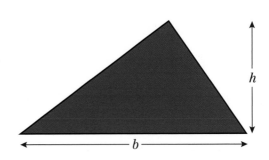

(4) Find the area of these trapeziums using the formula $A = \frac{1}{2}(a + b)h$.

a $a = 10\,\text{cm}, b = 8\,\text{cm}, h = 4\,\text{cm}$

b $a = 17\,\text{cm}, b = 90\,\text{mm}, h = 7\,\text{cm}$

c $a = 210\,\text{mm}, b = 15\,\text{cm}, h = 10\,\text{cm}$

d $a = 0.8\,\text{m}, b = 0.4\,\text{m}, h = 50\,\text{cm}$

(i) Did you know that...?

For many years weather forecasts in the UK used the Fahrenheit scale developed by the German **Gabriel Daniel Fahrenheit** in the eighteenth century. We now use the Celsius scale developed at about the same time by **Anders Celsius** from Sweden.

This formula changes degrees Celsius to Fahrenheit:

$$F = \frac{9}{5}C + 32$$

where F is the temperature in degrees Fahrenheit and C is the temperature in degrees Celsius.

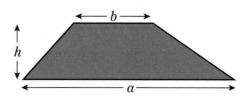

Anders Celsius

---

(5) Change these temperatures in degrees Celsius to degrees Fahrenheit.

a $C = 20$ b $C = 5$ c $C = 15$ d $C = 30$

(6) A little-known formula to change degrees Fahrenheit to degrees Celsius is.

$$C = \frac{5}{9}(F + 40) - 40$$

Change these temperatures in degrees Fahrenheit to degrees Celsius.

a $F = 50$ b $F = 212$ c $F = 23$ d $F = 32$

(7) The cooking time, T (minutes), to cook a joint of meat is given by the formula

$$T = 20w + 30$$

where w is the weight of the joint of meat in kilograms.

Use this formula to work out the cooking time when:

a $w = 5\,\text{kg}$ b $w = 3.5\,\text{kg}$

c $w = 750\,\text{g}$ d $w = 800\,\text{g}$

Extension problem

8 Find the period of a pendulum using the formula

$T = 2\pi\sqrt{\dfrac{l}{g}}$, where T is the period in seconds,

l the length in metres and g is the acceleration
due to gravity in m/s².

Use $\pi \approx 3$.

Give your answers to two decimal places.

a $l = 0.1\,\text{m}, g = 10\,\text{m/s}^2$

b $l = 0.25\,\text{m}, g = 9.8\,\text{m/s}^2$

c $l = 0.4\,\text{m}, g = 9.8\,\text{m/s}^2$

d $l = 0.18\,\text{m}, g = 9.81\,\text{m/s}^2$

Points to remember

- A **formula** is a way of describing a rule or relationship. A formula can be written using algebraic expressions. It must have an $=$ sign.
- When you substitute values into a formula always check that you are using the correct units.

---

4 Changing the subject of a formula

This lesson will help you to change the subject of a formula.

Did you know that...?

Leonhard Euler (1707–1783) was a Swiss mathematician who contributed to a wide range of mathematics.

A formula which shows the relationship between the number of faces, vertices and edges of a polyhedron is named after him (see question 3).

distance = speed × time

$$d = st$$

Distance d is the **subject** of the formula.

If you want to use the formula to work out the speed or the time, you have to rearrange the formula to make a different letter the subject.

To make t the subject divide both sides by s:

$$\frac{d}{s} = t$$

This can be written as:

$$t = \frac{d}{s}$$

1 Make x the subject of the formula:

a $y = x + 4$ b $y = 7x$ c $y = 2x + 1$ d $y = 4x - 5$

e $y = 3 - x$ f $y = 9 - 2x$ g $y = -x$ h $y = -3x + 6$

2 Make the letter in brackets the subject of each formula.

a $d = st$ (s) b $A = lw$ (l)

c $d = p + q$ (p) d $m = r - s$ (r)

e $b = ac + f$ (f) f $b = ac + f$ (a)

g $V = IR$ (R) h $V = IR$ (I)

i $V = lwh$ (w) j $A = \frac{1}{2}bh$ (b)

3 See if you can work out Euler's formula showing the relationship between the number of faces, vertices and edges of a polyhedron.

cuboid

tetrahedron

triangular prism

a Copy and complete this table.

Polyhedron	Number of faces (F)	Number of vertices (V)	Number of edges (E)
tetrahedron			
cuboid			
triangular prism			
octahedron			
square-based pyramid			

b Find a formula showing the relationship between the number of faces, vertices and edges of a polyhedron.

c Use Euler's formula to work out the number of edges for a polyhedron with 20 faces and 12 vertices.

4 Rearrange the formula $v = u + at$ to make:

a u the subject   **b** a the subject   **c** t the subject

Extension problem

5 The area A of a circle is given by the formula $A = \pi r^2$, where r is the radius.
Make r the subject of the formula.

⊙ Points to remember

⊙ In the formula $A = lw$, A is called the **subject** of the formula.

⊙ You can rearrange a formula to make a different letter its subject.

For example, the formula $A = lw$ can also be written as $l = \dfrac{A}{w}$ or $w = \dfrac{A}{l}$.

5 Solving linear equations

This lesson will help you to solve linear equations.

Exercise 5

What you do to one side of the equation you must do to the other to keep the equation in balance.

You can solve equations with a single bracket on one side of the equation by multiplying out the bracket.

Example 1

Solve $5(3x + 1) = 110$.

$$5(3x + 1) = 110$$

multiply out $\quad\quad 15x + 5 = 110$

subtract 5 $\quad\quad\quad 15x = 105$

divide by 15 $\quad\quad\quad x = 7$

$x \rightarrow \boxed{\times 15} \rightarrow \boxed{+ 5} \rightarrow 110$

$7 \leftarrow \boxed{\div 15} \leftarrow \boxed{- 5} \leftarrow 110$

Sometimes the number outside the bracket is a fraction.

Example 2

Solve $\frac{1}{5}(x + 19) = 5$.

$$\frac{1}{5}(x + 19) = 5$$

multiply by 5 $\quad\quad x + 19 = 25$

subtract 19 $\quad\quad\quad x = 6$

$x \rightarrow \boxed{+ 19} \rightarrow \boxed{\div 5} \rightarrow 5$

$6 \leftarrow \boxed{- 19} \leftarrow \boxed{\times 5} \leftarrow 5$

When there is more than one bracket in an equation you must work out the brackets first then simplify the algebraic expression before you solve the equation.

Example 3

Solve $3(2x + 1) + 4(3x + 1) = 43$.

Multiply out: $\quad 6x + 3 + 12x + 4 = 43$

Simplify: $\quad\quad\quad 18x + 7 = 43$

subtract 7 $\quad\quad\quad\quad 18x = 36$

divide by 18 $\quad\quad\quad\quad x = 2$

$x \rightarrow \boxed{\times 18} \rightarrow \boxed{+ 7} \rightarrow 43$

$2 \leftarrow \boxed{\div 18} \leftarrow \boxed{- 7} \leftarrow 43$

If there are x terms on both sides you must first rearrange the equation.
Get all the x terms on one side of the equation.
Then solve the equation as before.

Example 4

Solve $9x - 3 = 5x + 13$.

subtract $5x$	$4x - 3 = 13$
add 3	$4x = 16$
divide by 4	$x = 4$

$x \rightarrow \boxed{\times 4} \rightarrow \boxed{-3} \rightarrow 13$

$4 \leftarrow \boxed{\div 4} \leftarrow \boxed{+3} \leftarrow 13$

① Find the value of x in each equation.
Check your answers by substituting the value of x back into the equation.

a $5x + 4 = 19$ b $4x - 7 = 13$

c $8x + 31 = 47$ d $9x + 18 = 27$

e $7x - 3 = 25$ f $8x + 5 = 53$

g $9x - 0.7 = 1.1$ h $5x + 33 = 28$

i $\frac{x}{2} + 5 = 11$ j $\frac{x}{7} + 17 = 21$

② Find the value of the letter in each equation.

a $4h + 33 = 61$ b $5q + 24 = 9$

c $19 + \frac{t}{5} = 24$ d $\frac{a}{4} + 13 = 17$

③ Find the value of x in each equation.

a $6(4x + 2) = 84$ b $2(7x + 8) = 86$

c $7(3x - 1) = 77$ d $3(2x + 5) = 27$

e $2(9x - 3) = 12$ f $5(7 + 3x) = 125$

g $4(9 + 6x) = 48$ h $549 = 9(8x + 5)$

④ Find the value of x in each of these.

a $3(2x + 7) + 2(4x + 1) = 37$ b $4(3x + 5) + 2(6x + 1) = 94$

c $7(9x - 4) - 5(2x + 4) = 252$ d $2(3x + 5) + 3(2x - 6) = 40$

e $4(3x - 5) + 6(5x - 2) = 52$ f $5(4x + 6) - 7(2x + 1) = 59$

g $197 = 9x + 10(3x + 8)$ h $9(3x + 5) - 7(2x + 8) = 54$

Find the value of x in each of these.

a $\frac{1}{4}(x + 5) = 2$

b $\frac{1}{8}(x - 3) = 1$

c $\frac{1}{3}(x - 8) = 4$

d $\frac{2}{5}(x + 3) = 6$

e $\frac{3}{4}(x - 2) = 3$

f $\frac{1}{2}(9 + x) = 5$

 Find the value of x in each of these.

a $7x + 2 = 6x + 5$

b $4x + 1 = x + 10$

c $15x - 12 = 9x + 18$

d $24x - 17 = 19x + 3$

e $6x + 14 = 11x + 9$

f $2x + 13 = 5x - 8$

Extension problem

7 Find the value of x in each of these.

a $26 - 7x = 20 - 4x$

b $5 - 2x = 3x + 25$

c $7x + 16 = 49 - 4x$

d $65 - x = 2 - 8x$

e $44 - 14x = 5 - x$

f $46 - 2x = 6 - 7x$

Points to remember

- What you do to one side of an equation you must do to the other.
- If necessary, rearrange the equation so that all the terms with the unknown letter are on one side.
- Check your solution by substituting the value in the original equation.

6 Trial and improvement

This lesson will help you to solve non-linear equations by trial and improvement.

 Did you know that...?

The **Babylonians** (about 400 BC) and the **Hindus** (about AD 600) developed numerical approaches to solving some equations.

Euclid (about 300 BC) used geometric methods.

But none of these people had algebra to help them.

The **Arabs** (about AD 800) began to use algebra to solve some equations but they were limited because they had no zero or negative numbers in their system.

Nowadays, the speed of a computer allows us to use numerical approaches that would be far too time-consuming by hand.

Early Arabic mathematics

Exercise 6

Non-linear equations can be solved using **trial and improvement**.

You begin with a good estimate, try it out and from the result make an improvement.

Example

Solve $x^2 - x = 3$.

Try different whole numbers for x until you get close to the answer.

Try $x = 1$: $1^2 - 1 = 0$ (too small)

Try $x = 2$: $2^2 - 2 = 2$ (too small)

Try $x = 3$: $3^2 - 3 = 6$ (too big)

The solution must be between 2 and 3, so now start looking at 2.1, 2.2, and so on.

Keep going. You will find that the solution is 2.303 to three decimal places.

There is a second solution to $x^2 - x = 3$ at $x = -1.303$.

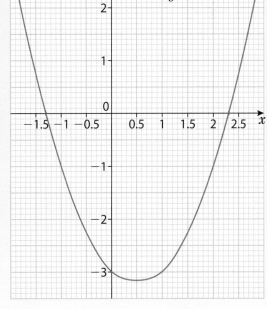

$y = x^2 - x - 3$

You can see these two solutions on the graph of $y = x^2 - x - 3$ at the points when $y = 0$.

① **Use a calculator** to find the solutions of these equations to four decimal places.

a $x^2 = 10$ b $x^2 = 50$

c $x^2 = 130$ d $x^2 = 250$

e $2x^2 = 66$ f $5x^2 = 350$

② Use **trial and improvement** to find two solutions for each equation.
Give your answers to three decimal places.
Start by making an estimate of each solution.

a $x^2 - x = 5$ b $x^2 - 3x - 5 = 0$

c $x^2 - 2x - 5 = 0$ d $x^2 + x = 9$

③ A cuboid has a base that is a square
of side x cm. Its height is 3 cm.

The total surface area of the cuboid
is 20 cm².

Form and solve an equation in x.
Give your answer to one decimal place.

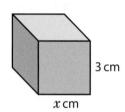

3 cm

x cm

④ Triangle ABC has an area of 20 cm².

Its height is x cm.
Its base is 4 cm more than its height.

Form and solve an equation in x.
Give your answer to two decimal places.

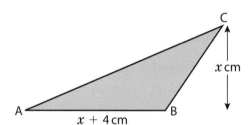

C

x cm

A

$x + 4$ cm

B

⑤ Trapezium ABCD has an area of 60 cm².

Its parallel sides are x cm and $(x + 6)$ cm.
Its height is x cm.

Form and solve an equation in x.
Give your answer to two decimal places.

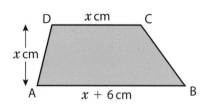

D x cm   C

x cm

A $x + 6$ cm   B

6 Use the method of trial and improvement to solve these equations.
Give your answer to two decimal places.
You can draw a graph to help you find the first estimate.

a $x^3 + x = 70$

b $a^3 - a = 35$

c $x^3 - x^2 = 40$

d $3x^3 - 2x^2 = 21$

7 The base of a cuboid is a square
of side x cm.
The height of the cuboid is $(x + 3)$ cm.
Its total surface area is 60 cm^2.

Form and solve an equation in x.
Give your answer to one decimal place.

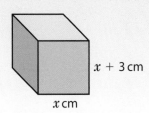

$x + 3$ cm

x cm

Points to remember

⊙ You can use **trial and improvement** to solve non-linear equations.

⊙ Trial and improvement is a step-by-step method that starts with an
estimate and gradually improves the answer with each step.

⊙ A graph can help you find a first estimate.

How well are you doing?

Can you:

- simplify algebraic expressions?
- add algebraic fractions?
- substitute numbers into formulae?
- change the subject of a formula?
- solve linear equations?
- use trial and improvement to solve non-linear equations?

1 *2007 level 6*

Jenny wants to multiply out the brackets in the expression $3(2a + 1)$.

She writes:

$$3(2a + 1) = 6a + 1$$

Show why Jenny is wrong.

2 *2006 level 6*

Multiply out this expression. Write your answer as simply as possible.

$$5(x + 2) + 3(7 + x)$$

3 *2005 level 6*

About 2000 years ago, a Greek mathematician worked out this formula to find the area of any triangle.

For a triangle with sides a, b and c

$$\text{Area} = \sqrt{s(s - a)(s - b)(s - c)}$$

$$\text{where } s = \frac{a + b + c}{2}$$

A triangle has sides, in cm, of 3, 5 and 6.

Use $a = 3$, $b = 5$ and $c = 6$ to work out the area of this triangle.

(4) *2001 level 6*

Solve these equations. Show your working.

a $7 + 5k = 8k + 1$

b $10y + 23 = 4y + 26$

c $\dfrac{3(2y + 1)}{14} = 1$

(5) *2004 level 6*

a Rearrange the equations.

$b + 4 = a$ Write $b = $ ....

$4d = c$ Write $d = $ ....

$m - 3 = 4k$ Write $m = $ ....

b Rearrange the equation to make t the subject.
Show your working.

$$5(2 + t) = w$$

(6) *1999 level 6*

The length of one side of a rectangle is y.
This equation shows the area of the rectangle:

$$y(y + 2) = 67.89$$

Find the value of y. Show your working.

You may find it helpful to make a table like this.

y	$y + 2$	$y(y + 2)$	
8	10	80	too large

Functional skills 2

Where is the mathematics?

This group activity will help you to:

⊙ identify the mathematics in a situation;

⊙ identify mathematical questions to ask;

⊙ choose appropriate language and forms of presentation to communicate conclusions.

Background

Mathematics is all around us.

Looking for the maths in a situation or in information will help you to understand how widely maths is used.

Problem 1

What mathematical questions could you ask about this picture?

What answers to your questions would you give?

What mathematical questions could you ask about this picture?

What answers to your questions would you give?

Problem 3

What mathematical questions could you ask about this picture?

What answers to your questions would you give?

Be prepared to justify your questions and answers to other groups.

2D and 3D shapes

This unit will help you to:

- use properties of shapes and angles and step-by-step reasoning to solve problems;

- visualise 3D objects, make isometric drawings of 3D solids, and draw plans and elevations;

- calculate the surface area and volume of right prisms.

1 Exploring angles and lines

This lesson will help you to understand the angle properties of regular polygons and parallel lines.

Exercise 1

Equal angles are formed when a transversal cuts parallel lines.

You often see parallel lines and equal angles in nature.

Fronds of a palm tree

Scorpion crossing sand

Veins on a leaf

Work with a partner for this exercise.

Use a computer with dynamic geometry software and the file **G5.2 Angle properties**.

You may need **G5.2 Resource sheets 1.1 and 1.2** to help you.

For question **7** you need a piece of A3 paper.

1. Open the file at page 1.

   ◎ Drag point C.

   ◎ Watch what happens to the size of angles ABC and DBC as you do so.

   ◎ Write what you notice about the sizes of the angles.

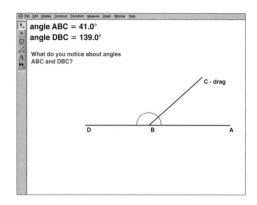

2. Change to page 2 of the file.

   ◎ Drag point D.

   ◎ Watch what happens to the size of angles BAC and DAE as you do so.

   ◎ Write what you notice about the sizes of the angles.

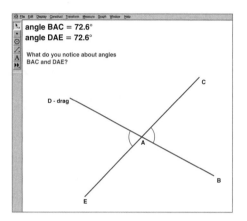

3. Change to page 3 of the file.

   ◎ Drag point C.

   ◎ Watch what happens to the size of angles a and b as you do so.

   ◎ Write what you notice about the sizes of the angles.

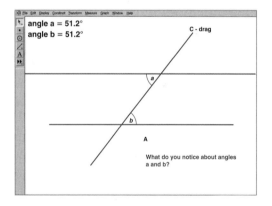

4. Change to page 4 of the file.

   ◎ Drag point C.

   ◎ Watch what happens to the size of angles a and b as you do so.

   ◎ Write what you notice about the sizes of the angles.

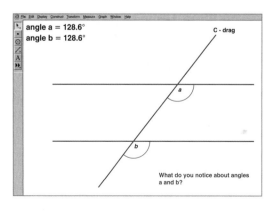

(5) Change to page 5 of the file.

- Drag any vertex of the triangle.

- Watch what happens to the size of angles a, b and c, and their sum, as you do so.

- Write what you notice about the sizes of the angles and their sum.

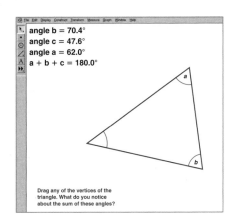

(6) Change to page 6 of the file.

- Use **G5.2 Resource sheet 1.2** to help you to draw a polygon and to measure its angles.

- Drag some of the vertices.

- Watch what happens to the sizes of the angles.

- Write what you notice about the angle sizes and their sum.

- Repeat for some different polygons.

(7) Choose one of the angle facts you have worked on during the lesson.

Make a poster to illustrate it on A3 paper. The poster should state your chosen fact clearly and contain some examples demonstrating it.

● Points to remember

- Angles on a straight line sum to 180°.
- **Vertically opposite angles** are equal.
- **Corresponding angles** on parallel lines are equal.
- **Alternate angles** on parallel lines are equal.
- The interior angles of a triangle sum to 180°.
- The interior angles of an n-sided polygon sum to $(n - 2) \times 180°$.

2 Solving problems

This lesson will help you to draw and label angles correctly and use angle facts, properties of polygons and step-by-step reasoning to solve problems.

Exercise 2

Angle facts

Here are some angle facts that you can use to help you to solve problems:

- angles on a straight line sum to 180°;
- vertically opposite angles are equal;
- corresponding angles on parallel lines are equal;
- alternate angles on parallel lines are equal;
- the interior angles of a triangle sum to 180°;
- the interior angles of an n-sided polygon sum to $(n - 2) \times 180°$;
- the base angles of an isosceles triangle are equal;
- in a triangle with two equal angles, the sides opposite the equal angles are equal and the triangle is isosceles.

Method of working

- **Solve the problem** on your own if you can.
  You will need to draw a diagram and label some points and angles.
- **Compare notes.** Take turns to explain your thinking to a partner.
  Ask questions so that your partner makes everything clear.
- **Agree on a solution.** Talk through the steps.
  Carefully write out your work.
  Make sure that you give a reason for each step.
- **Look for alternative solutions.** Could you have tackled the problem differently?
  Is there a better way to do it?

Example

Prove that the exterior angle of a triangle is equal to the sum of the interior angles at the other two vertices.

$x + y + z = 180°$ (angles in triangle ABC)

$y + w = 180°$ (angles on straight line ABD)

Therefore

$w = x + z$

or

$\angle CBD = \angle CAB + \angle ACB$

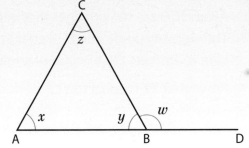

Work with a partner. For each question follow the 'Method of working' on the previous page. You may assume only the angle facts given on the previous page.

1. Triangle XYZ is isosceles with XY = XZ.
   P is any point on XZ.
   Through P, a straight line is drawn parallel to ZY to cut XY at Q.

   Prove that angle XQP = angle XPQ.

2. BD is the bisector of angle ABC.
   Through D, a straight line is drawn parallel to AB to cut BC at E.

   Prove that triangle BDE is isosceles.

3. ABC is an isosceles triangle with AB = AC.
   X is a point on the side BC.
   From X, a straight line is drawn at right angles to BC, cutting AB at Y and CA extended at Z.

   Prove that triangle AYZ is isosceles.

4. ABC is a triangle.
   CB is extended to D.
   BE bisects angle ABD and is parallel to CA.

   Prove that triangle ABC is isosceles.

5. ABCD is a quadrilateral.
   The bisector of angle A meets the bisector of angle B at E.

   Prove that angle AEB is equal to half the sum of angle C and angle D.

6. ABC is an isosceles triangle with AB = AC.
   BA is extended to D, so that AD = BA.
   Points D and C are joined.

   Prove that angle BCD is a right angle.

Extension problem

7. AB and CD are straight lines that intersect at E.
   Through any point Y on EC a straight line XYZ is drawn parallel to AB.
   Line XYZ meets the bisector of angle AEY at X and the bisector of angle BEY at Z.

   Prove that XY is equal to YZ.

Points to remember

- ⊙ Read the question carefully and draw a diagram.
- ⊙ Use given information to label the diagram. Look for:
  - equal angles;
  - equal lengths.
- ⊙ Use angle facts to find out information to help you to answer the question.
- ⊙ Write your solution giving a reason for each step.
- ⊙ When you have finished, check your reasoning and make sure that you have answered the question.

3 Solving longer problems

This lesson will help you to use angle facts, properties of polygons and step-by-step reasoning to solve harder problems.

Did you know that...?

Regular polygons can often be seen in both the man-made and natural environments.

The Pentagon

50p coin

The dome at Ely Cathedral

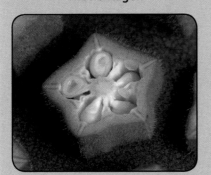

Okra

Snowflake

Honeycomb

G5.2 *2D and 3D shapes* | **119**

Exercise 3

You will need **G5.2 Resource sheet 3.1** for this exercise.

(1) **Regular polygons**

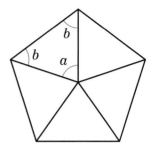

a A regular pentagon is made up of five identical isosceles triangles that fit together round a point without any gaps or overlaps.

Work out the size of angles a and b. Show your reasoning.

b Imagine a regular decagon.

How many sides does it have?

Work out the sizes of the angles a and b in the isosceles triangles that make up the decagon.

c All regular polygons can be made from isosceles triangles that fit together round a point with no gaps or overlaps.

Only 12 of these regular polygons have isosceles triangles where all the angles are whole numbers greater than or equal to 10°.

How many sides do these 12 polygons have?

d Explain how you can be certain that you have found them all.

(2) Use the diagrams on **G5.2 Resource sheet 3.1** if you need to.

ABCDE is a regular pentagon.

A regular pentagram (a star with five points) has been formed.

The intersections marked as P, Q, R, S, T.

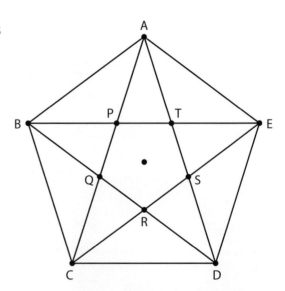

a How many pairs of parallel lines can you find?

b Work out all the angles in the diagram.

c How many different types of triangle can you find?

d How many different types of quadrilateral can you find?

Explain your reasoning.

(3) Answer the same questions as in question **2**
for a regular hexagram
(a star with 6 points).

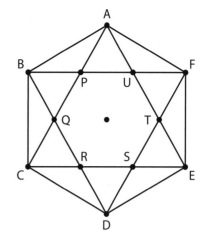

(4) Answer the same questions as in question **2**
for a regular octogram
(a star with 8 points).

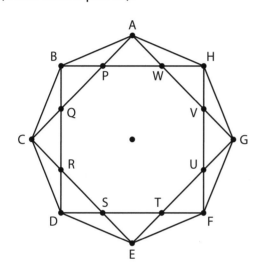

4 Drawing 3D objects

This lesson will help you to visualise 3D objects, make isometric drawings of 3D solids and draw plans and elevations.

Exercise 4

The picture shows a block with dimensions 3 by 4 by 2.

The diagrams below show the isometric view, the plan view from above (the bird's eye view), the view from the front and the view from the side.

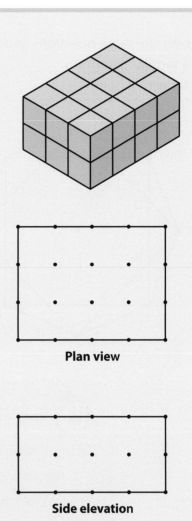

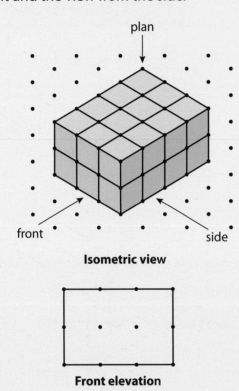

Isometric view

Plan view

Front elevation

Side elevation

You will need isometric dotty paper, square dotty paper, a ruler and a sharp pencil.

(1) Draw these in isometric view.

 a A single cube

 b A tower of five cubes

 c A tower two cubes wide and five cubes high

 d A block with dimensions 3 by 4 by 5

(2) For each solid in question **1** draw the plan view, front elevation and side elevation.

3 Draw the plan, front elevation and side elevation for each of these 3D shapes.

a

b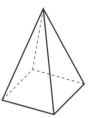

c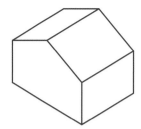

4 The drawing shows a flat-roofed house.

Draw the plan view, the front elevation and the side elevation.

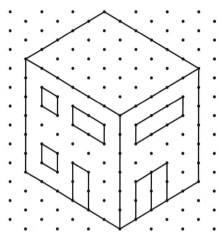

5 The drawing shows a model made out of linking cubes.

How many faces does the model have?

Draw the plan view, the front elevation and the side elevation.

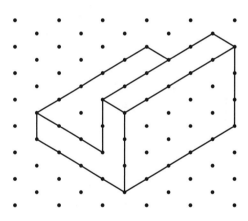

6 On isometric paper, draw a shape with six faces.

⊙ Points to remember

- ⊙ An **isometric drawing** shows an object that has been rotated and tilted.
- ⊙ The **plan view** looks at the object from directly above.
- ⊙ The **side and front elevations** show the object from the side and front.
- ⊙ Different objects can have the same plan view, front elevation and side elevation.

5 Drawing plans and elevations

This lesson will help you to visualise 3D objects and to use isometric drawings, plans and elevations of 3D solids to solve problems.

 Did you know that...?

In ancient times, architecture was regarded as part of mathematics.

Mathematics and architecture are still closely linked to the present day.

The Byzantine emperor Justinian I wanted an architect to build the Hagia Sophia in what is now Istanbul.

He chose two mathematics professors as the architects: **Anthemus of Tralles** and **Isodorus of Miletus**.

The Hagia Sophia took only six years to build. It was finished in AD 537.

Exercise 5

Sometimes using colour can make isometric drawing easier to understand.

All the faces in the same direction are coloured in the same colour.

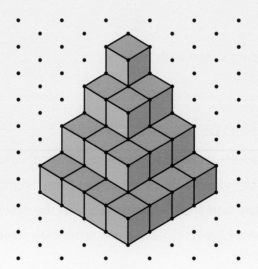

You will need isometric paper, square dotty paper, A3 plain paper, linking cubes, glue, a ruler and a sharp pencil.

1. **a** Make a model using at least 12 linking cubes. Make it quite complicated.

   b Draw an isometric view, a plan view and front and side elevations of your model.
   Use these to make a poster on A3 paper.

   c When you have finished, swap posters with someone else.
   Make sure you can't see each other's models.
   Try to create the other person's model from their poster.

   d When you have finished, compare your models with the originals.

2. Here are some isometric drawings of models made of linking cubes.
   Draw the front elevation, side elevation and plan view for each model.

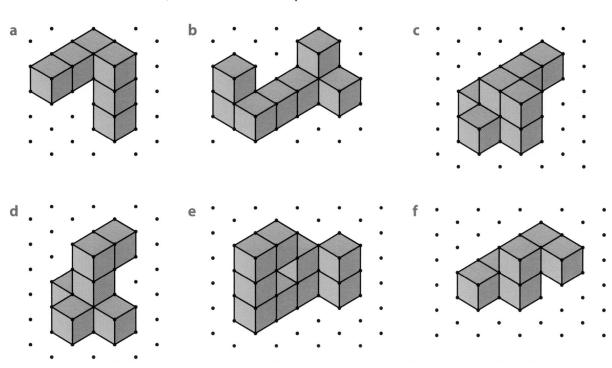

a   b   c

d   e   f

6 More plans and elevations

This lesson will help you to visualise 3D objects and to use isometric drawings, plans and elevations of 3D solids to solve problems.

Exercise 6

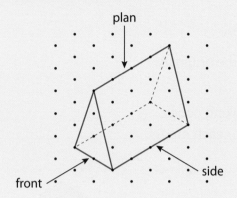

plan

front

side

The view from above is called the **plan view**.

The view from the front is called the **front elevation**.

The view from the side is called the **side elevation**.

You will need square dotty paper, isometric dotty paper, a ruler and a sharp pencil.

1 Identify each of the solids shown below.

a

plan view

side elevation

front elevation

b

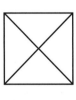
plan view

side elevation

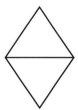
front elevation

c

plan view

side elevation

front elevation

2 Name some shapes with these front elevations:

   a triangle   **b** square   **c** rectangle

(3) What is the least number of cubes needed to make each shape into a cuboid?

a
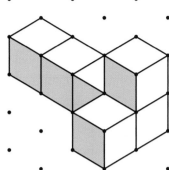

b
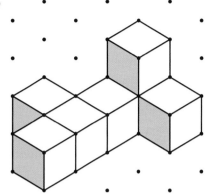

(4) Write the name of each shape. Draw its plan view, front elevation and side elevation.

a
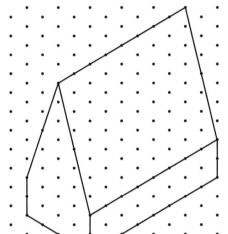

b
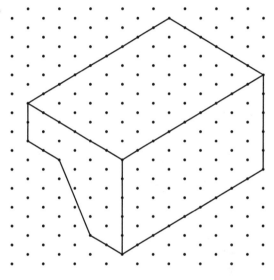

(5) The diagram shows a garden planter.

Draw the plan view, front elevation and side elevation.

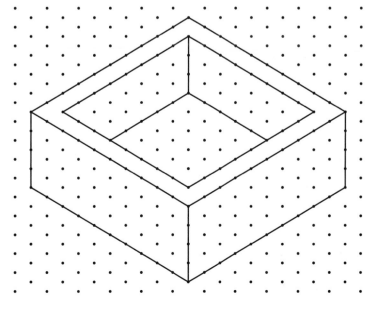

6 Each pair of diagrams shows two out of the plan view, front elevation and side elevation of the same model made of interlocking cubes.

Draw the missing elevation for each pair.

a

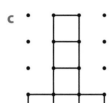

plan view   side elevation

b

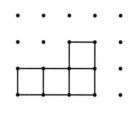

plan view   front elevation

c

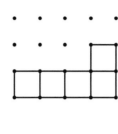

plan view   side elevation

d

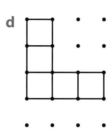

plan view   side elevation

Extension problems

7 Imagine a square-based pyramid.

Make a horizontal slice parallel to the base of the pyramid.
What shape is the cut area?

Imagine you make some more cuts parallel to the base of the pyramid but nearer to the apex (top point).
What shapes are the cross-sections?

How do the shapes change as the slices get nearer the apex?

8 Draw a cube on isometric dotty paper.

Show three different ways that it can be cut in half to form two triangular prisms.

⊙ Points to remember

- ⊙ The plan view looks at the object from directly above.
- ⊙ The side and front elevations show the object from the side and front.
- ⊙ Different objects can have the same plan view, front elevation and side elevation.

7 Solving problems using surface area and volume

This lesson will help you to calculate and solve problems involving surface area and volume.

 Did you know that...?

Female emperor penguins lay their eggs at the beginning of the Antarctic winter. The males incubate the eggs by holding them on their feet for 65 days until the eggs hatch in the middle of the winter.

To keep warm the penguins huddle together. As the penguins on the outside of the huddle get cold they move slowly from the outside to the inside of the huddle.

Exercise 7

Investigate how huddling can help the penguins keep warm.

You will need some linking cubes and a computer with spreadsheet software.
You will also need the Excel spreadsheet file **G5.2 Penguins** and **G5.2 Resource sheet 7.1**.

1. Put three linking cubes together to form a 3 by 1 by 1 cuboid. This is your basic 'penguin'.

   a What is the volume of your penguin in cubic units?

   b What is the surface area of your penguin in square units?

2. Make another penguin.
   Put the two penguins side by side to make a line.

   a What is the volume of your penguin line in cubic units?

   b What is the surface area of your penguin line in square units?

   c What is the average surface area per penguin?

(3) The surface area of one penguin can be broken down into:

- 3 square units for its front

- 3 square units for its back

- 6 square units for its two sides

- 1 square unit for its head

- 1 square unit for its feet.

a Open the Excel spreadsheet file **G5.4 Penguins**.
   Fill in the spaces for 2, 3, 4, 5 and 6 penguins standing in a straight line.

b What patterns do you notice in the table?

c Why do the sides stay at 6 square units?

d Why are the numbers in the 'Heads' and 'Feet' columns the same as
   the number of penguins?

e What happens to the average surface area per penguin as
   the number of penguins increases?

f Continue the patterns using the spreadsheet.

   Plot a graph to show what happens to the average surface area
   as the number of penguins increases.

Use G5.2 Resource sheet 7.1 to help.

(4) The diagram shows penguins lined up in pairs
    instead of a single line.

a Click on the sheet labelled 'Pairs'.

   Fill in the spaces in the table for
   the number of rows from 1 to 6.

b What patterns do you notice in the table?

c What happens to the average surface area
   per penguin as the number of rows
   of penguins increases?

d Continue the patterns using the spreadsheet.

   Plot a graph to show what happens to the average surface area as the number of
   penguins increases.

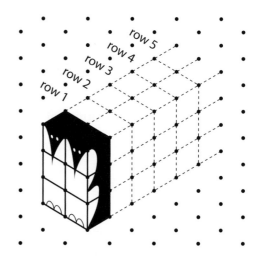

5 This time the penguins stand three in a line.

    a Click on the sheet labelled 'Triples'.
       Fill in the spaces in the table for the number of rows from 1 to 6.

    b What patterns do you notice in the table?

    c What happens to the average surface area per penguin
       as the number of rows of penguins increases?

    d Continue the patterns using the spreadsheet.

       Plot a graph to show what happens to the average surface area
       as the number of penguins increases.

6 Look at the results for all three sheets.

    a What do you notice about the average surface area as the number
       of penguins per row increases?

    b What would happen if there are even more penguins in a row?

Extension problem

7 Now consider what would happen
with a large 'huddle'.

    a What is the average surface
       area for a huddle of
       100×100 penguins?

    b Write an expression to show
       the average surface area for
       an $n \times m$ huddle of penguins.

🔘 Points to remember

- Surface area is measured in square units.
- To find the surface area of a cuboid, calculate the area of each of the six rectangular faces and add them together.
- Volume is measured in cubic units.

8 Surface area and volume of prisms

This lesson will help you to solve problems involving calculating the surface area and volume of prisms.

Exercise 8

The surface area of a 3D solid is the sum of the areas of each of the faces.

- To find the **surface area of a cuboid**, calculate the area of each of the six rectangular faces and add them together. Remember that opposite faces are identical.
- To find the **surface area of a prism**, calculate the area of the two identical bases and add this to the sum of the areas of all the rectangular faces.
- To find the **volume of a prism**, use this formula:

    volume of prism = area of cross-section × length

- To find the **area of a triangle**, use this formula:

    area of triangle = $\frac{1}{2}$ × (base × perpendicular height)

Example 1

Find the volume and surface area of this cuboid.

Volume is $5 \times 6 \times 8 = 240 \, \text{cm}^3$

Surface area is

$(2 \times 5 \times 6) + (2 \times 5 \times 8) + (2 \times 6 \times 8) = 236 \, \text{cm}^2$

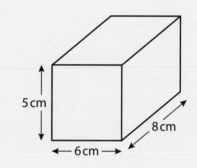

Example 2

This prism has a cross-section of $10 \, \text{cm}^2$.

Find the volume of the prism.

Volume = $10 \times 17 = 170 \, \text{cm}^2$

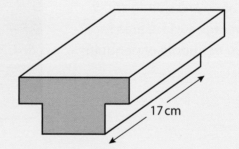

Work with a partner.

1. **a** Find a set of dimensions for a cuboid with volume $48 \, \text{cm}^3$.

    b Find as many different sets of whole number dimensions as you can for a cuboid with volume $48 \, \text{cm}^3$.

    c For each set of dimensions, find the surface area for that cuboid.

    d What are the dimensions of the cuboid with the smallest surface area?

2　**a** Can you find the dimensions for a triangular prism with volume 48 cm³?

> **Hint**
> ◉ Pick a length.
> ◉ What must be the area of the triangular cross-section?
> ◉ Find two numbers that multiply to make double the area of the cross-section.
>   These will be the base and perpendicular height of the cross-section.

　b Find the dimensions for two more triangular prisms.

　c What do you notice about the dimensions of your prisms?

　d Draw the cross-section of each of your three triangular prisms as accurately as you can.
　　Use these diagrams to work out the surface area of your triangular prisms.

> **Hint**
> ◉ You will need to measure the sides of your triangles.

3　Find some more prisms with different cross-sections that have a volume of 48 cm³.

> **Hint**
> ◉ You might need to make some accurate drawings to calculate or estimate the
>   areas of their cross-sections.

Extension problem

4　This cuboid has a volume of 1 litre.

　a Find a possible length, width and height for a cuboid with a volume of 1 litre.
　　You might find it helpful to use a spreadsheet.

　b Work out the surface area of your cuboid.

　c Now find some more cuboids that have a volume of 1 litre.
　　Find the surface area of each of your cuboids.
　　Which cuboid with a volume of 1 litre has the smallest surface area?

> **◉ Points to remember**
> ◉ A **prism** is a polyhedron with two parallel and congruent bases.
>   Its side faces are rectangles perpendicular to the bases.
>   Cross-sections parallel to a base are identical to the base.
> ◉ The **surface area of a prism** is the sum of the area of each of the faces.
> ◉ The **volume of a prism** is calculated by:
>   volume of a prism = area of cross-section × length

How well are you doing?

1 *1999 level 6*

The diagram shows a model made with nine cubes.

Five of the cubes are grey.
The other four cubes are white.

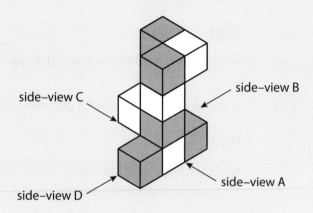

side-view C

side-view B

side-view A

side-view D

a The drawings below show the four side views of the model.

Which side view does each drawing show?

P 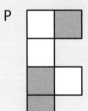   Q 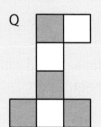   R 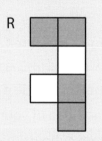   S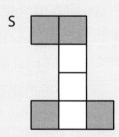

b Copy and complete this top view of the model by shading the squares which are grey.

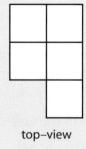

top-view

c Imagine you turn the model upside down. What will the new top view of the model look like?

Copy and shade the new top view.

new top-view

2 *2001 level 6*

A cuboid has a square base.

It is twice as tall as it is wide.

Its volume is 250 cubic centimetres.

Calculate the width of the cuboid.

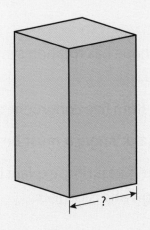

Not actual size

3 *1996 level 6*

This door wedge is the shape of a prism.

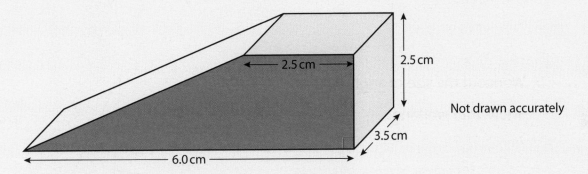

2.5 cm

2.5 cm

Not drawn accurately

3.5 cm

6.0 cm

a The shaded face of the door wedge is a trapezium.
Calculate the area of the shaded face. Show your working.

b Calculate the volume of the door wedge. Show your working.

4 *2003 level 6*

This pattern has rotation symmetry of order 6.

What is the size of angle w?

Show your working.

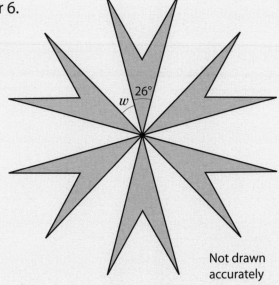

26°

w

Not drawn
accurately

This star shape has rotation symmetry of order 5.

It is made from five congruent triangles.

a   Jenny said: 'Angle a must be 72°.'

Without measuring, explain how you know she is correct.

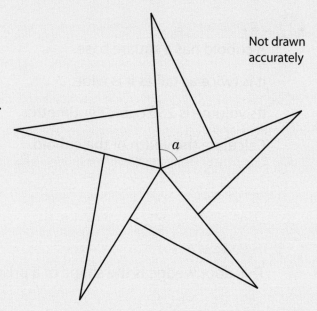

Not drawn accurately

b   Work out the size of angle b.

Show your working.

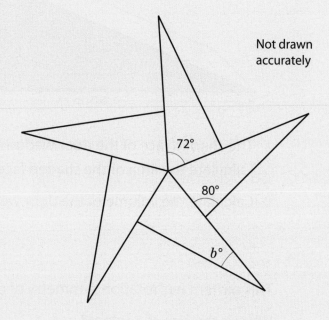

Not drawn accurately

Calculations and calculators

This unit will help you to:

- multiply and divide by integer powers of 10;
- understand the effects of multiplying or dividing by numbers between 0 and 1;
- round decimals and use rounding to make estimates;
- use efficient mental and written methods to calculate with decimals;
- use a calculator efficiently for complex calculations.

1 Powers of 10

This lesson will help you to multiply and divide by positive and negative integer powers of 10 and to understand the effects of multiplying or dividing by numbers between 0 and 1.

 Did you know that...?

Around 1920, the American mathematician **Edward Kasner** asked his nine-year-old nephew Milton Sirotta to invent a name for 10 to the power 100, or 10^{100}.

His nephew called it a **googol**. This is 1 with one hundred zeros after it.

A **googolplex** is 10 to the power googol.

The Internet search engine Google was named as a variation of the number googol. The Google headquarters in California is called Googleplex.

Exercise 1

The short way to write $10 \times 10 \times 10 \times 10$ is as 10^4, or '10 to the power 4'.
The small number 4 is called the **index**.

An index can be negative as well as positive. For example:

$$10^{-2} = \frac{1}{10 \times 10} = \frac{1}{100} = 0.01$$

1 Write down the answers.

    a 4.1×10 **b** 3.76×10^2 **c** 0.65×10^3 **d** $97 \div 10^3$

    e $325 \div 10^2$ **f** $8.02 \div 10^3$ **g** 51.98×10^2 **h** $8.76 \div 10^2$

    i 0.076×10^3 **j** $0.09 \div 10$ **k** 0.08×10^5 **l** $324 \div 10^4$

2 Write down the answers.

    a 7×10 **b** 50×10 **c** 0.8×10 **d** 7.2×10

    e $7 \div 10$ **f** $50 \div 10$ **g** $0.8 \div 10$ **h** $7.2 \div 10$

    i 7×0.1 **j** 50×0.1 **k** 0.8×0.1 **l** 7.2×0.1

    m $7 \div 0.1$ **n** $50 \div 0.1$ **o** $0.8 \div 0.1$ **p** $7.2 \div 0.1$

    Explain the connection between your answers to question **2**.

3 Multiply these by 0.01.

    a 4.5   **b** 63.2   **c** 0.08

    d 500   **e** 0.7   **f** 56 432

4 Divide these by 0.01.

    a 6.2   **b** 400   **c** 5

    d 91.4   **e** 29   **f** 28 017

5 This table shows approximate diameters in kilometres of the planets in the Solar System, and their distances in kilometres from the Sun.

Planet	Diameter (km)	Distance from Sun (km)
Earth	1.3×10^4	1.5×10^8
Jupiter	1.4×10^5	7.8×10^8
Mars	6.8×10^3	2.3×10^8
Mercury	4.9×10^3	5.8×10^7
Neptune	4.9×10^4	4.5×10^9
Pluto	2.4×10^3	5.9×10^9
Saturn	1.2×10^5	1.4×10^9
Uranus	5.2×10^4	2.7×10^9
Venus	1.2×10^4	1.1×10^8

    a Which is the smallest planet?

    b Which is the biggest planet?

    c Which planet is the furthest distance from the Sun?

d Which planet is the closest in size to Earth?

e Which planet is closest in distance to Earth?

f Which planet has a diameter that is 3000 km longer than the diameter of Neptune?

g Which planet has a diameter about ten times the diameter of Mercury?

h How many times bigger is the diameter of Saturn than the diameter of Venus?

i How many times bigger is the diameter of Venus than the diameter of Pluto?

j How many times further from the Sun is Neptune than Earth?

Points to remember

- $\times$ 0.1 is equivalent to $\div$ 10.
- $\times$ 0.01 is equivalent to $\div$ 100.
- $\times$ 0.001 is equivalent to $\div$ 1000.

- $\div$ 0.1 is equivalent to $\times$ 10.
- $\div$ 0.01 is equivalent to $\times$ 100.
- $\div$ 0.001 is equivalent to $\times$ 1000.

2 Rounding and approximation

This lesson will help you to round decimals and use rounding to estimate results of calculations.

Exercise 2A

When you round whole numbers, look at the first unwanted digit.
If it is 5, 6, 7, 8 or 9, add 1 to the last digit that you keep, otherwise make no changes.
Then replace all the unwanted digits by zeros.

Example 1

843 27**5** to the nearest 10 is 843 280.
843 2**75** to the nearest 100 is 843 300.
843 **275** to the nearest 1000 is 843 000.

When you round decimals, look at the first unwanted digit.
If it is 5, 6, 7, 8 or 9, add 1 to the last digit that you keep, otherwise make no changes.
Then leave off all the unwanted digits.

Example 2

39.9**65** correct to one decimal place is 40.0.
39.96**5** correct to two decimal places is 39.97.

① Round to the nearest ten:

   a 1395

   b 6 400 998

② Round to the nearest hundred:

   a 306 728

   b 9961

③ Round to the nearest thousand:

   a 49 700

   b 7 329 500

④ Round to the nearest hundred thousand:

   a 8 246 509

   b 999 999

⑤ Round to one decimal place:

   a 1.036

   b 79.98

⑥ Round to two decimal places:

   a 14.328

   b 3.9999

⑦ Round to three decimal places:

   a 0.059 67

   b 5.999 99

⑧ Round to the nearest pound:

   a 56p

   b £17.10

⑨ Estimate the answer to each of these calculations.

a $486 \div 19$	b 523×49	c $620 \div 5.8$
d 2.85×32	e 2.85×1.6	f 0.042×311
g 0.052×0.71	h $0.79 \div 0.09$	i $(0.062)^2$
j $\dfrac{17.3 - 4.2}{8.6 + 10.7}$	k $\dfrac{279 \times 19}{41}$	l $\dfrac{59.2 \times 18.5}{11.7 \times 5.8}$

Exercise 2B

⊙ An amount in £ correct to **2 d.p.** is correct to the nearest hundredth of a £, i.e. **the nearest penny**.

⊙ A length in metres correct to **2 d.p.** is correct to the nearest hundredth of a metre, i.e. **the nearest centimetre**.

⊙ A mass in kilograms correct to **3 d.p.** is correct to thousandth of a kilogram, i.e. **the nearest gram**.

① Give each of these lengths correct to the nearest centimetre.

   a 642.8 cm   b 4.123 m   c 26.0081 m

② Give each of these weights correct to the nearest gram.

   a 32.7 g   b 9.3295 kg   c 0.3217 kg

3 Give each of these distances correct to the nearest metre.

   a 32.0531 km   **b** 26.0 m   **c** 1.2599 km

4 Billiards is thought to have been invented by the Spaniards in the late 1500s.

The game became popular in England where at first it was played by royalty only.

It reached America in the 1770s where it quickly gained popularity. 'Pool' has become one of the USA's favourite pastimes.

Use your calculator.

   a 15 numbered billiard balls weigh 2.41 kg.
      What does 1 billiard ball weigh to the nearest gram?

   b A billiard cue is 1.4732 m long.
      6 billiard cues are laid end-to-end in a straight line.
      How long is the line to the nearest cm?

   c A set of 9 antique ivory billiard balls were sold for £191.50 on an auction website.
      What is the mean cost of 1 billiard ball to the nearest penny?

Extension problems

5 Estimate the number that the arrow is pointing to on each line.

a

0   6.6

b
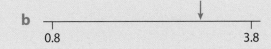
0.8   3.8

c

−5   +25

d

0.15   1.15

6 Work on this problem with a partner.

Estimate the number of dots below.
Explain how you made your estimate.

⊙ Points to remember

- ⊙ When you round an answer, make sure it has the required number of decimal places, e.g. 4.96 rounded to one decimal place is 5.0, not 5.
- ⊙ Round before a calculation to estimate the answer.
- ⊙ When you work out the actual answer, don't round until after you have completed the calculation.
- ⊙ A length in metres rounded to two decimal places is to the nearest centimetre.
- ⊙ A weight in kilograms correct to three decimal places is correct to the nearest gram.

3 Mental calculations with decimals

This lesson will help you to calculate mentally with decimals.

Exercise 3

Here are some examples of ways to calculate mentally by using facts that you know.

Example 1   £2.99 × 5

£2.99 × 5 = £3 × 5 − 1p × 5

        = £15 − 5p

        = £14.95

Example 2   £1.48 × 3

£1.48 × 3 = £1.50 × 3 − 2p × 3

        = £4.50 − 6p

        = £4.44

Example 3

Find the change from £10 for two cakes at £2.93 each.

£2.93 × 2 = £3 × 2 − 7p × 2

        = £6 − 14p

        = £5.86

Add on 4p to make £5.90.
Add on 10p to make £6.
Add on £4 to make £10

Total change £4.14.

1

  a Find the cost of two tins of paint at £4.99 each.

  b Find the cost of three cans of drink at 49p each.

  c Find the cost of six packets of sweets at 97p each.

  d Find the cost of 45 litres of petrol at 98p each litre.

2 This is an addition table.

Each number is the sum of the number at the beginning of the row and the number at the top of the column.

For example, 5.3 is the sum of 4.7 and 0.6.

+	0.6	1.5
0.8	1.4	2.3
4.7	5.3	6.2

Copy and complete this addition table.

+	0.3		2.9
			3.5
2.5		7.1	
	1.7		

3 Try this puzzle.

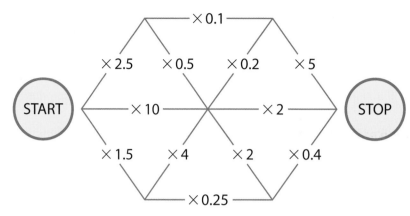

- Start with 1. The aim is to finish with a product of 5.
- Choose a route from START to STOP.
  Multiply by the number on each line that you travel along.
- You may go along each line only once.

Write in your book the numbers that you multiplied to make 5.

4 Play this **Decimal game** with a partner.

You need a copy of **N5.3 Resource sheet 3.2**,
a calculator and some counters in two colours.

0.1	0.2	0.3		×		0.1	0.2
	0.4	0.5					0.3
0.02	0.03	0.04		÷		0.4	0.5

The rules of the game are on the resource sheet.

0.25	0.004	0.012	1.0	0.008	0.03
0.8	0.3	0.2	0.003	0.04	1.25
1.5	0.01	0.08	0.016	0.75	0.02
0.12	0.5	0.006	2.0	0.15	0.6
0.04	0.1	0.015	0.05	0.4	0.06
0.09	0.002	0.16	2.5	0.009	0.075

Points to remember

- Given a calculation, check first to see if you can do it mentally.
- Use facts you know to work out new facts.
  For example, to multiply by 5, multiply by 10, then halve.
- When a is greater than 1:
  multiplying a number by a makes it bigger;
  dividing a number by a makes it smaller.
- When a is less than 1:
  multiplying a number by a makes it smaller;
  dividing a number by a makes it bigger.

4 Written calculations with decimals

This lesson will help you to use efficient written methods to calculate with decimals.

Exercise 4

Adding or subtracting decimals

Example

Find the total of 6.452 km, 2.78 km and 600 m.

Change the units so that they are all in kilometres.

Line up decimal points underneath each other.

$$
\begin{array}{r}
6.452 \\
2.78 \\
+ \ 0.6 \\
\hline
9.832 \\
\scriptstyle 1
\end{array}
$$

Estimate $6 + 3 + 1 = 10$

Answer 9.832

Multiplying by a decimal

Example

4.82 × 2.7

Do the equivalent whole-number calculation, then divide by the appropriate power of 10.

Check that the number of decimal places in the answer is the same as in the product.

$$
\begin{array}{r}
482 \\
\times \ 27 \\
\hline
9640 \\
3374 \\
\hline
13014 \\
\scriptstyle 1 \ 1
\end{array}
$$

Estimate $5 \times 3 = 15$

$4.82 \times 2.7 = 13014 \div 10^3$

Answer 13.014

Dividing by a decimal

Example

154 ÷ 2.8

Multiply both numbers by the same power of 10 to make the divisor a whole number.

$$154 \div 2.8 = \frac{154}{2.8} = \frac{154 \times 10}{2.8 \times 10} = \frac{1540}{28}$$

$$
\begin{array}{r}
55 \\
28 \overline{)1540} \\
-1400 \quad 50 \times 28 \\
\hline
140 \\
-140 \quad 5 \times 28 \\
\hline
0
\end{array}
$$

Estimate $1500 \div 30 = 50$

Answer 55

Do this exercise **without using a calculator**. Show your working.

 Work out:

    a 8 + 4.6 + 7.21

    b 36.463 + 8.79

    c 29.54 − 6.79

    d 24.7 − 6.93

2. Work these out.

   a 9.3×4 **b** 4.35×5 **c** 5.1×6.2 **d** 0.32×7.5

3. Work these out.

   a $75.6 \div 0.3$ **b** $46.2 \div 0.03$ **c** $0.84 \div 0.004$ **d** $5.44 \div 1.7$

4. A kitchen worktop is a rectangle of length 2.365 metres and width 65 centimetres. What is the perimeter of the worktop?

5. There are 5 metres of sticky tape on a roll.
   Lengths of 94 cm, 1.36 m and 58 mm are cut from it.
   How many metres of sticky tape are left on the roll?

6. A circular tablecloth is to have lace stitched round its circumference.
   The tablecloth has a radius of 1.25 metres.

   a What is the circumference of the tablecloth?
   Use a value of 3.1 for π.

   b Lace costs £1.40 per metre.
   What is the cost of the lace for the tablecloth?

7. The floor of a disco is a circle of radius 4 metres.

   a What is the area of the floor?
   Use a value of 3.1 for π.

   b The floor needs polishing.
   Polishing costs £2.70 per square metre.
   What does it cost for the floor to be polished?

Extension problem

8. The 'ink blots' cover missing digits.

   Without using a calculator, work out what the digits are.

   Copy, complete and check each calculation. Show your working.

   a $9.3 \times 8.\bullet = 7\bullet.\bullet8$ **b** $2.\bullet \times 2.\bullet = 6.96$

   c $3.\bullet \times \bullet.9 = 18.13$ **d** $1.\bullet2 \times 4.\bullet = 5.94$

   e $\bullet.\bullet6 \times 4.\bullet = 14.448$ **f** $3.\bullet\bullet \times \bullet.7 = 14.171$

Points to remember

- To add or subtract decimals in columns, line up decimal points under each other.
- To multiply by a decimal:
  - do the whole-number calculation, then divide by the appropriate power of 10;
  - check that the number of decimal places in the answer is the same as in the product.
- To divide by a decimal, multiply both numbers by the same power of 10 to make the divisor a whole number.
- For written calculations with decimals:
  - estimate the answer;
  - choose an efficient method;
  - use the estimate to check the size of the answer and to make sure that any decimal point is in the right place.
- You can also check calculator answers by using inverse operations.

5 Using a calculator

This lesson will help you to use a calculator efficiently for complex problems.

Exercise 5

You may need to use brackets before you can work out the value of an expression using your calculator.

Example 1

Work out $\dfrac{1.23 + 4.5}{3.8}$.

Put brackets round the numerator: $\dfrac{(1.23 + 4.5)}{3.8}$.

(1 · 2 3 + 4 · 5) ÷ 3 · 8 =

Answer: 15.08 correct to two decimal places

Use brackets if you have more than one term under a square root.

Example 2

Work out $7\sqrt{9^2 + 6^2}$.

Put brackets round the expression under the square root: $7\sqrt{(9^2 + 6^2)}$
Work out the brackets first, then the square root.

(9 x^2 + 6 x^2) √ × 7 =

Answer: 75.72 correct to two decimal places

When you have an answer, key in Mode 7 2 to round it to two decimal places.

You may need to adapt these instructions for your type of calculator.

Example 3

Work out $32.6 \div 9.71$ correct to two decimal places.

3 2 . 6 ÷ 9 . 7 1 = ◯ Mode 7 2

Answer: 3.36 correct to two decimal places

Use your calculator.
Give your answers correct to two decimal places where appropriate.

① Work out the value of each expression.
Put brackets in where you need them.

a $\dfrac{21.7 + 101.5}{0.18 + 0.56}$

b $\dfrac{721}{94 - 46}$

c $\dfrac{70.3 - 29.7}{13.2 - 8.8}$

d $\sqrt{24^2 + 13^2}$

e $4.3^2 - (6.9 - 2.2)$

f $(2.45 - 1.63)^2$

g $\dfrac{11.2^2 - 9.3^2}{28.7}$

h $\dfrac{\sqrt{16.2 - 4.28}}{3.25}$

i $\sqrt{\dfrac{3.6 + 5.4}{2.8 - 1.9}}$

② Find the value of B in each of these formulae.

a $B = \dfrac{a^2 + c^2}{a - c}$ $a = 12.6, c = 9.2$

b $B = 5\sqrt{a^2 + c^2}$ $a = 15, c = 17$

③ Robert fills his car with 32.6 litres of petrol costing 99.7p per litre.
What does the petrol cost?

Use your calculator's memory to help answer questions **4–6**.

(4) Ranjit gets paid £6.85 per hour for an 8-hour shift.
For overtime after this, he gets paid £13.65 per hour.

How much does Ranjit earn if he works:

a a 10-hour shift?

b a 12-hour shift?

(5) The table below shows the number of people taking rides at a theme park on a Saturday afternoon.

Ride	Number of people
£4.75	421
£3.35	118
£1.65	327
£2.40	228

a How much did the theme park take for the rides on that Saturday afternoon?

b What was the mean price paid for one ride?

(6) Mike went to the supermarket. He bought:

- 2 packs of French cheese at £2.79 each
- 8 lamb chops at £3.48 for a packet of two
- 5 cartons of fresh tomato soup at £2.11 each
- 400 g of broccoli at £3.40 per kg
- 4 loaves of bread at 78p each
- 2 packets of butter at £1.39 each
- 1 pineapple at £1.29
- 1.5 litres of orange juice at £1.60 per litre

How much did Mike spend altogether?

Extension problem

(7) Investigate with your calculator.

Each ★ represents a missing sign (+, −, × or ÷). Copy and complete the calculations.

a (6.5 ★ 3.8) ★ 9.7 = 26.19

b (20.3 ★ 3.5) ★ 4.8 = 10.6

c 15.04 ★ (7.8 ★ 4.6) = 4.7

d 2.7 ★ (6.3 ★ 2.9) = 24.84

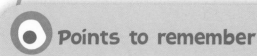
6 Problems involving measures

This lesson will help you to solve problems involving decimals.

Exercise 6

Do questions 1–7 **without using a calculator**.

1. Sharifa pays a 50p connection charge for each international phone call.
   She also pays 8.9p per minute for the call.
   Calculate what it costs Sharifa to make international calls lasting:

   a 7 minutes

   b 15 minutes

2. Two oarsmen weigh in at 85.3 kg and 92.75 kg. What is their mean weight?

3. Find the perimeter of a rectangle with sides of 1.67 m and 89 cm.

4. A parcel contains two items weighing 1 kg 342 g and 869 g.
   A third item is added to bring the total mass to 5 kg.
   What is the mass of the third item?

5. A cylindrical tin has a diameter of 7 cm.
   What is the length of a label going round the tin, if it overlaps itself by 1 cm at its ends?
   Use a value of 3.14 for π. Give your answer to one decimal place.

6 Estimate the area of a small circular table top with a diameter of 50 cm. Use a value of 3 for π.

7 A child's toy brick has a cross-section of area 6.1 cm². Its height is 1.1 cm.

    a Calculate the volume of the brick in cubic centimetres.

    b What is the volume of the brick in cubic millimetres?

Use your calculator to help answer questions **8–14**.

8 Mary pays £79 to join a gym, then £18.75 a month to use it.

Work out what it costs in total for Mary to be a member of the gym, for:

    a 5 months

    b 12 months

9 Find the area of a rectangle with length 2.38 cm and width 45 mm.

10 Calculate each area. Give your answers to one decimal place.

    a a semicircle   **b** a parallelogram   **c** a trapezium

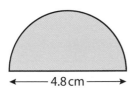

← 4.8 cm →

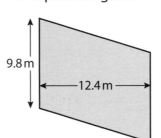

9.8 m   ← 12.4 m →

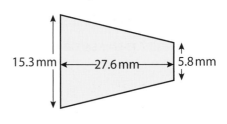

15.3 mm   ← 27.6 mm →   5.8 mm

11 The Earth has a radius of approximately 6400 km. Estimate the distance round the Equator to the nearest 100 kilometres. Use a value of 3.14 for π.

12 A CD is made from plastic. Its diameter is 11.6 cm.

The hole in the centre is 1.5 cm wide.

    a Work out the area of the hole.

    b Work out the area of the plastic.

13 The diameter of each wheel on Natasha's bike is 70 cm.

    a Calculate the circumference of each wheel to the nearest centimetre.

    b How many times does each wheel turn when Natasha rides her bike for a distance of 5 km? Give your answer to the nearest 10 turns.

Extension problem

14 The diagram shows the measurements of a prism.

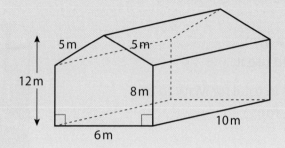

    a Calculate the total surface area of the prism.

    b Calculate the volume of the prism.

Points to remember

- Read word problems carefully.
- Change units to the same unit.
- Show your working, particularly when you use a calculator.
- When you use a calculator, consider the meaning of the numbers in the final display.
- Round only the final answer.
- Include the units in the answer.

How well are you doing?

Can you:

- ⊙ multiply and divide by positive and negative integer powers of 10?
- ⊙ round decimals and use rounding to make estimates?
- ⊙ use mental and efficient written methods to calculate with decimals?
- ⊙ use a calculator efficiently for complex calculations?

Calculations and calculators (no calculator)

① What is the value of $(0.1)^3$?

② A family uses about 6000 litres of water per week.
Approximately how many litres of water does the family use each year?

$$30\,000 \qquad 240\,000 \qquad 300\,000 \qquad 2\,400\,000 \qquad 3\,000\,000$$

③ Which of these is the best estimate of the answer to $72.48 \div 7.91$?

$$6 \quad 7 \quad 8 \quad 9 \quad 10 \quad 11$$

④ Estimate the answer to $\dfrac{50.03 \times 19.8}{9.76}$.

⑤ In a javelin competition, the winning throw was 81.7 metres.
The second-place throw was 79.86 metres.
How much longer was the winning throw?

⑥ *Year 8 Optional test level 6*
Calculate 57.3×2.1
Show your working.

Calculations and calculators (calculator allowed)

⑦ *2005 level 5*
Use your calculator to work out the answers.

a $(48 + 57) \times (61 - 19)$ 　　　　　　b $\dfrac{48 + 57}{61 - 19}$

8 *2002 level 6*

A company sells and processes films of two different sizes.
The tables show how much the company charges.

Film size: **24** photos

Cost to **buy** each film	£2.15
Postage	free

Cost to **print** each film	£0.99
Postage for each film	60p

Film size: **36** photos

Cost to **buy** each film	£2.65
Postage	free

Cost to **print** each film	£2.89
Postage for each film	60p

I want to take 360 photos.
I need to buy the film, pay for the film to be printed, and pay for the postage.

a Is it cheaper to use all films of size 24 photos, or all films of size 36 photos?

b How much cheaper is it? Show your working.

9 *2007 level 6*

The value of π correct to seven decimal places is:

3.1415927

a Write the value of π correct to 4 decimal places.

b Which value below is closest to the value of π?

A $\frac{179}{57}$ B $3\frac{1}{7}$ C $\left(\frac{16}{9}\right)^2$ D $\frac{355}{113}$

Probability 1

This unit will help you to:

- ◉ calculate theoretical probability when outcomes are equally likely;

- ◉ estimate experimental probability from the results of an experiment;

- ◉ appreciate the connection between experimental probability and theoretical probability;

- ◉ understand when outcomes and events are mutually exclusive;

- ◉ appreciate that the sum of probabilities of all mutually exclusive outcomes is 1;

- ◉ find all the mutually exclusive outcomes of an experiment;

- ◉ use theoretical and experimental probabilities to make informed choices when playing games of chance.

1 Simple probability

This lesson will help you to calculate theoretical probabilities for equally likely outcomes.

 Did you know that...?

Abraham De Moivre was an 18th-century French mathematician who pioneered the development of the theory of probability.

He is famous for predicting the day of his own death.

He found that he was sleeping 15 minutes longer each night. He calculated that he would die on the day that he slept for 24 hours. He was right!

When all the outcomes are equally likely, the theoretical probability of a particular event is:

$$\frac{\text{number of successful outcomes}}{\text{total number of possible outcomes}}$$

Example

In a pack of playing cards there are 52 cards.

There are four suits:

hearts, diamonds, clubs and spades.

Each suit contains 13 different cards:

ace, 2, 3, 4, 5, 6, 7, 8, 9, 10, jack, queen and king

a If you pick a card at random, what is the probability of getting a heart?

There are 13 hearts in the 52 cards so the probability is $\frac{13}{52}$ or $\frac{1}{4}$.

b If you pick a card at random, what is the probability of getting a 5?

There are four 5s in the 52 cards so the probability is $\frac{4}{52}$ or $\frac{1}{13}$.

c If you pick a card at random, what is the probability of getting a king or queen?

There are eight kings and queens out of 52 cards so the probability is $\frac{8}{52}$ or $\frac{2}{13}$.

---

1 Adrian has this set of digit cards from 1 to 9.

He shuffles them and picks one at random.

a What is the probability that he picks a red card?

b What is the probability that he picks a multiple of 3?

c What is the probability that he picks a red multiple of 3?

d What is the probability that he picks a number less than 4?

e What is the probability that he picks a 4 or a 6?

f What is the probability that he picks a number greater than 7 or less than 3?

g Is he more likely to pick an odd number or an even number?

h Is he more likely to pick an number greater or less than 6?

2 The diagram shows three different spinners.

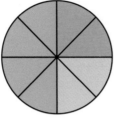 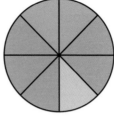 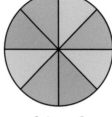

Spinner A   Spinner B   Spinner C

a Write a sentence comparing the probability of getting green on each of the three spinners.

b Which spinner has the highest probability of getting red?

c Which spinner has the lowest probability of getting blue?

3 Dyan makes this rectangular spinner. All the sections have equal areas.

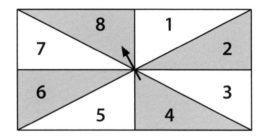

She says: 'All the numbers on my spinner have the same probability of coming up.'

Explain why Dyan is not correct.

4 A treasure hunt game at a fair is based on a grid.
There are prizes under some of the squares.

a Here are three possible grids for the game. The crosses indicate squares with prizes.

On which grid is there the best chance of winning? Explain your answer.

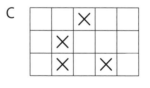

b Three more grids are designed:

Grid P   6 by 7 with 8 prize squares
Grid Q   12 by 14 with 20 prize squares
Grid R   8 by 11 with 15 prize squares

Which grid gives the best chance of winning? Explain your answer.

(5) Some counters are put in a bag. The table shows the probability of getting each colour.

Colour	Probability
Pink	0.4
Grey	0.1
Purple	0.2
Orange	0.3

a If there are 20 counters, how many are there of each colour?

b If you pick a counter at random, what is the probability of getting a pink or purple counter?

c If you pick a counter at random, what is the probability of getting a blue counter?

d Write down an outcome that has a probability of 0.5.

Extension problem

(6) Two bags, A and B, contain coloured cubes.

Bag A

Bag B

Each has the same number of cubes in it.

The probability of pulling a red cube out of bag A is 0.4.
The probability of pulling a red cube out of bag B is 0.2.

The cubes are all put in a new bag.

a What is the probability of taking a red cube out of the new bag?

b Barnaby says: 'There are 16 cubes altogether in the new bag.'
Explain why he cannot be correct.

Points to remember

⊙ When all the possible outcomes are equally likely, the **theoretical probability** of a particular event is given by:

$$\frac{\text{number of successful outcomes}}{\text{total number of possible outcomes}}$$

2 Equally likely outcomes with two events

This lesson will help you to calculate probabilities when two events happen at the same time or one after the other.

Exercise 2

It is important in probability to list all the possible outcomes of an event.

Example 1

When you throw two coins there are four possibilities.

The probability of getting two heads is $\frac{1}{4}$.

The probability of getting two tails is $\frac{1}{4}$.

The probability of getting one head and one tail is $\frac{1}{2}$.

Example 2

Make a table to show all the possible outcomes for rolling two dice and adding the scores.

What is the probability of getting a total score of 6?

There are 36 equally likely possible outcomes.

Five of these give a total of 6.

The probability of getting a total score of six is $\frac{5}{36}$.

+		First dice					
		1	2	3	4	5	6
Second dice	1	2	3	4	5	6	7
	2	3	4	5	6	7	8
	3	4	5	6	7	8	9
	4	5	6	7	8	9	10
	5	6	7	8	9	10	11
	6	7	8	9	10	11	12

Record your answers to questions **1** to **3** on **S5.2 Resource sheet 2.1**.

1. Nadia spins two spinners. One has eight equal sections numbered 1 to 8. The other has four equal sections numbered 1 to 4. She records the positive difference between the two scores.

   a Complete the table on **S5.2 Resource sheet 2.1** to show all the possible outcomes.

   b How many possible outcomes are there?

   c Use your completed table to work out the probability of getting a score of 0.

   d Calculate the probability of getting a score higher than 5.

   e Calculate the probability of getting a score of less than 2.

(2) Khalid rolls a fair 1 to 6 dice and flips a coin.

    a Complete the table on the resource sheet to show all the possible outcomes.

    b How many possible outcomes are there?

    c Use the completed table to work out the probability of getting a head and a 3.

    d Calculate the probability of getting a tail with a number greater than 4.

(3) Two fair dice are rolled and the scores added.
One dice is labelled 0, 0, 1, 1, 2, 2.
The other is labelled from 1 to 6.

    a Complete the table on the resource sheet to show the total scores.

    b How many possible outcomes are there?

    c Use the completed table to work out the probability of getting a score of 8.

    d Calculate the probability of getting a score of more than 5.

    e Calculate the probability of getting a score of less than 3.

(4) Two friends go to a café.
They each choose a drink from tea, coffee, milk shake or orange juice.

    a Make a table to show the two drinks they could choose.

    Write down the probability that:

    b they choose two different drinks

    c neither of them chooses a milk shake.

(5) A room is painted using two different colours.
The colours are chosen from white, cream, yellow and blue.

    a Make a list of the six different ways of choosing two different colours.

    b Write down the probability of choosing:
      i white and blue   **ii** cream with any other colour   **iii** not yellow.

◉ Points to remember

⊙ When two events occur at the same time or one after the other, you can use a table to show the equally likely outcomes.

⊙ This type of table is called a **sample space diagram**.

3 Mutually exclusive events

This lesson will help you to know that the sum of the probabilities of all the possible mutually exclusive outcomes of an experiment is 1.

Exercise 3

Example

You have some red, blue and green counters. You pick a counter at random.

a The probability of picking a green counter is 0.6.
What is the probability of picking a blue or red counter?

The only possibilities are red, green or blue so all the probabilities must add up to 1.

If the probability of getting a green is 0.6, the probability of getting a counter that is not green is $1 - 0.6 = 0.4$.

So the probability of picking a blue or red counter is 0.4.

b The probability of getting a red counter is 0.25.
What is the probability of getting a blue counter?

The three colours are mutually exclusive so their probabilities add up to 1.

$1 - 0.6 - 0.25 = 0.15$.

So the probability of getting a blue counter is 0.15.

c There are 20 counters in total. How many green counters are there?

The probability of green is $0.6 = \frac{6}{10} = \frac{12}{20}$.

So the number of green counters is 12 out of 20.

---

1 Rob chooses a number from 1 to 20.
Some possible events are shown on the right.

State whether these pairs of events are mutually exclusive or not.

a A and B	**b** A and C	**c** A and E
d B and C	**e** B and E	**f** C and D
g A and D	**h** C and E	**i** D and E

Events for Rob's number

The number chosen is:

A greater than 10

B less than 5

C a square number

D a triangular number

E a multiple of 8

2 a The probability of Abigail catching the bus for school is 0.07.
What is the probability that she misses the bus?

b Enrico goes home on the bus twice a week.
What is the probability that he will go home on the bus today?

c The punctuality rate for GoGo Buses is 86%.
What is the probability that a particular bus is late?

3 This table shows the probabilities of getting different scores on a biased six-sided dice.

a Work out the probability of getting a score of 4.

b What is the probability of getting a score greater than 3?

c What is the probability of getting a score less than 4?

Score	Probability
1	$\frac{1}{6}$
2	$\frac{1}{4}$
3	$\frac{1}{12}$
4	
5	$\frac{1}{3}$
6	$\frac{1}{12}$

4 The table shows the probabilities of getting different scores on a spinner with five sections of varying size. Part of it is hidden by a large ink blot.

The probability of getting a score greater than 3 is 0.5.

a Work out the probability of getting a score of 3.

b The probability of getting 2, 3, or 4 is 0.8.
What is the probability of getting a score of 5?

c What is the probability of getting a score of 4?

Score	Probability
1	$\frac{1}{10}$
2	$\frac{1}{4}$
3	
4	
5	

5 Two fair spinners are spun. The scores are added together.

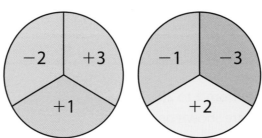

Work out the probability of getting:

a a total score of 5

b a total score of 0

c a score that is not 0

d a positive score

e a negative score

6 Vicky has lots of 1p, 2p, 5p, 10p, 20p, 50p, £1 and £2 coins.
She puts two coins in a charity box.

   a Write a list of all the possible amounts Vicky could have put in the charity box.

   b Work out the probability that Vicky put more than 50p in the charity box.

Extension problem

7 Two bags A and B contain coloured cubes.
Each bag has the same number of coloured cubes in it.

The probability of taking a purple cube at random from bag A is 0.4.
The probability of taking a purple cube at random from bag B is 0.8.

The contents of both bags are tipped into a new empty bag and mixed up.

   a What is the probability of picking a purple cube out of the new bag?

   b Suppose bag A had contained twice as many cubes as bag B.
   What would be the probability of picking a purple cube out of the new bag?

   c Suppose bag A had contained n times as many cubes as bag B.
   Find a rule to work out the probability of picking a purple cube out of the new bag.

 Points to remember

⊙ Outcomes that cannot occur at the same time are **mutually exclusive**.

⊙ The sum of the probabilities of all the possible mutually exclusive outcomes of an experiment is 1.

⊙ If the probability of an event occurring is p, then the probability of it not occurring is $1 - p$.

⊙ If A and B are mutually exclusive events then:
   probability of A **or** B = probability of A + probability of B

4 Practical probability experiments

This lesson will help you to estimate experimental probability and use probabilities to make informed choices when you play games of chance.

The experimental probability of an event is:

$$\frac{\text{number of successful trials}}{\text{total number of trials}}$$

Example

The frequency table shows the results from throwing a dice 50 times.

What is the experimental probability of getting each score?

Probability of getting a 1 $= \frac{7}{50}$

Probability of getting a 2 $= \frac{11}{50}$

Probability of getting a 3 $= \frac{9}{50}$

Probability of getting a 4 $= \frac{6}{50} = \frac{3}{25}$

Probability of getting a 5 $= \frac{10}{50} = \frac{1}{5}$

Probability of getting a 6 $= \frac{7}{50}$

Score	Frequency
1	7
2	11
3	9
4	6
5	10
6	7
TOTAL	50

1. Play **Odds and evens** with a partner.

You need a dice and 20 counters.

Rules

- Decide who will be 'odds' and who 'evens'.
  Start with 10 counters each.

- Throw the dice.

- If the score is odd then the person who is 'odds' takes that many counters from the other person.
  For example, a score of 3 means that 'odds' takes 3 counters from 'evens'.

- If the score is even then the person who is 'evens' takes that many counters from the other person.
  For example, a score of 2 means that 'evens' takes 2 counters from 'odds'.

- Continue playing the game until one player runs out of counters.

Play the game four or five times.

a Who won the most games?
Is the game fair? If not, why not?

b Think of other, fairer, scoring systems.

Work in a group of three or four. You need an envelope containing a set of cards made from **S5.2 Resource sheet 4.1**.

Don't take the cards out of the envelope to look at them!

1 Choose one person to take charge of the cards.

- Shuffle the cards by shaking them in the envelope without looking at them.
- Ask someone to pick a card without looking.
- Record the object on the card. Put the card back.
- Repeat this 10 times.

2 Now discuss these questions in your group and record your answers.

a How many different objects do you think are shown on the set of cards?

b There are 24 cards altogether.
How many of each card do you think there are?

c Can you be sure of your answers to questions **a** and **b**? If not, why not?

- Use a tally chart to record your ten results so far.
- Repeat the experiment another 40 times. Record your results.

3 Now answer these questions.

a Calculate the experimental probability of getting each object.

b How many different objects do you think there are in the set of cards?

c How many of each card do you think there are now?

d How sure are you of your answers to questions **b** and **c**? Explain why.

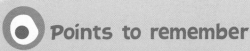

Points to remember

- The **experimental probability** of an event is given by:

$$\frac{\text{number of successful trials}}{\text{total number of trials}}$$

- Experimental probability becomes closer in value to theoretical probability the greater the number of trials.

5 Simulating probability experiments

This lesson will help you to estimate experimental probability and compare it with theoretical probability.

Exercise 5

A **simulation** is an easy-to-do experiment that behaves in the same way as the original experiment.

You can use a **random number generator** to simulate other situations more quickly than carrying out the actual experiment.

Simulating a coin toss using random numbers

You could use:

- odd numbers for tails and even numbers for heads;
- or 1–5 for tails and 6–10 for heads.

Simulating a dice using random numbers

You could use the first decimal place and ignore any values that are not 1, 2, 3, 4, 5 or 6.

Work in a group of three or four.

You will need a scientific calculator and a copy of **S5.2 Resource sheet 5.1**.

1. **Simulating spinning a coin 30 times**

   a Use your calculator to generate 30 random numbers from 0 to 99. For example, take the first two decimal places generated by the calculator. So:

   0.67932865 on the calculator would give you 67

   Record these numbers in the table on **S5.2 Resource sheet 5.1**.

   b If the number is odd, the outcome is tails, if the number is even, the outcome is heads.

   Record the outcome for each number in the table on the resource sheet.

   c Count up the number of tails and the number of heads.

   d Calculate the experimental probability of getting tails and heads.

(2) **Simulating throwing a dice 30 times**

a Use your calculator to generate 30 random numbers. For example, take the digit in the first decimal place only if it is a 1, 2, 3, 4, 5 or 6. For example:

  ⊙ 0.67932865 on the calculator would give you 6;

  ⊙ 0.78765482 would be ignored as the first digit is 7.

  Record these numbers in the table on **S5.2 Resource sheet 5.1**.

b If the number is 1 the score is 1, if the number is 2 the score is 2, and so on. Work out the frequency for each score on the dice.

c Calculate the experimental probability for each score on the dice.

(3) **Simulating spinning two coins**

Design your own simulation to simulate spinning two coins.

a What are the three possible outcomes? (They are not equally likely.)

b Decide how to allocate numbers to these three outcomes.

> **Hint**
>
> You will need to allocate twice as many numbers to the outcome one head and one tail, as the theoretical probability is that this happens twice as often as two heads or two tails.

c Use the table on **S5.2 Resource sheet 5.1** to record your random numbers.

d Record the outcome for each number in the table on the resource sheet.

e Count up the number of two tails, the number of two heads and the number of one head and one tail, in either order.

f Calculate the experimental probability of getting:

  i two tails   ii two heads   iii one head and one tail.

> ⊙ **Points to remember**
>
> ⊙ A **simulation** is an easy-to-do experiment that behaves in the same way as the original experiment.
>
> ⊙ A **random number generator** can simulate situations more quickly than carrying out an actual experiment.
>
> ⊙ Repeated experiments usually give different outcomes.

How well are you doing?

Can you:

- calculate theoretical probability when outcomes are equally likely?

- estimate experimental probability from the results of an experiment?

- find all the mutually exclusive outcomes of an experiment?

① *2007 level 6*

In a bag there are only red, blue and green counters.

a I am going to take a counter out of the bag at random.
Copy and complete the table below.

Colour of counters	Number of counters	Probability
Red	6	
Blue		$\frac{1}{5}$
Green	6	

b Before I take a counter out of the bag, I put one extra blue counter into the bag.

What effect does this have on the probability that I will take a red counter?

Which one of these four statements is correct?

A The probability has increased.

B The probability has decreased.

C The probability has stayed the same.

D It is impossible to tell.

a   A bag has 20 cubes in it. 6 of the cubes are green.

You take one cube out of the bag at random.

Which values below show the probability that you take out a cube that is green?
Write down the correct four values from the table.

$\frac{6}{14}$	30%	0.6	$\frac{3}{10}$
6%	$\frac{3}{5}$	$\frac{6}{20}$	0.03
0.3	$\frac{6}{10}$	60%	$\frac{6}{26}$

b   A box has 20 counters in it. 11 of the counters are red.

You take one counter out of the box at random.

What is the probability that the counter you take out is not red?
Write your answer as a fraction and then as a percentage.

3   Amy has two spinners.

One has five equal sections labelled 1 to 5.
The other has five equal sections labelled 6 to 10.

a   Make a table to show all the possible totals from spinning the two
spinners together.

b   How many different scores are there?

c   What is the probability of getting a score of 11?

d   Write down two possible events with equal probabilities.

e   Write down two different events whose probabilities sum to 1.

Functions and graphs

This unit will help you to:

- generate graphs using ICT;

- recognise properties of linear graphs;

- sketch, draw and interpret linear graphs;

- solve problems and justify your solutions or generalisations.

1 Generating linear graphs using ICT

This lesson will help you to generate linear graphs using ICT.

Exercise 1

You can rearrange a linear equation in the form $y = ax + b$ so that you can enter it into a graphing program or a calculator.

Remember that what you do to one side of an equation you must do to the other.

Example 1 $y - 3x = 7$

Add $3x$ $y = 3x + 7$

Example 2 $y + 5x - 6 = 0$

Add 6 $y + 5x = 6$

Subtract $5x$ $y = -5x + 6$

When the number in front of x is not 1, divide every term in the equation by that number before you rearrange it in the form $y = ax + b$.

Example 3 $3y - 12x = 21$

Divide by 3 $y - 4x = 7$

Add $4x$ $y = 4x + 7$

Example 4 $5y + 15x - 45 = 0$

Divide by 5 $y + 3x - 9 = 0$

Add 9 $y + 3x = 9$

Subtract $3x$ $y = -3x + 9$

Work with a partner for questions **4** and **7**.
You will need a **computer with graph-plotting software** or a **graphics calculator**.

1 Which of these equations are the same as $y = 2x - 5$?

A $y - 2x + 5 = 0$ 　　　　　　　　B $y - 2x = 5$

C $y + 2x - 5 = 0$ 　　　　　　　　D $y - 2x = -5$

E $2x - y = 5$ 　　　　　　　　　　E $2x - y = -5$

2 Rearrange these equations in the form $y = ax + b$.

a $y - 4x + 9 = 0$ 　　　　　　　　b $y - 8x = 1$

c $3x - y = 10$ 　　　　　　　　　　d $y - 6x = -3$

e $y + 7x - 8 = 0$ 　　　　　　　　f $y - x + 2 = 0$

g $y + 2x + 9 = 0$ 　　　　　　　　h $y - 4x - 7 = 0$

i $8x - y + 5 = 0$ 　　　　　　　　j $5 + 6x - y = 0$

3 Write the gradient and intercept on the y-axis for each of the graphs of the equations in question **2**.

4 Work with a partner.
Use a **computer** or **graphics calculator**.
Draw each of the graphs of the equations in question **2**.

How many out of the 10 graphs did you imagine correctly?

5 Rearrange these equations in the form $y = ax + b$.

a $2y - 16x + 14 = 0$ 　　　　　　　b $5y - 30x = 10$

c $9x - 3y = 21$ 　　　　　　　　　d $6y - 42x = -24$

e $10y + 60x - 70 = 0$ 　　　　　　f $4y - 20x + 36 = 0$

g $8y + 32x + 64 = 0$ 　　　　　　h $3y - 27x - 33 = 0$

i $18x - 9y + 27 = 0$ 　　　　　　j $49 + 28x - 7y = 0$

6 Write the gradient and intercept on the y-axis for each of the graphs of the equations in question **5**.

7 Work with a partner.
Use a **computer** or **graphics calculator**.
Draw each of the graphs of the equations in question **5**.

How many out of the 10 graphs did you imagine correctly?

8 **a** Write the equation of the red line.

b Write the equation of the blue line.

c Write the coordinates of the point where the lines cross.

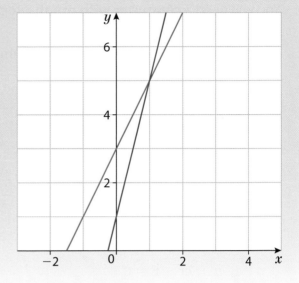

Points to remember

⊙ The equation of a linear graph is usually written in the form $y = ax + b$.

⊙ What you do to one side of an equation you must do to the other side.

⊙ You can divide each term in an equation by the same number.

2 Sketching graphs

This lesson will help you to sketch and transform linear graphs.

Exercise 2

A **sketch** of a graph is a neat drawing using a pencil and ruler.
Mark special points on the graph, such as the origin and the intercept on the y-axis.

Before you sketch a linear graph, put the equation in the form $y = ax + b$.

The coefficient of x is the number in front of x, which is a.
This gives you the **gradient** or steepness of the graph.

The number b gives you the **intercept** on the y-axis.

Equations of the form $y = ax + b$ always give straight-line graphs.

A **translation** is a movement horizontally and/or vertically.

The diagram shows the graphs of:

$y = x$
$y = x + 3$

The two lines are parallel.

They cross the y-axis at different points.

You can think of $y = x + 3$ as a translation of $y = x$ by 3 units upwards.

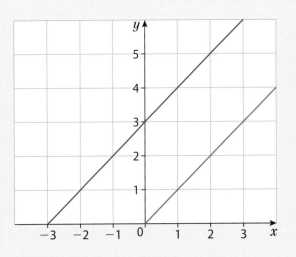

In a **reflection**, each point of the image is the same distance from the mirror line as the corresponding point of the object.

The diagram shows the graphs of:

$y = 2x$
$y = -2x$

You can think of the graph of $y = -2x$ as the reflection of the line $y = 2x$ in the y-axis.

For example, A is the point (2, 4) on $y = 2x$.
A' is the point $(-2, 4)$ on $y = -2x$.

A' is the reflection of A in the y-axis, so
AB = A'B

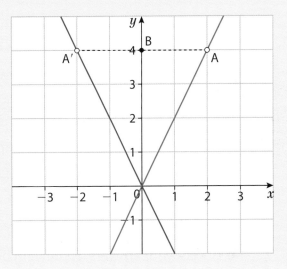

Work with a partner. You will each need squared paper, pencil and ruler.
You will need a **computer with graph-plotting software** or a **graphics calculator**.

1. On squared paper, sketch each graph on a blank set of axes.
   Check your sketches by drawing them on the computer or graphics calculator.

   a $y - 2x + 3 = 0$ **b** $y - 3x = 6$

   c $x - y = 5$ **d** $y - 5x = -1$

   e $y + 2x - 4 = 0$ **f** $y - 6x + 4 = 0$

   g $2y + 8x + 4 = 0$ **h** $3y - 9x - 30 = 0$

   i $10x - 5y + 25 = 0$ **j** $22 + x - 2y = 0$

2 a On squared paper, sketch the graph of $y = x$ on unnumbered axes.

   b On the same set of axes, sketch the graph when
      $y = x$ has been translated 7 units up.

   c Write the equation of the graph you have just sketched.

   d Check your answers by drawing both graphs on a computer or graphics calculator.

3 a On squared paper, sketch the graph of $y = 3x + 4$ on unnumbered axes.

   b On the same set of axes, sketch the graph when
      $y = 3x + 4$ has been translated 3 units down.

   c Write the equation of the graph you have just sketched.

   d Check your answers by drawing both graphs on a computer or graphics calculator.

4 a On squared paper, sketch the graph of $y = 2x + 1$ on unnumbered axes.

   b On the same set of axes, sketch the graph when
      $y = 2x + 1$ has been reflected in the y-axis.

   c Write the equation of the graph you have just sketched.

   d Check your answers by drawing both graphs on a computer or graphics calculator.

5 a On squared paper, sketch the graph of $y = 2x + 1$ on a blank set of axes.

   b On the same set of axes, sketch the graph when
      $y = 2x + 1$ has been reflected in the x-axis.

   c Write the equation of the graph you have just sketched.

   d Check your answers by drawing both graphs on a computer or graphics calculator.

◉ Points to remember

⊙ When a linear equation is in the form $y = ax + b$:
   a, the coefficient of x, is the **gradient** of the graph;
   b, is the **intercept** on the y-axis.

⊙ When the line $y = 2x + 3$ is **translated** 4 units up,
   the equation of the new line is $y = 2x + 7$.
   The gradient of the line does not change.

⊙ When the line $y = 2x + 3$ is **reflected** in the y-axis,
   the equation of the new line is $y = -2x + 3$.

⊙ When the line $y = 2x + 3$ is reflected in the x-axis,
   the equation of the new line is $y = -2x - 3$.

3 Drawing accurate graphs

This lesson will help you to draw linear graphs accurately.

Exercise 3

To make an accurate drawing of a straight-line graph you need to plot two points that lie on the graph. You need a third point to act as a check.

Plot the points with small neat dots or crosses and use a ruler to draw the line.

Example

Draw the graph of $y = -x + 5$.

When $x = 0$, $y = 5$, so $(0, 5)$ is a point on the graph.

When $y = 0$, $x = 5$, so $(5, 0)$ is a point on the graph.

Use a ruler to draw the straight line through $(0, 5)$ and $(5, 0)$.

When $x = 1$, $y = 4$, so $(1, 4)$ should lie on the graph.

As it does, this tells you that the graph is drawn accurately.

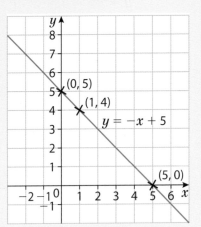

You will need graph paper.

1. Copy and complete these tables of values.

   a

x	−2	0	2
$y = 2x - 3$			

   b

x	−1	0	4
$y = 3x + 1$			

   c

x	0	1	2
$y = 5x - 2$			

   d

x	−3	0	1
$y = 4x + 0.5$			

   e

x	−1	0	1
$y = -2x + 5$			

(2) Use graph paper, pencil and ruler.
Draw an accurate graph of each equation in the tables in question **1**.
Draw each graph on a new grid.
Remember to continue the line to the edge of the grid.

(3) Work out three points that satisfy each of these equations.

On graph paper, draw each graph accurately using a pencil and a ruler.

a $y = x + 5$

b $y = 3x - 4$

c $x - y = 7$

d $y - 5x = -2$

e $y + 2x - 7 = 0$

f $2y - 4x + 6 = 0$

(4) The coordinate pairs in these tables lie on straight lines.
Work out the equations of each line.

a

x	−1	0	1
$y = ?$	2	3	4

b

x	−2	0	2
$y = ?$	−6	−4	−2

c

x	0	1	2
$y = ?$	−1	1	3

d

x	−3	0	1
$y = ?$	−1	5	7

e

x	0	1	2
$y = ?$	−1	2	5

Draw an accurate graph of each equation in the tables.

Points to remember

⊙ For **any** value of x in an equation such as $y = 3x + 2$, you can find a value of y.

⊙ To draw an accurate straight-line graph, you need the coordinates of three points: two to define the line and the third to check your accuracy.

4 Direct proportion

This lesson will help you to draw graphs showing direct proportion.

Exercise 4

Relationships between two quantities can be shown using a graph.

When the two quantities are directly related in **direct proportion** to one another, the graph is a straight line passing through the origin.

For example, the cost in pounds (£) of petrol y is directly proportional to the number of litres of petrol x that the motorist buys.

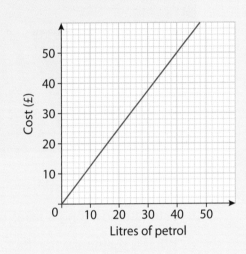

We write: $y \propto x$
or $y = kx$, where k is a constant.

The $\propto$ symbol means 'is proportional to'.

---

① Aisha has a bag of counters. She puts them on the table.

   a What is the ratio of red counters to blue counters?

   b What is the ratio of red counters to yellow counters?

   c What is the ratio of blue counters to yellow counters?

   d What proportion of counters is red?

   e What proportion of counters is blue?

   f What proportion of counters is yellow?

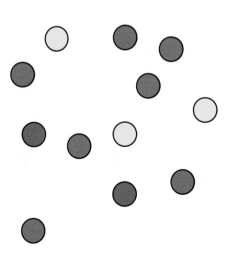

(2) Thomas drives from London to Manchester. He leaves home at 6:30 am.
The graph shows part of his journey using average speed.

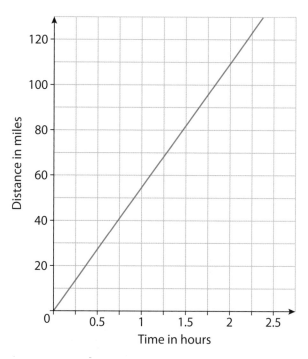

a Use the graph to estimate how far Thomas has travelled after three quarters of an hour.

b Estimate how long it takes him to travel 100 miles.

c What is the time when he has travelled 100 miles?

d Estimate his average speed.

e Thomas continues to travel at the same average speed.

His total journey is 200 miles.

At about what time does he arrive?

(3) Work out the formula for these directly proportional relationships.

a The perimeter P of a square is directly proportional to the length x of a side.

b The cost C of cheese is directly proportional to the weight w.

c The cost C of hiring skis is directly proportional to the number of hours t for which the skis are hired.

d The number of sandwiches n made for a picnic is directly proportional to the number of people p going on the picnic.

4   These tables represent directly proportional relationships $y \propto x$ or $y = kx$.
    Work out the value of k in each case.

a

x	1	2	3
y	5	10	15

b

x	0	1	2
y	0	2.5	5

c

x	−1	1	3
y	1	−1	−3

d

x	2	3	4
y	13	19.5	26

e

x	3	5	7
y	0.6	1.0	1.4

5   These tables represent directly proportional relationships $y \propto x$ or $y = kx$.
    Work out the value of k in each case.

a

x	3.2	5.7	8.6
y	4.16	7.41	11.18

b

x	1.7	2.9	5.8
y	1.19	2.03	4.06

c

x	−2.3	−4.6	−7.5
y	0.69	1.38	2.25

d

x	0.2	0.5	0.7
y	2.1	5.25	7.35

Extension problem

6 In these tables $y \propto x^2$ or $y = kx^2$.
Work out the value of k in each case.

a

x	0	2	4
y	0	24	96

b

x	0	3	5
y	0	4.5	12.5

c

x	-2	0	2
y	9.2	0	9.2

d

x	2	3	4
y	-12	-27	-48

◉ Points to remember

- ◉ When y is **directly proportional** to x you write $y \propto x$, giving the equation $y = kx$.
- ◉ The graph of $y = kx$ is a straight line passing through the origin with gradient k.

5 Reflecting graphs in $y = x$

This lesson will help you to sketch and transform linear graphs.

Exercise 5

A point P is reflected in a mirror line.

The point P and its image P′ are the same distance from the mirror line.

The line joining P and P′ is perpendicular to the mirror line.

When all the points on a straight line are reflected in a mirror line you get a new straight line.

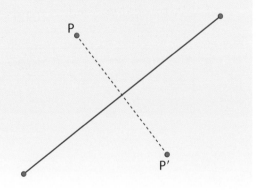

Example

Draw the reflection of the line $y = 3x$ in the line $y = x$.

The red line is the graph of $y = 3x$.

The black dashed line is the graph of $y = x$.

The blue line is the reflection of the red line in $y = x$.

The equation of the blue line is $y = \frac{1}{3}x$.

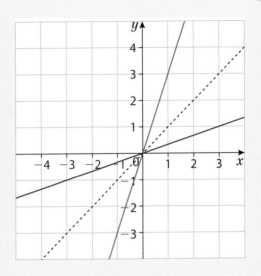

1 a The coordinates of the points A to I are reflected in the dashed line $y = x$.

Write the coordinates of each of the reflected points A′ to I′.

b What do you notice about any coordinate point (x, y) after it is reflected in $y = x$?

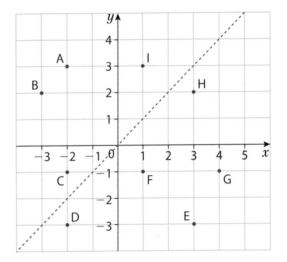

2 a Write the equation of the green line.

b The orange line is the reflection of the green line in the dashed line $y = x$.

Write the equation of the orange line.

c Write what you notice about the two equations.

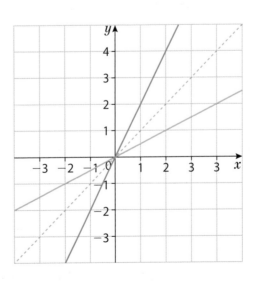

3 a Write the equation of the purple line.

b The pink line is the reflection of the purple line in the dashed line $y = x$.
Write the equation of the pink line.

c Write what you notice about the two equations.

d Work with a partner. Use a computer or graphics calculator to reflect your own lines in $y = x$.

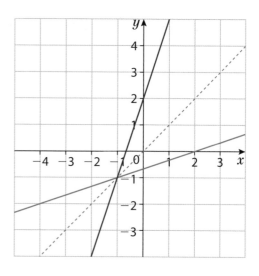

Extension problem

 4 Work with a partner.
You will each need squared paper, pencil and ruler.
You will need a **computer with graph-plotting software** or a **graphics calculator**.

a On squared paper, sketch the graph of $y = 6x + 2$.

b On the same set of axes, sketch the graph when $y = 6x + 2$ has been reflected in the line $y = x$.

c Write the equation of the graph you have just sketched.

d Check your answers by drawing both graphs using a computer or graphics calculator.

Points to remember

⊙ When the point (a, b) is reflected in the line $y = x$, the image is the point (b, a).

⊙ When the line with equation $y = ax + b$ is reflected in the line $y = x$, the equation of the image line is $x = ay + b$.

6 Simple quadratic graphs using ICT

This lesson will help you to use ICT to generate quadratic graphs.

Exercise 6

A **quadratic equation** is one that contains x and x^2 but no higher powers of x.

The graph of a quadratic equation is always U-shaped.

Example

Draw the graph of $y = x^2$.
Use values of x from $x = -3$ to $x = 3$.

When $x = 3$, $y = 3 \times 3 = 9$ When $x = -3$, $y = -3 \times -3 = 9$

When $x = 2$, $y = 2 \times 2 = 4$ When $x = -2$, $y = -2 \times -2 = 4$

When $x = 1$, $y = 1 \times 1 = 1$ When $x = -1$, $y = -1 \times -1 = 1$

When $x = 0$, $y = 0 \times 0 = 0$

x	−3	−2	−1	0	1	2	3
y	9	4	1	0	1	4	9

The lowest point of this graph is where it turns.

It is the origin (0, 0).

It is called the **minimum point**.

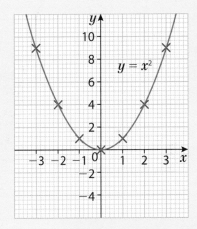

Work with a partner.

You will need a **computer with graph-plotting software** or a **graphics calculator**.

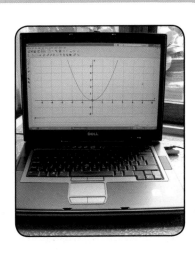

① a Plot the curves:
$y = x^2 - 3$, $y = x^2 - 2$, $y = x^2 - 1$, $y = x^2$,
$y = x^2 + 1$, $y = x^2 + 2$, $y = x^2 + 3$, …

  b Explain what happens to the graph of $y = x^2$ as you add or subtract a number to the equation.

2 **a** Plot the curves:

$$y = -x^2, y = -x^2 + 1, y = -x^2 + 2,$$
$$y = -x^2 + 3, y = -x^2 - 1, y = -x^2 - 2.$$

b Explain what happens when the coefficient of x^2 is a negative number.

Extension problem

3 **a** Plot the curves:

$$y = x^2, y = 2x^2, y = 3x^2, y = 4x^2, y = 5x^2$$

b Describe what happens when you multiply x^2 by a number other than 1.

c Plot the curves:

$$y = -x^2, y = -2x^2, y = -3x^2, y = -4x^2, y = -5x^2$$

d Describe what happens when you multiply $-x^2$ by a number other than 1.

 Points to remember

⊙ **Quadratic graphs** are always U-shaped.
⊙ Quadratic graphs do not always cut the x-axis.

How well are you doing?

Can you:

- recognise properties of linear graphs?
- sketch, draw and interpret linear graphs?
- solve problems involving graphs and justify your solution?

1 *2002 level 6*

The graph shows a straight line.
The equation of the line is $y = 3x$.

Does the point (25, 75) lie on
the straight line $y = 3x$?

Write **Yes** or **No**.
Explain how you know.

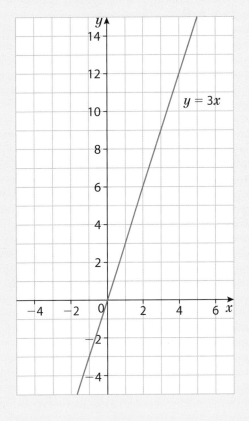

2 *2004 level 6*

Use graph paper.

Draw the straight line $x + y = 12$.

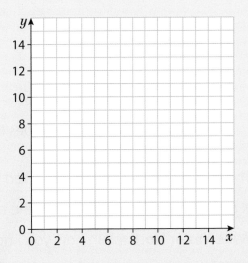

3 Write the gradient and intercept on the y-axis for the graph of the equation $2y - 8x = 14$.

4 *2000 level 6*

The diagram shows a square drawn on a square grid.

The line $y = 0$ passes through the vertices A and C.

Through which two vertices do these lines pass?

a $x = 0$

b $x + y = 2$

c $x + y = -2$

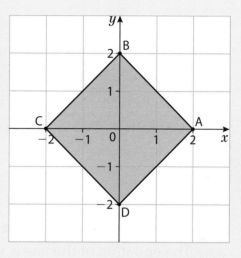

5 *Year 8 optional test level 6*

a You can write the equation $y = x + 4$ in different ways.

Which of these equations are the same as $y = x + 4$?

A $x + y = 4$ B $x = 4 + y$ C $y - x = 4$

D $y + 4 = x$ E $x = y - 4$

b The equation of the line AB is $y = x + 4$.

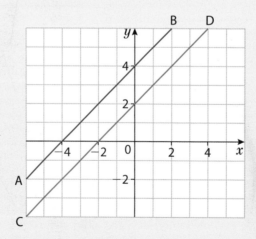

Write an equation that describes line CD.

6 The graph of $y = 2x + 1$ is reflected in the y-axis.

Is $y = -2x + 1$ the equation of the new line?

Write **Yes** or **No**. Explain how you know.

Transformations

This unit will help you to:

- ⊙ find planes of symmetry in 3D shapes;

- ⊙ transform 2D shapes by enlarging them and by combining reflections, rotations and translations;

- ⊙ understand the effect of enlargement on perimeter, area and volume;

- ⊙ appreciate some of the ways in which mathematics is used in real life.

1 Planes of symmetry

This lesson will help you to find planes of symmetry in 3D shapes.

 Did you know that...?

When a plane cuts a 3D shape in two so that each half is a mirror image of the other half, the plane is called a **plane of symmetry**.

Buildings often have a plane of symmetry.

The terrace houses on the right are divided by a plane of symmetry.

Pyramids have planes of symmetry. **The Great Pyramid** in Giza, Egypt, was built about 2570 BC. It is 147 m tall and its square base is 230 m wide. It has four planes of symmetry.

Pyramids are still built today. The pyramid on the right above is outside Le Louvre in Paris.

These 3D shapes have several **planes of symmetry**.

Hexagonal prism

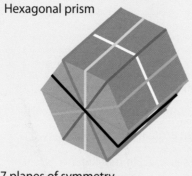

7 planes of symmetry

Cube

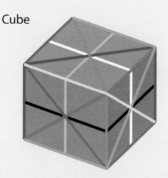

9 planes of symmetry

In this exercise, prisms are all right prisms and pyramids are all right pyramids.

1 The cross-section of each of these prisms is a regular polygon.
How many planes of symmetry are there in each prism?

a pentagonal prism

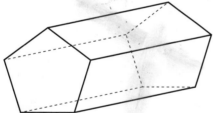

b octagonal prism

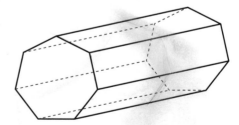

c triangular prism

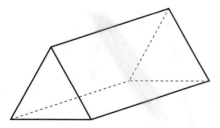

d heptagonal prism

2 A prism with a cross-section that is a regular polygon has 10 planes of symmetry.
How many sides does the polygon have?

3 A prism with a cross-section that is a regular polygon has 7 planes of symmetry.
What is the name of the polygon?

(4) How many planes of symmetry are there in each of these prisms?

a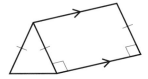

b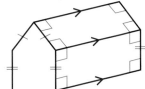

c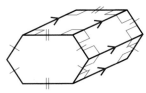

d

e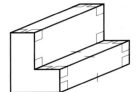

f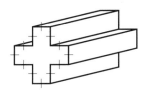

(5) Write the number of planes of symmetry in each of these prisms.

a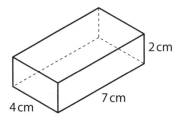

2 cm
7 cm
4 cm

b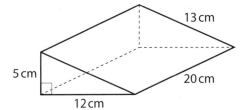

13 cm
5 cm
20 cm
12 cm

c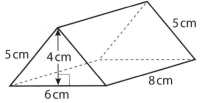

5 cm
5 cm
4 cm
8 cm
6 cm

d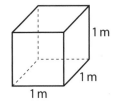

1 m
1 m
1 m

(6) The base of each pyramid is a regular polygon.
How many planes of symmetry are there in each pyramid?

a square base

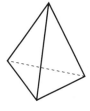

b regular pentagon base

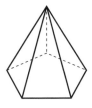

c isosceles triangle base

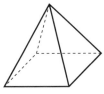

d rectangle base

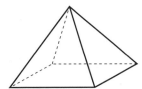

7 a The base of a pyramid is a regular polygon.
The pyramid has six planes of symmetry.
How many triangular faces does the pyramid have?

b The base of a pyramid is a regular decagon (ten-sided polygon).
How many planes of symmetry does this pyramid have?

8 A regular tetrahedron is a pyramid whose base and side faces are all equilateral triangles.

a How many faces does it have?   b How many edges?

c How many vertices?   d How many planes of symmetry?

9 This 3D shape is made up from a triangular prism
and a tetrahedron that fit together exactly.

a How many faces does it have?

b How many edges?

c How many vertices?

d How many planes of symmetry?

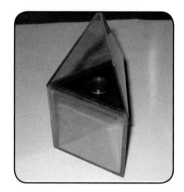

Extension problem

10 The following objects are placed on a mirror.
Write the name of the shape formed from each object and its reflection.

a A cube

b A cuboid

c A square-based pyramid on its square base

⊙ Points to remember

⊙ A plane of symmetry divides a 3D shape into two equal halves that are
mirror images of each other.

⊙ The number of **planes of symmetry** in a right prism is one more than
the number of lines of symmetry of the cross-section.

⊙ A cube has 9 planes of symmetry.

⊙ A right pyramid has the same number of planes of symmetry as the lines
of symmetry of the base.

2 Combined transformations

This lesson will help you to transform 2D shapes by combining reflections, rotations and translations.

Exercise 2

After a rotation, reflection or translation, the image is the same size and shape as the object.

Rotations, reflections and translations can be combined to transform an object.

After any combination of reflections, rotations and translations, the image is the same size and shape as the original object.

Example 1

This shape has been reflected twice, once in a vertical mirror line and once in a horizontal mirror line.

Draw the mirror lines.

Write down the single transformation that moves the object to the image.

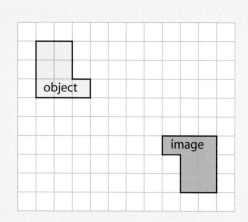

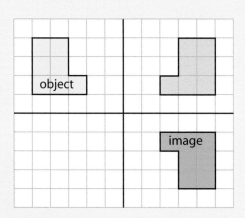

The object is reflected in the vertical mirror line and then in the horizontal mirror line.

It could also be reflected first in the horizontal mirror line and then in the vertical mirror line.

A single transformation would be a rotation of 180° clockwise about the point at which the two lines cross.

Example 2

a Write down a single transformation that moves the object to the image.

Rotate the object 90° clockwise about centre of rotation A.

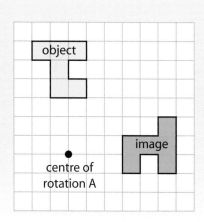

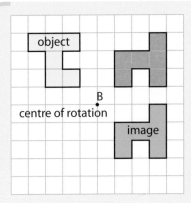

b Write down a combination of two transformations that move the object to the image.

Rotate the object 90° clockwise about centre of rotation B followed by a translation across 0 down 4.

You will need squared paper and squared dotty paper or a pinboard for this exercise.

1 The diagram shows eight right-angled triangles.

a Triangle A maps onto four of the unshaded triangles by a reflection.

Name these four triangles and write down the reflection in each case.

b Triangle A maps onto three of the unshaded triangles by a rotation.

Name these three triangles.

Write down the rotation in each case.

c How many unshaded triangles are congruent to triangle A?

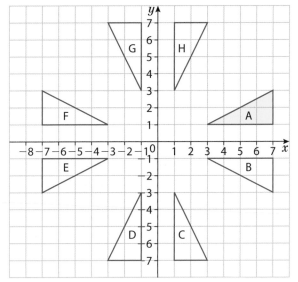

2 This shape has been reflected twice, once in a vertical mirror line and once in a horizontal mirror line.

a Copy the diagram on squared paper. Draw the two mirror lines.

b What single transformation could have made the same movement?

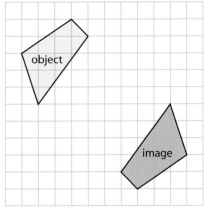

3 Copy this diagram on squared paper.

Rotate the object 90° clockwise about the centre of rotation marked 1. Label this 'image 1'.

Now rotate image 1 90° clockwise about the centre of rotation marked 2. Label this 'image 2'.

Write down the single transformation that transforms the object to image 2.

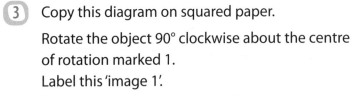

④ Copy this diagram on squared paper.

Rotate the object through 90° clockwise three times about the centre of rotation marked with a dot.

Label the images in order 'image 1', 'image 2' and 'image 3'.

Rotating the object twice transforms it to image 2.

Write down three different transformations or combinations of transformations that could transform the object to image 2.

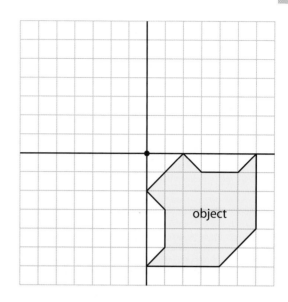

⑤ Copy this diagram on squared paper.

a Rotate triangle P 90° anticlockwise about (3, 5). Label the new triangle Q.

b Rotate triangle Q 90° clockwise about (6, 2). Label the new triangle R.

c Write down the single transformation which maps triangle P onto triangle R.

Extension problem

⑥ Copy this triangle on a 5 by 5 pinboard or 5 by 5 dotty paper.

Now draw two more congruent triangles but in different positions and orientations.

Choose one of the triangles to be the object.

Write down the transformations from the object onto each of the other triangles you drew.

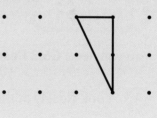

⊙ Points to remember

⊙ For rotation, translation and reflection, the image is always **congruent** to the object, although its **orientation** may change.

⊙ Rotation, translation and reflection can be combined to move an object.

⊙ Different combinations of transformations can have the same effect.

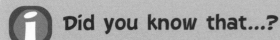

3 Islamic patterns

This lesson will help you to appreciate the mathematics underlying some patterns.

Did you know that...?

Pattern has always been an important part of Islamic culture.

Exercise 3

You will need **G5.3 Resource sheets 3.1 and 3.2**.

1. Look closely at the photographs above. Describe the transformations that you can see.

2. Add more lines to the starting point on **G5.3 Resource sheet 3.1** so that the shape always has four lines of symmetry and order of rotation 4.

   Choose some lines.
   Draw over them in a coloured pen or pencil to create your individual pattern.
   Repeat your pattern on all the squares on **G5.3 Resource sheet 3.2**.

Points to remember

⊙ Islamic patterns are often based on tiles that have four lines of symmetry and rotation symmetry of order 4.

4 Enlargements

This lesson will help you to transform 2D shapes by enlarging them.

Exercise 4

The larger photograph is an **enlargement** with **scale factor** 4 of the smaller photograph.

Each length in the **enlargement** is 4 times the corresponding length in the small photograph.

Each angle in the enlargement is the same as the corresponding angle in the original photograph.

The width of the enlargement is 12 cm and the width of the original photograph is 3 cm.
The scale factor of the enlargement is 12 ÷ 3 = 4.

$$\text{scale factor} = \frac{\text{length of side in image}}{\text{length of corresponding side in object}}$$

Example 1

Find the scale factor of the enlargement.

The scale factor is:

$$\frac{\text{length of side in image}}{\text{length of corresponding side in object}}$$

$$\frac{EF}{AB} = \frac{12}{4} = 3$$

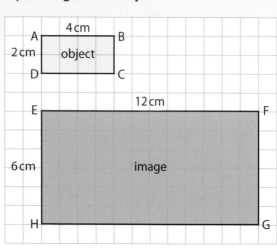

In the diagram below, triangle P has been enlarged by a scale factor of 2 to give triangle Q.

The corner A of triangle P corresponds to the corner A′ of triangle Q.
A line has been drawn joining A and A′.

Lines have been drawn to join the other pairs of corresponding points of triangles P and Q.

The lines meet at point C, called the **centre of enlargement**.

C to A is 2 squares across and 3 squares up.

C to A′ is 4 squares across and 6 squares up.

So $\dfrac{CA'}{CA} = 2$, the **scale factor**.

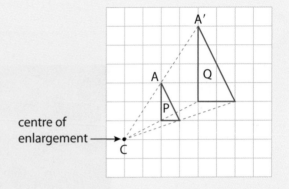

centre of enlargement →

Example 2

Enlarge the triangle with scale factor 2 and centre O.

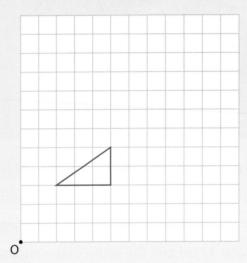

Choose a point A of the triangle.

Measure from the centre of enlargement. Join O, the centre of enlargement, to A and extend this line.

O to A is 5 to the right and 3 up.

The scale factor is 2, and

$2 \times 5 = 10$ and $2 \times 3 = 6$

so O to A′ is 10 to the right and 6 up.

Mark A′ on the diagram.

Find the other two corners of the enlarged triangle in the same way or draw it making its sides twice the length of the sides of the original triangle.

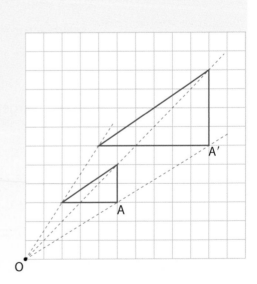

You will need squared paper.

1 What is the scale factor for each of these enlargements?

   a Triangle A to triangle B

   b Triangle D to triangle C

   c Triangle D to triangle A

   d Triangle A to triangle C

   e Triangle C to triangle B

   f Triangle D to triangle B

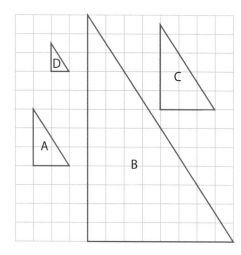

2 Shape B is an enlargement of shape A.

   a Copy the diagram on squared paper.
      Mark the centre of enlargement with a cross.

   b What is the scale factor of the enlargement?

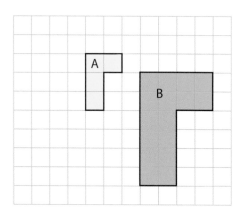

3 Copy this diagram on squared paper.

   Leave enough space for an enlargement.

   Enlarge the object by a scale factor of 2 about the centre of enlargement.

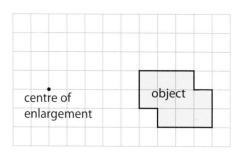

4 Shape A is shown in the diagram.

   Shape B is part of an enlargement of shape A.

   a Copy the diagram on squared paper leaving space for an enlargement.

   b What is the scale factor of the enlargement?

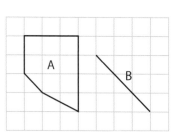

5 A right-angled triangle has a base of 4 cm and a height of 3 cm.
The triangle is enlarged with a scale factor of 5.
How long are the base and the height of the new triangle?

6 Copy this diagram on squared paper.

Enlarge the shape by a scale factor of 3 about the centre of enlargement (2, 14).

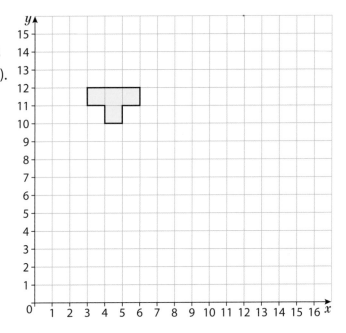

Extension problem

7 Write down the single transformation that transforms the object to the image.

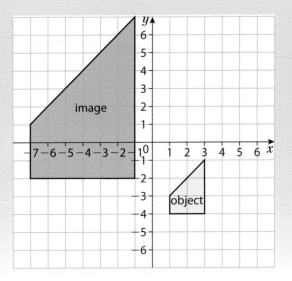

⬤ Points to remember

⊙ All angles remain unaltered by an **enlargement**.

⊙ **Scale factor** = $\dfrac{\text{length of side in image}}{\text{length of corresponding side in object}}$

⊙ Lines joining corresponding points of the object and image meet at the **centre of enlargement**.

⊙ If O is the centre of enlargement, then for corresponding points A′ and A on the image and object:

OA′ = scale factor × OA

5 Enlargements in real-life applications

This lesson will help you to solve 'real-life' problems involving enlargements.

Scale drawings and **scale models** are drawings and models of places and objects.

The lengths and distances in scale drawings and models are shorter than in the actual places and objects but the proportions and angles stay the same.

A **scale** of 1 : 10 means that every 1 unit of length on the model or map represents 10 of the same units of length of the real object.

A scale of 1 cm to 5 m means that every 1 cm of the model or map represents 5 m of the real object.

Since 5 m = 500 cm, this can also be written without the units as a scale of 1 : 500.

Example 1

These two rectangles are similar.
Find the length of the side marked x.

Scale factor = 15 ÷ 5 = 3

$x = 3 \times 3 = 9$ cm

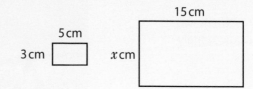

Example 2

Anna builds a model car with a scale of 1 : 15.
The length of the model car is 30 cm.
How long is the real car?

Real car length = 30 × 15 = 450 cm

Example 3

The scale of a map is 2 cm to 5 km.
On the map the distance between two towns is 14 cm.
How far apart are the two towns?

2 cm to 5 km means that for every 2 cm on the map there is 5 km on the ground.

Distance between the two towns = $14 \div 2 \times 5 = 35$ km

① Find the lengths of the missing sides in these pairs of similar shapes.

a
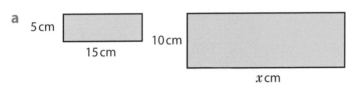
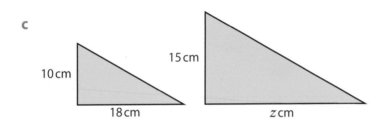

b
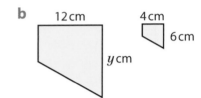

c

② Here are two photographs.
The small photograph is enlarged by a scale factor of 4 to produce the larger photograph.
What are the dimensions of the larger photograph in centimetres?

Not drawn
accurately

20 mm

←— 25 mm —→

3 A model car is built to a scale of 1 : 32.

    a The length of the model car is 15 cm. How long is the real car?

    b In the model the angle between the bonnet and the windscreen is 125°.
       What is the angle between the bonnet and the windscreen on the real car?

4 A ship is 100 m long in real life.
    The scale of a model of the ship is 1 cm to 10 m.

    How long is the model of the ship?

5 On a map the distance between two towns is 4.6 cm.
    The scale of the map is 2 cm to 5 km.

    How far apart are the two towns?

6 The scale of a map is 1 : 100 000.

    Work out the distance on the map between two towns, if the
    real distance between the towns is:

    a 6 km   **b** 10.5 km

7 The scale of a model aeroplane is 1 : 72.

    a The length of the model aeroplane is 93 cm.
       Find, in metres, the real length of the aeroplane.

    b The wingspan of the real aeroplane is 32.4 m.
       Find, in centimetres, the wingspan of the model.

8 Poppy uses a map with a scale of 1 to 50 000.
    She measures the distance between two points on the map as 7.4 cm.

    What is the actual distance between the two points in kilometres?

Extension problems

9 Triangle ADE is an enlargement of triangle ABC.

    AC = 8 mm, BC = 5 mm, DE = 15 mm.

    What is the length of CE?

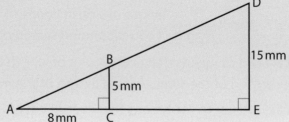

10 Blackpool Tower is approximately 160 m tall.

Peter stands at Y so that the end of his shadow coincides with the end of the shadow from Blackpool Tower at point X.

Peter is 2 m tall.

The length of Peter's shadow is 4 m.

How far from point Z at the base of the Blackpool Tower is Peter standing?

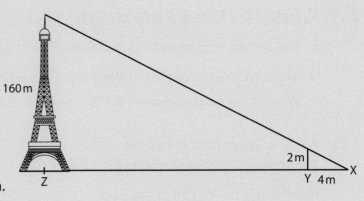

11 Which of these pictures were taken at the same time of day?

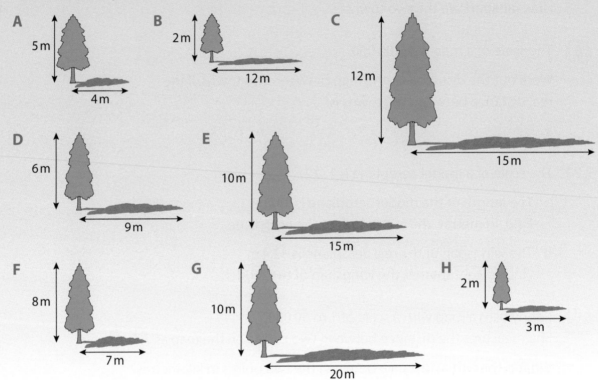

A 5 m 4 m

B 2 m 12 m

C 12 m 15 m

D 6 m 9 m

E 10 m 15 m

F 8 m 7 m

G 10 m 20 m

H 2 m 3 m

Points to remember

⊙ Scale factor = $\dfrac{\text{length of side in image}}{\text{length of corresponding side in object}}$

⊙ A scale of 1 : 8 means that every 1 unit of length on the model or map represents 8 of the same units of length of the real object.

⊙ A scale of 1 cm to 4 m means that every 1 cm of the model or map represents 4 m of the real object.
This can also be written as a scale of 1 : 400.

6 Length, area and volume

This lesson will help you to understand the effect of enlargement on perimeter, area and volume.

Exercise 6

The diagram shows squares of side 1 cm and 2 cm.

The area of the square of side 1 cm is 1 cm².

The area of the square of side 2 cm is 4 cm².

When lengths are multiplied by 2, area is multiplied by 4 = 2².

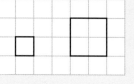

The diagram shows squares of side 1 cm and 3 cm.

The area of the square of side 1 cm is 1 cm².

The area of the square of side 3 cm is 9 cm².

When lengths are multiplied by 3, area is multiplied by 9 = 3².

For enlargements of shapes, if the length is multiplied by f, the area is multiplied by f^2.

Example 1

A rectangle is 6 mm by 13 mm.

It is enlarged by a scale factor of 4.

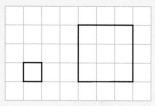

a Calculate the perimeter of the original rectangle.

Perimeter of original rectangle is

$2 \times (6 + 13) = 2 \times 19 = 38$ mm

b Calculate the area of the original rectangle.

Area of original rectangle = $6 \times 13 = 78$ mm²

c Calculate the perimeter of the enlarged rectangle.

Perimeter of enlarged rectangle is

scale factor × original perimeter = $4 \times 38 = 152$ mm

d Calculate the area of the enlarged rectangle.

Area of enlarged rectangle = (scale factor)² × original area

$= 4^2 \times 78 = 16 \times 78 = 1248$ mm²

The diagram shows cubes of side 1 cm and side 2 cm.

The volume of the cube of side 1 cm is 1 cm³.

The volume of the cube of side 2 cm is $2 \times 2 \times 2 = 8$ cm³.

When lengths are multiplied by 2,
volume is multiplied by $8 = 2^3$.

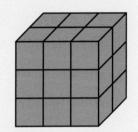

The diagram shows cubes of side 1 cm and side 3 cm.

The volume of the cube of side 1 cm is 1 cm³.

The volume of the cube of side 3 cm is $3 \times 3 \times 3 = 27$ cm³.

When lengths are multiplied by 3,
volume is multiplied by $27 = 3^3$.

For enlargements of shapes, if the length is multiplied by f, the volume is multiplied by f^3.

Example 2

A cuboid has dimensions 5.2 cm by 6.1 cm by 7.3 cm.

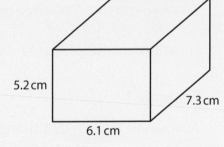

a   Calculate the volume and total surface area
of the cuboid.

Volume $= 5.2 \times 6.1 \times 7.3 = 231.556$ cm³

Total surface area $= 2 \times (5.2 \times 6.1) + 2 \times (5.2 \times 7.3) + 2 \times (6.1 \times 7.3)$

$\qquad = 2 \times 31.72 + 2 \times 37.96 + 2 \times 44.53$

$\qquad = 63.44 + 75.92 + 89.06$

$\qquad = 228.42$ cm²

b   The sides of the cuboid are enlarged by a scale factor of 2.
Calculate the volume and total surface area of the enlarged cuboid.

Volume of enlarged cuboid $=$ original volume $\times$ (scale factor)³

$\qquad = 231.556 \times 2^3$

$\qquad = 231.556 \times 8$

$\qquad = 1852.448$ cm³

Total surface area of enlarged cuboid $=$ original surface area $\times$ (scale factor)²

$\qquad = 228.42 \times 2^2 = 228.42 \times 4$

$\qquad = 913.68$ cm²

You will need isometric dotty paper.

1. A rectangle has dimensions 3 cm by 5 cm.

   a Work out the perimeter of the rectangle.

   b The rectangle is enlarged by a scale factor of 2.
   Work out the perimeter of the enlarged rectangle.

2. The perimeter of a triangle is 15 mm.
   The triangle is enlarged by a scale factor of 3.
   What is the perimeter of the image?

3. A parallelogram has an area of 25 cm^2.
   The parallelogram is enlarged by a scale factor of 4.
   Work out the area of the enlarged parallelogram.

4. This 9 cm by 6 cm photo is enlarged by a scale factor of 2.

   a What are the dimensions of the enlargement?

   b What is the perimeter of the enlargement?

   c Work out the area of the enlargement

   d How many times bigger is the area of the enlargement
   than the area of the small photograph?

5. A trapezium has a perimeter of 23 cm and an area of 24 cm^2.
   The trapezium is enlarged by a scale factor of 5.

   a What is the perimeter of the enlarged trapezium?

   b What is the area of the enlarged trapezium?

6. An equilateral triangle is enlarged by a scale factor of 2.
   How many of the original equilateral triangles could be placed
   inside the enlarged equilateral triangle?

⑦ The edges of this cuboid are enlarged by a scale factor of 2.
Draw the enlargement on dotty paper.

How many of the original cuboid would
fit into the enlarged cuboid?

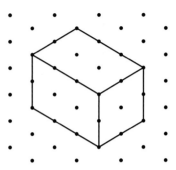

⑧ A cuboid has dimensions 2 cm by 3 cm by 4 cm.

a What is the volume of the cuboid?

b The sides of the cuboid are enlarged by a scale factor of 2.
What is the volume of the enlarged cuboid?

c How many times bigger is the enlarged cuboid than the original cuboid?

⑨ The area of a rhombus is 20 cm² and the perimeter is 25 cm.
The rhombus is enlarged so that the area of the enlarged rhombus is 80 cm².

What is the perimeter of the enlarged rhombus?

⑩ Rhodri makes this shape with 8 small cubes.
He enlarges all the edges by a scale factor of 3.

How many small cubes will he need to make an
enlarged version of his shape?

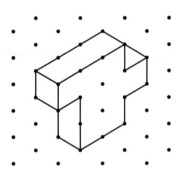

Extension problems

⑪ On a map with scale 1 to 1000 the area of a school playing field is 20 cm².
Work out the area of the playing field.

⑫ A cuboid has dimensions 3 cm by 5 cm by 10 cm.

a Work out the surface area of the cuboid.

b All the sides of the original cuboid are enlarged by a scale factor of 4.
Work out the total surface area of the enlarged cuboid.

13 Each of these Russian dolls is an enlargement of the previous doll.

Each doll is 1.5 times taller than the next doll.
The smallest doll is 16 cm³.

What is the volume of the middle sized doll?

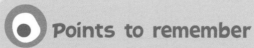 **Points to remember**

⊙ For enlargements, if the length is multiplied by the scale factor k, then:
  – the perimeter is multiplied by k;
  – the area is multiplied by k^2;
  – the volume is multiplied by k^3.

How well are you doing?

1 How many planes of symmetry do these 3D shapes have?

  a A prism with a cross-section that is a regular hexagon

  b A prism with a cross-section that is an equilateral triangle

  c A prism with a cross-section that is an isosceles triangle

  d A square-based pyramid

2 *2005 level 5*

These diagrams show a rectangle that is rotated, then rotated again.

The centre of rotation is marked ●.

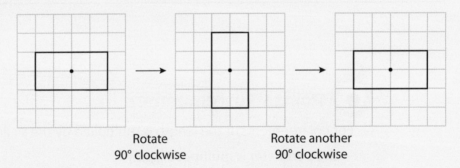

Rotate   Rotate another
90° clockwise   90° clockwise

Copy and complete the diagrams below on squared paper.

The centre of rotation is marked ●.

Draw the triangle after it has been rotated, then rotated again.

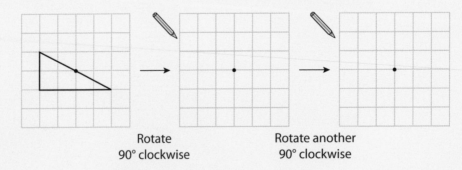

Rotate   Rotate another
90° clockwise   90° clockwise

3 Copy this diagram on squared paper.

a Mark the centre of enlargement with a cross.

b What is the scale factor of the enlargement?

c What is the area of the object?

d What is the area of the image?

e How many times bigger is the area of the image than the area of the object?

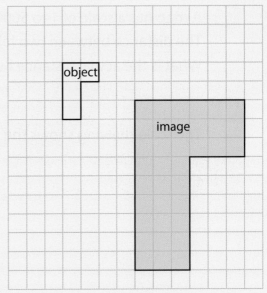

4 Copy this diagram on squared paper.
Enlarge the object by a scale factor of 2 about the centre of enlargement (1, 12).

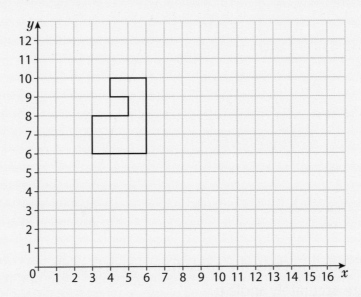

5 *2006 level 6*

Look at the square grids. Each diagram shows an enlargement of scale factor 2.
Copy each grid carefully on squared paper.
Mark the centre of enlargement with a cross.

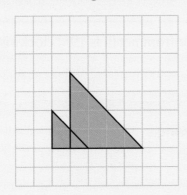

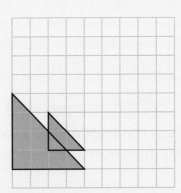

6 A map has a scale of 1 to 5000.
The distance between two hilltops on the map is 6.8 cm.
What is the actual distance between the hilltops?

7 *2005 level 5*

The scale drawing shows the positions of London and Paris.

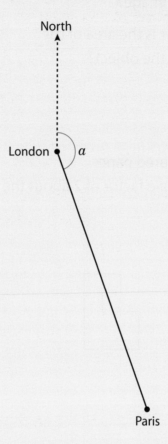

North

London • ⟩ *a*

Paris

a From London to Paris, the angle from north is angle *a*.
Measure accurately angle *a*.

b On the scale drawing, 1 cm represents 50 km.
What is the distance, in km, from London to Paris?

c A newspaper printed this information about London and Madrid.

> From London to Madrid, the angle from north is 195° clockwise.
> Madrid is 1300 km from London.

Show this information on a scale drawing.
Use the scale 1 cm represents 200 km.

Using algebra

This unit will help you to:

- use algebra to investigate and solve problems;
- represent problems using equations, diagrams and graphs;
- derive and use formulae;
- plot and interpret graphs arising from real-life problems;
- see connections between different mathematical topics.

1 Using graphs to solve problems

This lesson will help you to use graphs to solve problems.

Exercise 1

If y is directly proportional to x, then:

$$y = kx$$

where k is a constant number.

The graph of $y = kx$ is always a straight line passing through the origin.

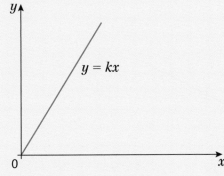

The gradient of the straight line is k.

Example

y is directly proportional to x.
When $x = 5$, $y = 50$.

Find y when $x = 40$.

Since y is directly proportional to x, $y = kx$, where k is a constant.

Substituting $y = 50$ and $x = 5$ gives $50 = k \times 5$.

So $k = \frac{50}{5} = 10$.

Now substitute $x = 40$ and $k = 10$ in the equation $y = kx$.

$y = kx = 10 \times 40 = 400$.

So when $x = 40$, $y = 400$.

1. y is directly proportional to x.

   a $y = 10$ when $x = 2$.

   Find y when $x = 3$.

   b $y = 5$ when $x = 3$.

   Find y when $x = 4.5$.

   c $y = 3$ when $x = 8$.

   Find y when $x = 6$.

(2) The height, T mm, of a pile of printer paper is directly proportional to the number of sheets, N, in the pile.

When $N = 196$, $T = 28$.

a Write a formula for N in terms of T.

b Find the value of N when $T = 50$.

c Find the value of T when $N = 420$.

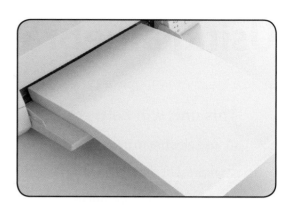

(3) The distance, D miles, travelled by a car is directly proportional to the amount, A litres, of petrol used.

When $A = 5$, $D = 27$.

a Write a formula for D in terms of A.

b Find the value of D when $A = 2$.

c How many litres of petrol are needed to drive a distance of 216 miles?

(4) A tool hire company has a fixed charge of £4 plus £3 per day to hire a tool.

a Write the total hire charge £C as a formula in terms of the number of days n.

b Work out the cost of hiring a tool for 10 days.

c The company decides to change its fixed charge and daily rate.
The new hire charges are shown on the graph below.
Use the graph to work out the fixed charge and the daily rate.

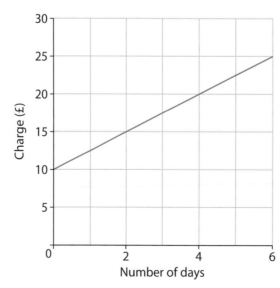

d Does it cost more to hire a tool for 10 days with the old charges or the new charges?

5 You will need some **squared paper** for this question.

Rob does an experiment.
He attaches weights to the end of a spring.
Then he measures the total length of the spring.

When he attaches a 1 kg weight, the spring is 30 cm long.

For each extra 1 kg weight that Rob adds, the spring
extends a further 5 cm.

a How long is the spring when 2 kg is attached?

b How long is the spring when 3 kg is attached?

c Copy and complete this table to show the length of the spring for different weights.

Mass (kg)	1	2	3	4	5
Total length of spring (cm)					

d Look at the values in your table.
Are they in proportion?

e Plot the values on a graph on squared paper.
Join up the points and describe the graph.

f What is the original length of the spring?

g Plot a graph of the extension of the spring against mass.
What do you notice?

6 With one mobile phone company, the cost of an overseas
call is a fixed charge of 16p plus 2p per minute.

With another mobile phone company the cost of an overseas
call is a fixed charge of 10p plus 3p per minute.

For how many minutes is the cost of an overseas call
the same with both companies?

⦿ **Points to remember**

⊙ You can explore many mathematical problems by using algebra.

⊙ For example, you may be able to set up an equation and draw a graph.

⊙ Put values that you estimate from a graph back into the original
equation to check them.

2 Using algebra in geometry problems

This lesson is about using algebra to solve problems.

Did you know that...?

The **Rhind Mathematical Papyrus** is one of the oldest surviving examples of how our ancestors used mathematics. The papyrus, written in an ancient Egyptian script, is 33 centimetres tall and over 5 metres long. It was copied by the scribe **Ahmes** from a lost text from the reign of King Amenemhat III (1860 to 1840 BC).

Sphinx of Amenemhat III

Rhind papyrus, now in the British Museum

The papyrus shows 84 maths problems. Fifteen of these involve using algebra to solve equations. The simplest problem shows how to find the value of an unknown x when x plus one seventh of x equals 19.

Exercise 2

Work with a partner.
You will need a **computer with graph-plotting software** or a **graphics calculator**.

1 a Write the formula for the area of the triangle.

   b Use a computer or graphics calculator to draw the graph of the equation for the area.

   c Use the graph to estimate the value of x when the area of the triangle is 60 cm².

   d Use trial and improvement to find the value of x to two decimal places.

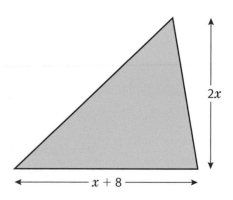

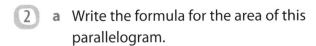

 a Write the formula for the area of this parallelogram.

b Use a computer or graphics calculator to draw the graph of the equation for the area.

c Use the graph to estimate the value of x when the area of the parallelogram is 80 cm².

d Use trial and improvement to find the value of x to two decimal places.

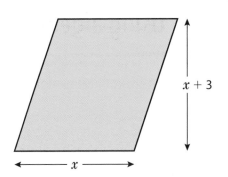

 a What is the height of the trapezium?

b What is the sum of the two parallel sides of the trapezium?

c What is the area of the trapezium?

d What is the height of the triangle?

e What is the area of the triangle?

f The trapezium and the triangle have the same area.

Write an equation to show this relationship.

g Work out the value of x to two decimal places.

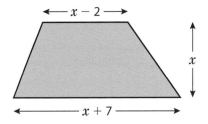

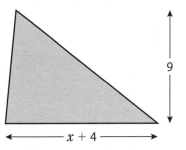

Extension problem

 This rectangle has an area of 108 m².

Find the area of the square in the top left corner of the rectangle.

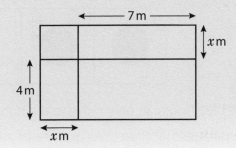

Points to remember

⊙ You can explore many mathematical problems by using algebra.

⊙ For example, you may be able to set up an equation and solve it.

⊙ Put the values you have found into the original equation to see if your answer is sensible.

3 Using algebra in investigations

This lesson is about using algebra to investigate patterns.

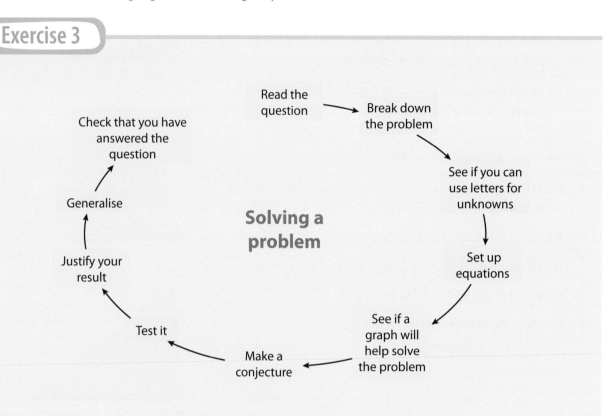

1. Solve the **Frogs and toads puzzle** with a partner.

   Rules

   ○ The blue frogs can only move to the right and the yellow toads can only move to the left.

   ○ To move, either slide one square into an empty space or hop over a different colour into an empty space.

   ○ The aim is to get the blue frogs in the position of the yellow toads and the yellow toads in the position of the blue frogs.

   a What is the least number of moves needed for 2 blue frogs and 2 yellow toads to change over their positions?

   b Try one blue frog and one yellow toad. How many moves are needed?

   c Try three blue frogs and three yellow toads. How many moves are needed?

   d What is the least number of moves needed to exchange ten frogs and ten toads?

   e What is the least number of moves needed to exchange n counters of each colour?

2   Investigate the **Frogs and toads puzzle** further. For example:

- What if you had different numbers of frogs and toads?
- What if you had a different shaped grid?
- What if …?

Points to remember

- When you start an investigation, break the problem down into smaller parts.
- Work systematically and record your results in a table as you go along.
- Look for patterns.
- Make a conjecture and test it.
- See if you can make a generalisation.
- Check that you have answered the question and ask yourself further questions.

How well are you doing?

1 *2003 level 6*

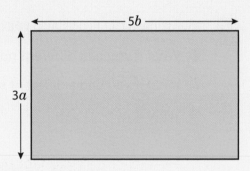

a The diagram shows a rectangle.
Its dimensions are $3a$ by $5b$.

Write simplified expressions for the area and the perimeter of this rectangle.

b A different rectangle has area $12a^2$ and perimeter $14a$.

What are the dimensions of this rectangle?

2 *2000 level 6*

Here is the start of a sequence of shapes using rectangles and triangles
Each rectangle has been numbered.

 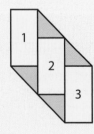 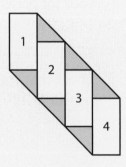

The pattern continues to grow in this way.

a How many triangles will there be in the shape that has 50 rectangles in it?

b T stands for the number of triangles in each shape.

R stands for the number of rectangles in each shape.

What is the rule connecting T and R?

3 *1999 level 6*

A number grid is inside a large triangle.

The small triangles are numbered consecutively.

The diagram shows the first four rows.

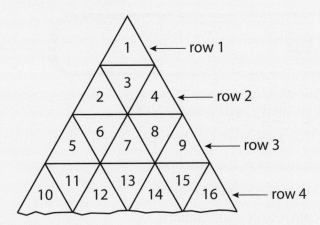

An expression for the last number
in row n is n^2.

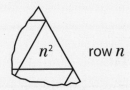

row n

a Write an expression for the last but one
number in row n.

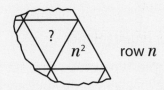

row n

b An expression for the first number in row n is $n^2 - 2n + 2$.
Calculate the value of the first number in row 10.

c Copy and complete the table by writing an expression.

First number in row n	$n^2 - 2n + 2$
Second number in row n	

4 *2001 level 6*

A cuboid has a square base.

It is twice as tall as it is wide.

Its volume is 250 cubic centimetres.

Calculate the width of the cuboid.

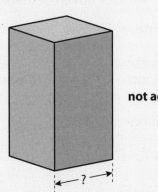

not actual size

Functional skills 3

Cutting it up

This group activity will help you to:

- recognise that a situation can be represented using mathematics;
- choose how to model the situation;
- examine patterns and relationships;
- communicate results and solutions.

Background

A common problem in industry is how to divide or cut up an area to suit particular requirements.

For example, typesetters who set out the pages for newspapers and magazines have to work out how to fit photographs and advertisements of different sizes on a page without leaving gaps.

Problem 1

Newspaper adverts

A newspaper sets out its pages with 7 columns.

Each page is 48 cm tall.

It has orders for these block advertisements:

One column wide	Two columns wide
1 advert 16 cm long	2 adverts 8 cm long
1 advert 12 cm long	2 adverts 4 cm long
8 adverts 8 cm long	
7 adverts 4 cm long	

The adverts have to be laid out on half a page.

Will they all fit?

Remember, they must all be the right way up!

The next problem is a related problem. Can you see the connections?

Background

Sheets of metal are used to make a wide range of items. These metal trays have been made from sheet metal.

Sheet metal is supplied in sheets of fixed dimensions. Pieces have to be cut from the sheets to required width and length.

The aim is to have as little waste as possible.

Problem 2

Heating ducts

Metal sheets are supplied in squares measuring 10 metres by 10 metres.

A construction worker wants these pieces for heating ducts at his building site.

    18 pieces of 3 m by 1 m

    13 pieces of 4 m by 2 m

    4 pieces of 7 m by 5 m.

How should the metal sheets be cut to reduce waste to a minimum?

How many 10 m by 10 m squares will be needed?

Be prepared to present your solutions to other groups.

Enquiry 2

This unit will help you to:

- ☉ calculate and use statistics;
- ☉ draw and interpret scatter graphs and line graphs for time series;
- ☉ ask questions and find answers by carrying out a statistical project.

1 Calculating statistics

This lesson will help you to calculate and use statistics.

Exercise 1

In statistics there are three different measures of average — the median, mode and mean.

The **median** is the middle value when the values in the data set are listed in order of size.

The **mode** is the value in the data set that appears most often.

The **mean** is found by adding up all the values in the data set and dividing by the number of values in the set.

Example

A garage sold these numbers of cars over 10 days.

   3   2   7   8   4   9   7   5   7   3

Find the median, the mode and the mean.

The numbers arranged in order are:

   2   3   3   4   5   7   7   7   8   9

The middle two numbers are 5 and 7, and their mean is

$$\frac{5+7}{2} = \frac{12}{2} = 6$$

So the **median** number of cars is 6.

The number of cars that occurs most frequently is 7, so 7 is the **mode**.

The **mean** number of cars is

$$\frac{3+2+7+8+4+9+7+5+7+3}{10} = \frac{55}{10} = 5.5$$

1 **a** The **median** is the middle value when the values in the set are listed in order of size.

The median of a set of seven numbers is 9.

Write down five different sets of numbers that fit this description.
Make the sets of numbers as different as you can.

   i What remains unchanged in each set of numbers?

   ii How can you change the numbers without affecting the median?

 b The **mode** is the value that appears most often.

The mode of a set of seven numbers is 9.

Write down five different sets of numbers that fit this description.
Make the sets of numbers as different as you can.

   i What remains unchanged in each set of numbers?

   ii How can you change the numbers without affecting the mode?

 c The **mean** is found by adding up all the values in the set and dividing by the number of values in the set.

The mean of a set of seven numbers is 9.

Write down five different sets of numbers that fit this description.
Make the sets of numbers as different as you can.

   i What remains unchanged in each set of numbers?

   ii How can you change the numbers without affecting the mean?

2 Work with a partner.

Decide which measure of average (mean, median or mode) you would use to answer each question. Give your reasons.

 a What is the most common eye colour in your class?

 b What is the average hand span for 14-year-olds?

 c What is the average salary of supermarket workers?

 d What is the best-selling computer game in December?

 e Who is the best goal-scorer in the Premier League?

 f What is the average mark in a spelling test?

 g What size shoe should a shop stock the most of?

Points to remember

⊙ The **range** is the difference between the smallest value in the data set and the largest.

⊙ The **median** is the middle value when the values in the data set are listed in order of size. It is less affected by extreme values than the mean.

⊙ The **mode** is the value in the data set that appears most often. It is affected by how often values are repeated, not by the values themselves.

⊙ The **mean** is the sum of all the values in the data set divided by the number of values. It gives an indication of all the values but it is more affected by extreme values than either the median or the mode.

2 Line graphs for time series

This lesson will help you to draw and interpret line graphs for time series.

Did you know that...?

In 1838, the Office of the Registrar-General was established for registering births, marriages and deaths.

William Farr (1807—1883) was appointed as the first 'compiler of abstracts' (chief statistician).

Farr became one of the leading campaigners for cleaner conditions, especially in urban areas.

In those days little was understood about diseases and how they spread. Diseases such as cholera killed many people.

Farr collected data to show that the pollution of the river Thames was directly responsible for deaths from cholera.

Exercise 2

Line graphs

Line graphs are useful for displaying time series data, where the variable on the horizontal axis is time (e.g. minutes, hours, days, months or years).

They are also useful for comparing several sets of data on the same axes.

The axes should have the lines labelled in equal steps.

Example

Number of polio cases in 1970 in the USA

Month	Jan	Feb	Mar	Apr	May	Jun	Jul	Aug	Sep	Oct	Nov	Dec
Cases	0	1	0	0	1	3	9	2	3	5	3	5

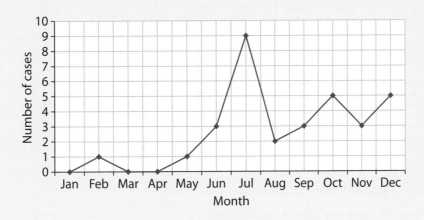

You will need graph paper, a ruler and a sharp pencil.

Work with a partner. Use the data in the tables to answer the questions on the next page.

Reported monthly cases of measles, New York City

	Jan	Feb	Mar	Apr	May	Jun	Jul	Aug	Sep	Oct	Nov	Dec
1931	750	2010	4858	6172	7095	4238	907	165	43	54	93	134
1941	6336	13 226	25 826	22 741	8195	2527	436	100	63	67	55	74
1951	282	381	549	1079	1915	1770	948	380	184	246	515	1360
1961	227	298	374	384	644	683	343	185	109	123	383	1043
1971	283	557	818	844	501	472	206	60	23	22	12	21

Reported monthly cases of mumps, New York City

	Jan	Feb	Mar	Apr	May	Jun	Jul	Aug	Sep	Oct	Nov	Dec
1931	116	177	288	299	315	329	143	50	59	74	110	180
1941	930	899	1261	1245	847	626	348	168	132	142	201	399
1951	616	634	808	902	1003	833	475	243	167	152	182	279
1961	361	350	551	488	631	717	452	293	165	180	230	276
1971	146	149	248	300	223	294	235	110	88	68	88	132

Reported monthly cases of chickenpox, New York City

	Jan	Feb	Mar	Apr	May	Jun	Jul	Aug	Sep	Oct	Nov	Dec
1931	956	927	1585	1536	1448	1272	303	68	62	116	275	565
1941	1409	1218	1543	1477	987	935	495	126	109	197	397	880
1951	1427	1545	1951	2200	1964	1284	523	142	93	148	198	374
1961	619	691	1022	858	953	913	332	127	82	62	147	384
1971	211	331	471	639	569	718	391	123	72	63	86	141

Data source: Time Series Data Library www-personal.buseco.monash.edu.au/~hyndman/TSDL

1. Plot a line graph to find out how the number of cases of a disease changes during the year.

   ◉ Choose one of measles, mumps or chickenpox.
   Then choose a year.

   ◉ Use graph paper in landscape format.
   Put months on the horizontal axis. Use 2 cm for each month.

   ◉ Choose a scale for the vertical axis for the number of cases of the disease.
   Draw and label the vertical axis.

   ◉ Plot the points for the year, marking each one with a cross.
   Join the crosses up with straight lines.

   ◉ Write a title for the graph.
   Write one or two sentences to say what the graph shows.
   How does the number of cases of the disease change during the year?

2. Plot a line graph to compare the number of cases of a disease in different years.

   ◉ Choose one of measles, mumps or chickenpox.
   Choose three years to plot.

   ◉ Use graph paper in landscape format.
   Put months on the horizontal axis. Use 2 cm for each month.

   ◉ Choose a scale for the vertical axis for the number of cases of the disease.
   Make sure you can get the data for all three years on your scale.
   Draw and label the vertical axis.

   ◉ Plot the points for the first year, marking each one with a cross, and join them up with straight lines.
   Label the line with the year.
   Do the same for the other two years, using a different coloured pen.

   ◉ Add a key to the graph, and write a title.
   Write two or three sentences to say what the graph shows.
   How does the number of cases of the disease change over time?

3 Plot a line graph to compare the number of cases of the three diseases in the same year.

- Choose a year.
- Use graph paper in landscape format.
  Put months on the horizontal axis. Choose a sensible scale.
- Choose a scale for the vertical axis for the number of cases of the disease.
  Make sure you can get the data for all diseases on the scale.
  Draw and label the vertical axis.
- Plot the points for one disease, marking each one with a cross, and join them up with straight lines.
  Label the line with the name of the disease.
  Do the same for the other two diseases but use a different coloured pen.
- Add a key to the graph, and write a title.
  What are the differences and similarities between the three lines?

 Points to remember

- Line graphs are useful for looking at how data changes over time.
- Displaying several line graphs on one set of axes allows related data to be compared.

3 Scatter graphs

This lesson will help you to draw and interpret scatter graphs and understand correlation.

Did you know that...?

Scatter graphs and line graphs are plotted using coordinates.

The coordinate system was developed by **Rene Descartes** in the 17th century.

The story is that he was ill and as he lay in bed he saw a fly buzzing around on the ceiling. His ceiling was made of square tiles and as he watched he realised he could describe the position of the fly by the ceiling tile he was on.

Scatter graphs

Scatter graphs are useful for looking for connections between quantities.

The scales are labelled evenly.

Each data point has a value for both quantities.

Where the data point is located it is marked with a small cross.

Correlation

The different types of correlation are

Strong positive correlation

When one variable increases as the other increases, this is called **positive correlation**. When the points are grouped closely the correlation is strong.

Weak positive correlation

When the points are more spread out, the correlation is weak.

Strong negative correlation

When one variable decreases as the other increases, this is called **negative correlation**. When the points are grouped closely the correlation is strong.

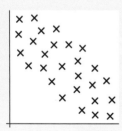

Weak negative correlation

When the points are more spread out, the correlation is weak.

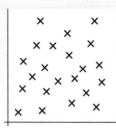

No correlation

When the points are all spread out, indicating no relationship between the two variables, this is called having **no correlation**.

Example

The table shows, for each of 10 men, his age and the number of his own teeth each has.

Age (years)	22	28	33	37	41	49	52	56	64	68
Number of own teeth	29	29	26	28	26	21	23	21	17	15

Draw a scatter graph to show this information.

Describe the relationship between the men's ages and the number of their own teeth.

The scatter graph shows strong negative correlation.

For these 10 men, the older a man is, the fewer of his own teeth he has.

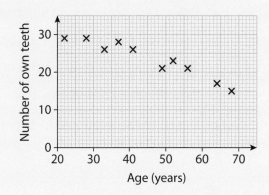

You will need graph paper, a ruler and a sharp pencil.

1. This table shows the prices and ages of 11 used Ford Fiesta cars.

Age (years)	12	15	11	10	13	9	8	3	1	4	5
Price (£)	300	400	400	600	700	1200	1300	6000	6500	3300	4500

Data source: www.adtrader.co.uk

a Draw a scatter graph to illustrate the data.

Use a scale of 1 cm to 1 year on the horizontal axis from 0 to 16.
Use a scale of 2 cm to £1000 on the vertical axis from £0 to £7000.

b Describe the correlation.

c Describe the relationship between price and age of car.

2. This table shows pupils' marks in English and maths tests.

English test mark	12	15	19	17	11	13	15	16	8	14
Maths test mark	14	13	17	20	8	13	14	19	12	7

a Draw a scatter graph to illustrate the data.
Use a scale of 1 cm to 1 mark on both axes from 5 marks to 20 marks.

b Describe the correlation.

c Describe the relationship between English and mathematics test scores.

3 This table shows the average temperature and average rainfall for each month in Toronto, Canada.

	Jan	Feb	Mar	Apr	May	Jun	Jul	Aug	Sep	Oct	Nov	Dec
Temperature (°C)	−6.4	−5.6	−0.8	6.3	12.3	17.6	20.7	19.7	15.4	9.1	3.2	−3.3
Rainfall (mm)	47	46	58	66	67	66	72	82	70	63	67	62

Data source: www.worldclimate.com

a Draw a scatter graph to illustrate the data.

Use a scale of 2 cm to 5 °C on the horizontal axis from −10 °C to 25 °C.

Use a scale of 4 cm to 10 mm on the vertical axis from 40 mm to 85 mm.

b Describe the correlation.

c Describe the relationship between temperature and rainfall in Toronto.

Points to remember

⊙ A **scatter graph** shows the relationship between two variables.
The relationship can show:
- negative correlation;
- or positive correlation;
- or no correlation.

4 Collecting and organising data

In the rest of this unit you will be working on a statistical project about recycling.

This lesson will help you to:

⊙ ask questions and consider possible answers;

⊙ decide what information you need and where to get it.

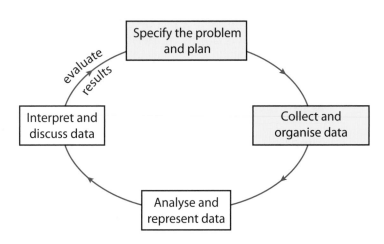

Scrap metal for recycling

Rubber tyres for recycling

Work in a group of four.

You will need a large sheet of paper and some marker pens.

1. Make a poster about recycling.
   - What do you know about recycling?
   - What would you like to find out more about?

2. For each question on your poster:
   - Decide what you would need to find out in order to answer some of your questions.
   - How would you find this information?

Exercise 4B

Work with a partner.

You will each need a copy of **S5.3 Resource sheet 4.1**.

Pick a question or statement about recycling.
You will work on a project about this for the rest of the unit.

The question or statement could be one from your poster, one of your own or one from this list:

1. Other countries in Europe are better at recycling than the UK.

2. The UK is getting better at recycling.

3. Some parts of the UK are improving their recycling rates more quickly than others.

4. The composition of recycled material is the same across the UK.

Identify the data from **S5.3 Resource sheet 4.1** that you need for your project.

5 Analysing and representing data

This lesson will help you to organise and present the data for your project.

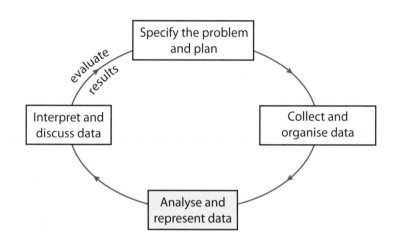

Specify the problem and plan

Collect and organise data

Analyse and represent data

Interpret and discuss data

evaluate results

Exercise 5

Glass for recycling

Bins for separating clear and coloured bottles

Work with your partner. You will need your work from the last lesson.

You may use **spreadsheet software** to plot your graphs.

(1) To continue your project you need to:

◉ analyse and organise the data;

◉ draw some graphs;

◉ come to some conclusions;

◉ put together a short report.

You will have time in this and the next two lessons to do all this.

Before you begin, think about these questions.

◉ What type of data do you have?

◉ What type of chart do you need to draw?

   – Is it a time series?

   – Are you considering proportions of a whole?

   – How can you show data that allows for comparison?

◉ Will the chart type you have chosen allow you to find out what you need to?

◉ Will you need to present the data in another way as well?

You can now start your investigation by organising your data and drawing some graphs.

◉ Points to remember

◉ Different charts and diagrams are good for showing different kinds of data and different features of the data.

◉ Choose a graph, chart or diagram that helps you to answer your question. Explain why you chose it.

◉ You can use spreadsheet software to produce graphs and charts of tables of data.

6 Interpreting data

This lesson will help you to interpret and discuss the data for your project.

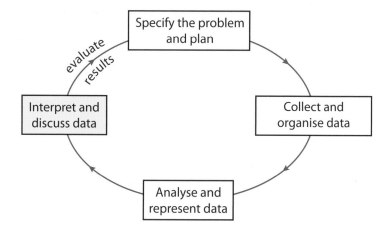

Specify the problem and plan

Collect and organise data

Analyse and represent data

Interpret and discuss data

evaluate results

Exercise 6

Paper for recycling in Devon

Pellets of recycled paper

Work with your partner. You will need your graphs from the previous lesson.

For each of your graphs and charts:

1. Each write down as much detail as you can about what the graph shows.

2. Compare what you have both written.
   Draft a joint statement saying what the graph shows.

3. Check your statement using the points below before deciding finally what you will say about the graph.

   ○ What general shape, or trend, does the graph show?

   ○ What does that mean in terms of the original question?

   ○ Look at the maximum and minimum values on the graph. What do these show?

   ○ Are there any places where the shape of the graph changes?

   ○ Can you think of any reasons why this might be?

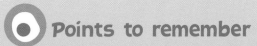

Points to remember

- Graphs can show general trends and patterns.
- Useful points to comment on are the greatest and least values, and any points where the shape of the graph changes.
- Interpret graphs in the context of the original question.
- Try to explain why any changes have happened.

7 Reporting and evaluating

This lesson will help you to communicate what you have found in your project and to evaluate your work.

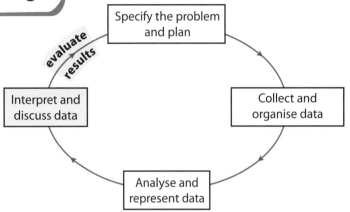

Specify the problem and plan

Collect and organise data

Analyse and represent data

Interpret and discuss data

evaluate results

Exercise 7A

plastics
paper
rubber
steel
aluminium
glass
electronics

Work with your partner. You will need all the work you have done so far on your project.

1. Produce a leaflet explaining what you found out in your project.

   The points below will help you to plan how to do this. Include:

   - what your question was;
   - the data you used;
   - what your results were — include your graphs and charts;
   - what your graphs show;
   - your conclusions.

   Remember to relate all your work to your original question.

The three bar charts and the table show information about recycling in Cambridgeshire.

The data source is www.cambridgeshire.gov.uk.

1 Describe how often people use the recycling centres.

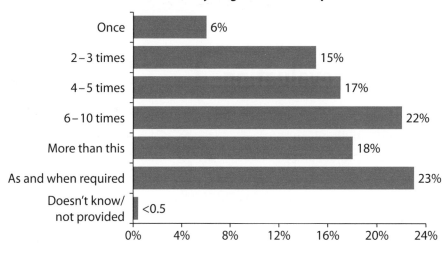

Users of household waste recycling centres in the past twelve months

Once — 6%
2–3 times — 15%
4–5 times — 17%
6–10 times — 22%
More than this — 18%
As and when required — 23%
Doesn't know/not provided — <0.5

2 **a** What are the most common materials recycled at the centres?

b What are the least common materials recycled at the centres?

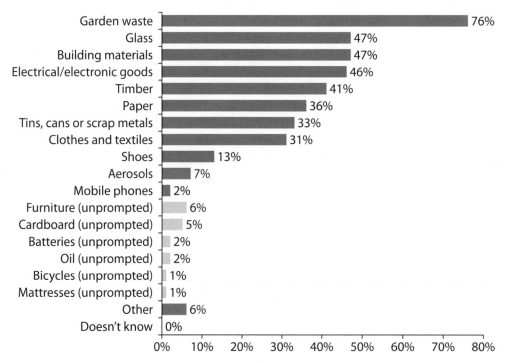

Users of household waste recycling centres in the past twelve months

Garden waste — 76%
Glass — 47%
Building materials — 47%
Electrical/electronic goods — 46%
Timber — 41%
Paper — 36%
Tins, cans or scrap metals — 33%
Clothes and textiles — 31%
Shoes — 13%
Aerosols — 7%
Mobile phones — 2%
Furniture (unprompted) — 6%
Cardboard (unprompted) — 5%
Batteries (unprompted) — 2%
Oil (unprompted) — 2%
Bicycles (unprompted) — 1%
Mattresses (unprompted) — 1%
Other — 6%
Doesn't know — 0%

3 **a** What are the main reasons people state for not using recycling centres?

b Pick four common reasons for people not using the recycling centres.

What do you think the council could do to encourage more use of the recycling centres?

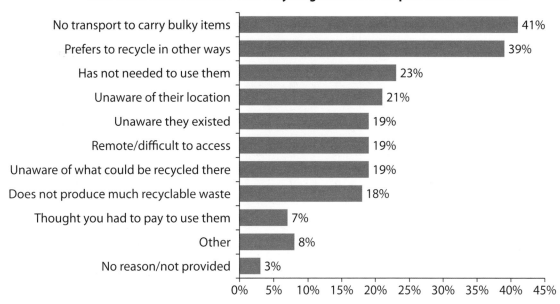

Non-users of household waste recycling centres in the past twelve months

Reason	%
No transport to carry bulky items	41%
Prefers to recycle in other ways	39%
Has not needed to use them	23%
Unaware of their location	21%
Unaware they existed	19%
Remote/difficult to access	19%
Unaware of what could be recycled there	19%
Does not produce much recyclable waste	18%
Thought you had to pay to use them	7%
Other	8%
No reason/not provided	3%

4 Look at this table.

Proportion of households that recycle specified materials or goods, by district (all respondants)						
	Cambs city	East Cambs	Fenland	Hunts	South Cambs	All
	%	%	%	%	%	%
Paper	96	93	84	96	94	**93**
Glass	90	86	76	85	93	**87**
Clothes and textiles	67	70	67	83	79	**75**
Tins, cans, scrap metals	77	56	60	75	79	**71**
Plastic bags	65	63	64	73	57	**65**
Timber	44	49	47	56	53	**51**
Shoes	45	42	42	54	47	**47**
Building materials	33	46	36	49	46	**43**
Electrical/electronic goods	37	39	29	40	45	**39**
Metal foil	42	21	24	36	34	**33**
Mobile phones	24	22	16	28	30	**25**
Aerosols	26	12	16	23	16	**20**

a What material is recycled the most?

b What material is recycled the least?

c Describe any differences you notice in recycling across the different districts.

d Which district do you think is the best at recycling?

Extension problem

 5 The table shows the 2004 results of the 'Recycling Olympics' from www.planetark.com.

Countries are ranked according to how good they are at recycling each type of material. For example, Germany recycles the most paper and cardboard.

Type of waste	Australia	France	Italy	Germany	Japan	Portugal	Spain	Sweden	Switzer- land	UK	USA
Paper and card	7	5	11	1	4	8	6	2	3	10	9
Aluminium cans	5	9	7	4	3	10	11	2	1	8	6
Glass	6	5	8	3	4	7	9	2	1	10	11
Steel cans	9	6	7	2	1	11	8	4	3	10	5
Municipal waste	10	5	4	7	1	2	8	3	9	6	11

Find ways to compare the countries.

Give them an overall ranking for recycling.

 Points to remember

When you finish a statistical project, evaluate your results:

⊙ make sure that you have answered the original question;

⊙ give a conclusion by summarising what you have found out;

⊙ consider whether there are further questions you could ask;

⊙ consider how you could improve your work next time.

How well are you doing?

1. Selina thinks that there are more girls in the families of the pupils in her year group than there are boys.

   Write two questions she could include in a survey to find out whether or not she is right.

2. Seth is growing a bean plant for a school project.

   He records its height each day once it has sprouted and produced this line graph.

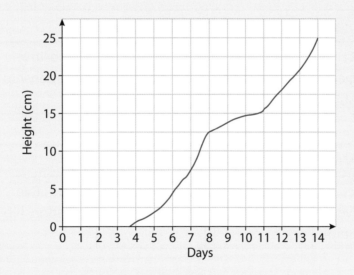

   a What happened between day 3 and day 4?

   b How tall is the bean plant on day 8?

   c Describe how the bean plant is growing.

   d How tall will the bean plant be on day 24?

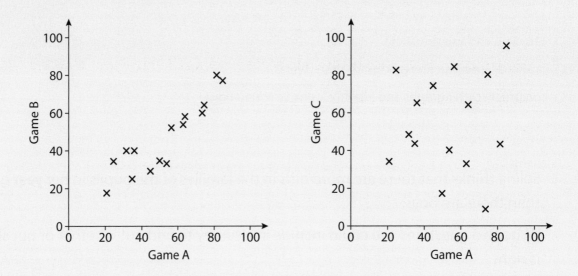

A competition has three different games.

a The scatter graphs show the scores of everyone who plays all three games.

Look at the scatter graphs.

Which statement most closely describes the relationship between the games?

Game A and Game B				
perfect negative relationship	negative relationship	no relationship	positive relationship	perfect positive relationship

Game A and Game C				
perfect negative relationship	negative relationship	no relationship	positive relationship	perfect positive relationship

b What can you tell about the relationship between the scores on game B and the scores on game C?

Game B and Game C				
perfect negative relationship	negative relationship	no relationship	positive relationship	perfect positive relationship

c Jeff plays two of the games.

	Game A	Game B	Game C
Score	62	53	

To win, Jeff needs a mean score of 60.

How many points does he need to score in game C? Show your working.

d Imran and Nia play the three games.

Their scores have the same mean.

The range of Imran's scores is twice the range of Nia's scores.

Copy the table and fill the missing scores:

Imran's score	....	40	....
Nia's score	35	40	45

G 5.4

Angles and constructions

This unit will help you to:

- ◉ know that the sum of the exterior angles of any polygon is 360°;
- ◉ find the sum of the interior angles of a polygon;
- ◉ know that the sum of the exterior and interior angle at the vertex of a polygon is 180°;
- ◉ know that the vertices of a regular polygon lie on a circle and that a regular polygon with n sides can be split into n equal-sized isosceles triangles;
- ◉ prove that for a regular polygon the exterior angle equals the angle at the centre;
- ◉ use the angle properties of regular polygons and parallel lines to solve problems;
- ◉ construct lines and shapes using a straight-edge and compasses.

Did you know that...?

An important part of the work of the Greek mathematician **Euclid** (about 325 to 265 BC) was constructing geometric shapes using only compasses and a straight edge.

In this unit, you will construct some regular polygons using Euclid's methods. Euclid thought that all regular polygons could be constructed but we now know that this is not possible.

In 1796, the German **Carl Friedrich Gauss** proved that it was possible to construct a heptadecagon (a polygon with 17 sides).

The actual construction was done by **Jonannes Erchinger** in 1800. It had 64 steps.

This house at Sleepy Hollow in Vermont in the USA is being built in the shape of a heptadecagon.

In 1894 a mathematician called **Johann Gustav Hermes** completed the construction of a regular polygon with 65 537 sides. It took him about 10 years!

1 Angles in polygons

This lesson will help you to find the sum of the interior and exterior angles of a polygon.

Exercise 1

A **polygon** is a 2D shape with three or more straight sides.

A polygon with n sides has n **vertices**.

A polygon's **interior angles** are the angles *inside* the polygon.

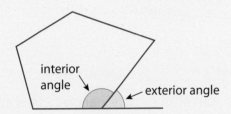

Extend a side to make an **exterior angle**, which is *outside* the polygon.

At each **vertex** (corner), the interior angle and the exterior angle are on a straight line. So their sum is 180°.

interior angle + exterior angle = 180°

The sum of the exterior angles of any polygon is 360°.

Imagine someone standing at P on this quadrilateral, facing in the direction of the arrow.

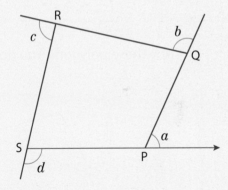

They turn through angle a, so that they are facing in the direction PQ, and then walk to Q.

At Q, they turn through angle b, so that they are facing in the direction QR, and then walk to R.

At R, they turn through angle c, so that they are facing in the direction RS, and then walk to S.

At S, they turn through angle d.

They are now facing in the direction of the arrow again and so they have turned through 360°.

The total angle they have turned through is also the sum of the exterior angles of the quadrilateral.

So $a + b + c + d = 360°$

The same argument can be used with *any* polygon, not just a quadrilateral. So:

The sum of the exterior angles of any polygon is 360°.

Example

Show that the sum of the interior angles of a triangle is 180°.

In triangle ABC

a and x, b and y, c and z are pairs of angles on a straight line.

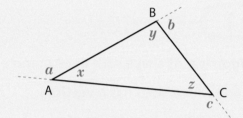

So
$a + x = 180°$
$b + y = 180°$
$c + z = 180°$

Adding:

$a + b + c + x + y + z = 3 \times 180$

So the sum of the exterior angles + the sum of the interior angles = $3 \times 180°$

But the sum of the exterior angles is 360°.

So 360° + the sum of the interior angles = $3 \times 180°$

So the sum of the interior angles = $3 \times 180° - 360° = 540° - 360° = 180°$.

The sum of the interior angles of a triangle is 180°.

① Copy these polygons. You do not need to make an exact copy.

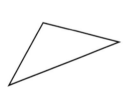  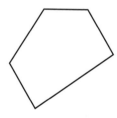

   a On each polygon, extend lines to form the exterior angles.
      Label the angles with *I* for interior angles and *E* for exterior angles.

   b For each polygon, write down the number of sides and the sum of all the interior and exterior angles.

   c Explain why, for a polygon with n sides, the sum of all the interior and exterior angles is $180 \times n$.

   d Explain why, for each polygon, the sum of the exterior angles is 360°.

(2) Copy this diagram of a quadrilateral.
You do not need to make an exact copy.

Copy and complete this proof that the sum of
the interior angles of a quadrilateral is 360°.

A quadrilateral has ... sides and ... vertices.

Sum of the exterior angles a, b, c and d = ...°

$a + w = 180°$

...... + ... = 180°

...... + ... = 180°

...... + ... = 180°

Adding: $a + b + c + d + w + x + y + z$ = ... × ......°

Sum of the exterior angles + sum of the interior angles = ...°

......° + sum of the interior angles = ...°

Sum of the interior angles = ...° − ......°

So the sum of the interior angles of a quadrilateral is ......°.

(3) **a** Prove that the interior angles of a pentagon add up to 540°.

  b Prove that the sum of the interior angles of a hexagon is 720°.

  c Copy and complete this table.

Polygon	Number of sides (n)	Sum of interior and exterior angles	Sum of interior angles
Triangle	3	3 × 180°	3 × 180 − 360 = 180°
Quadrilateral	4	4 × 180°	4 × 180 − 360 = 360°
Pentagon			
Hexagon			

◉ Points to remember

⊙ A **polygon** is a 2D shape with three or more straight sides.
The number of sides equals the number of vertices.

⊙ The **sum of the exterior angles** of any polygon is **360°**.

⊙ At each vertex, the **interior angle + exterior angle = 180°**.

⊙ The sum of the interior angles of a **triangle** is **180°**; a **quadrilateral** is **360°**, a **pentagon** is **540°** and a **hexagon** is **720°**.

2 Regular polygons

This lesson will help you to find the exterior angle and interior angle of any regular polygon.

Did you know that...?

Logo is a language for writing computer programs. It was developed in Massachusetts in the USA in 1967 by **Wally Feurzeig** and **Seymour Papert**.

It was used to control a small robot connected to the computer. As the robot moved it drew lines that formed shapes and patterns. These are called **turtle graphics**.

Logo turtle graphic

A 'turtle'

The first turtle was a radio-controlled floor robot named 'Irving'. Irving was a domed Perspex device with wheels. It had touch sensors and could go forward, back, rotate right or left, and ding (Irving had a bell). Its domed shell made it look like an electronic turtle.

On the screen, the 'turtle' is represented as a triangular pointer.

Exercise 2

Work with a partner.

You need a computer with Logo software and the help sheet on **G5.4 Resource sheet 2.1**.

1   This Logo procedure will draw a square.

```
TO SQUARE
    REPEAT 4 [FD 100 RT 90]
END
```

Type in the procedure and check that it works.

(2) Change the procedure in question **1** to generate other regular polygons: triangle, pentagon, hexagon, octagon and decagon.

Record your procedures in a table like this.

Polygon	n	Procedure
Triangle		
Quadrilateral	4	REPEAT 4 [FD 100 RT 90]
…		

(3) What do you think the Logo procedure would be to draw an n-sided regular polygon?

 Points to remember

⊙ The sum of the exterior angles of any polygon is 360°.

⊙ A regular polygon has equal sides and equal angles.

⊙ The exterior angle of a regular polygon with n sides is $360 \div n$.

3 Regular polygons and the circle

This lesson will help you to know that vertices of a regular polygon lie on a circle and that a regular polygon with n sides can be split into n equal-sized isosceles triangles.

Exercise 3

A **regular polygon** has equal sides and equal angles.
Its vertices lie on the circumference of a circle.

Regular pentagon –
slices of okra

Regular hexagon –
tiles

Regular dodecagon –
Australian 50 cent coin

Example

The diagram shows a regular octagon with centre O.

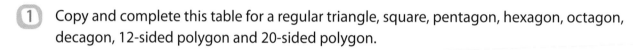

a Work out the size of the **angle at the centre**.

The octagon is split into 8 isosceles triangles.
Each of the angles at the centre O is equal.

So each angle at the centre is 360 ÷ 8 = 45°.

b Work out the size of the **exterior angle** CBX.

The sum of the exterior angles is 360°. All the exterior angles are equal.

So each exterior angle is 360 ÷ 8 = 45°.

c Work out the size of each **interior angle** ABC.

Exterior angle + interior angle = 180° (angles on a straight line)

So interior angle = 180 − 45 = 135°

---

① Copy and complete this table for a regular triangle, square, pentagon, hexagon, octagon, decagon, 12-sided polygon and 20-sided polygon.

Polygon	n	Exterior angle	Interior angle	Angle at centre
Triangle	3			
Quadrilateral	4			
Pentagon	5			
Hexagon	6			
Octagon	8	360 ÷ 8 = 45°	180 − 45 = 135°	360 ÷ 8 = 45°
...				

② **a** Radii are drawn from the centre of a regular pentagon to each of its vertices.

How many equal-sized isosceles triangles are formed?

Sketch one of these isosceles triangles and work out all of its angles.

Check that these angles give the correct interior angle.

b Repeat part **a** for each regular polygon in question **1**.

③ The angle at the centre of a regular polygon is 20°.

a How many sides has the polygon?

b Work out the size of each interior angle of the polygon.

4 For a regular 40-sided polygon, work out:

   a the size of each exterior angle

   b the size of each interior angle.

5 The size of each interior angle of a regular polygon is 168°. Work out:

   a the size of each exterior angle

   b the number of sides the polygon has.

⦿ Points to remember

- ⦿ The vertices of a regular polygon lie on the circumference of a circle.
- ⦿ Lines joining the centre of a regular n-sided polygon to each vertex divide the regular polygon into n equal-sized isosceles triangles.
- ⦿ Each angle at the centre of an n-sided regular polygon is equal to $360 \div n$, the exterior angle of the polygon.

4 Angle problems and polygons

This lesson will help you to use the angle properties of regular polygons to solve problems.

Exercise 4

The properties of polygons can be used to solve problems.

Example 1

Calculate the size of angles a and b.

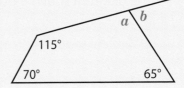

The interior angles of a quadrilateral add up to 360°.

So $a + 65 + 70 + 115 = 360°$

So $a + 250 = 360°$

So $a = 360 - 250 = 110°$

The interior and exterior angles of a polygon at a vertex add up to 180°.

So $a + b = 180°$

So $b = 180 - 110 = 70°$

Example 2

Calculate the size of angles a, b and c.
Explain the method in each case.

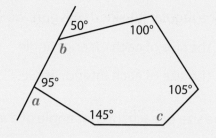

The sum of the interior and exterior angles
at a vertex is 180°.

So $\qquad a + 95 = 180°$ $\qquad\qquad\qquad b + 50 = 180°$

So $\quad a = 180 - 95 = 85°$ $\qquad\qquad b = 180 - 50 = 130°$

The interior angles of a hexagon add up to $6 \times 180 - 360 = 720°$.

So $\qquad c + 95 + 145 + b + 100 + 105 = 720°$

So $\qquad c + 95 + 145 + 130 + 100 + 105 = 720°$

So $\qquad\qquad\qquad\qquad\qquad c + 480 = 720°$

So $\qquad\qquad\qquad\qquad\qquad c = 720 - 575 = 145°$

---

① The diagram shows a pentagon.

Work out the size of:

a angle h

b angle i.

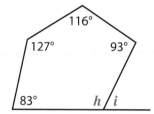

② The diagram shows a hexagon.

Work out the size of:

a angle j

b angle k.

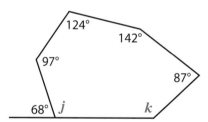

③ The diagram shows a quadrilateral.

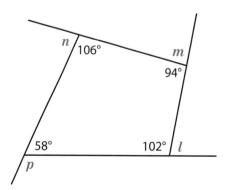

a Work out the size of each of the angles marked with a letter.

b Work out $l + m + n + p$.

(4) Find the size of each of the angles marked with a letter.

a
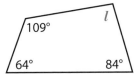

b
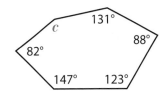

c
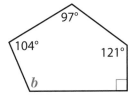

d
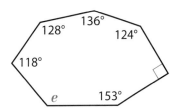

(5) The polygons below are not drawn accurately.

Calculate the sizes of angles a to f. Give reasons for your answers.

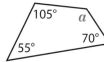

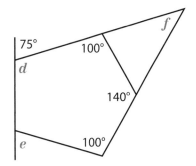

(6) In this decagon:

- four of the interior angles are right angles;

- three of the interior angles are each 135°;

- the three remaining interior angles are of equal size.

Work out the size of the unknown interior angles.
Show your working.

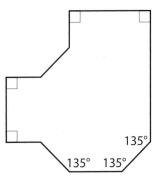

(7) ABCDE is a regular pentagon with centre O.

a Explain why triangle AED is isosceles.

b What is the size of the interior angle of a regular pentagon? Show your working.

c Work out the sizes of angles a, b and c.

d Work out the sizes of angles d, e and f.

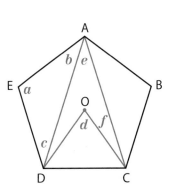

8 ABCDE is a regular pentagon.
DEF and BAF are straight lines.

Use the hints below to help you to calculate:

a angles FEA and FAE;

b angles AED, DCB and BAE;

c angles CDB and CBD;

d angles EDB and ABD;

e angle AFE.

Give a reason for each answer.

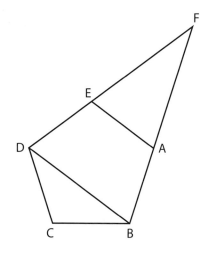

Hint

a Angles FEA and FAE are **both** exterior angles of the pentagon ($360 \div n$).

b Angles AED, DCB and BAE are interior angles of the pentagon ($180° -$ exterior angle).

c Triangle CDB is an isosceles triangle. Explain why.

d Angles EDB and CDB make up an interior angle. So do angles ABD and DBC.

e Triangle AFE is an isosceles triangle. Explain why.

Extension problem

9 ABCDEFGH is a regular octagon with centre O.

ABX and EDX are straight line segments.

a Angles a, b and c are exterior angles of the octagon.

Write down the size of angles a, b and c.

b Angles d and e are angles at the centre of the regular octagon.

Write down the sizes of angles d and e.

c Calculate the size of angle f.

d Calculate the size of angle g.

e Calculate the size of angle h.

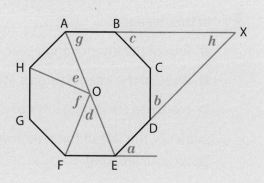

10 The diagram shows part of a regular polygon constructed inside a circle.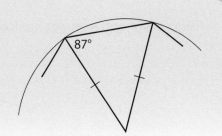

How many sides does the polygon have?

Show all of your working.

⊙ Points to remember

⊙ When you solve problems involving polygons, use these facts:

- the sum of the interior angles of the polygon;
- the sum of the exterior angles of a polygon is 360°;
- the sum of the interior and exterior angles is 180°.

⊙ Given an n-sided regular polygon, use these facts:

- exterior angles are equal to $360 \div n$;
- interior angles are equal to $180 - (360 \div n)$;
- the angles at the centre are equal to $360 \div n$.

⊙ You may be able to use the properties of isosceles triangles.

---

5 Polygons and parallel lines

This lesson will help you to use the angle properties of regular polygons and parallel lines to solve problems.

Exercise 5A

Parallel lines are lines in the same direction.

The pipes in the foreground of the photograph are parallel.

In real life any two of these pipes are always the same distance apart.

On a diagram parallel lines are shown by arrows on each line.

A line crossing a pair of parallels is called a **transversal**.

Two sets of equal angles are formed when a transversal crosses a pair of parallel lines.

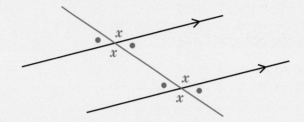

All angles marked with a dot are equal. All angles marked with a cross are equal.

The angles marked • and the angles marked x occur in pairs on a straight line.

So • + x = 180°.

Pairs of equal angles have special names.

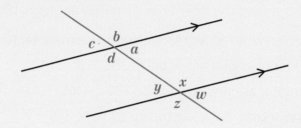

Corresponding angles:	**Alternate angles:**	**Vertically opposite angles:**
a and w	a and y	a and c
b and x	b and z	b and d
c and y	c and w	y and w
d and z	d and x	x and z

Example

Work out the size of angle d.

Explain how you worked out your answer.

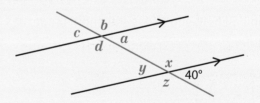

$z = 140°$ (z and 40° lie on a straight line)

$d = 140°$ (d and z are corresponding $\angle$s)

Regular polygons with an even number of sides have pairs of parallel sides.

In the regular hexagon ABCDEF:

- ⊙ side AB is parallel to side ED and diagonal FC;

- ⊙ side BC is parallel to side FE and diagonal AD;

- ⊙ side CD is parallel to side AF and diagonal BE.

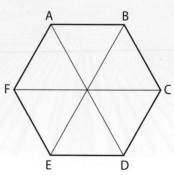

The properties of angles in a regular hexagon can be used to show that angles x and y are both 60°.

In a regular hexagon, triangle OAB is equilateral. So angle $y = 60°$.

Angle x and angle y are corresponding angles, since AD is parallel to BC.

So angle x is also 60°.

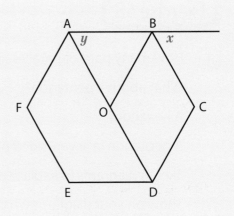

1   **a**   Work out the size of angle b.

    b   Work out the size of angle c.

       Show your working.

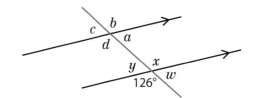

2   The diagram shows three parallel lines and a transversal. One angle is given.

   Copy the diagram.

   Fill in all the angles.

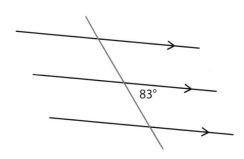

3   The diagram shows a pair of parallel lines and two transversals. Two angles are given.

   Work out the size of each of these angles.

   a   Angle a **b**   Angle b

   c   Angle c **d**   Angle d

   e   Angle e

   Give a reason for each answer.

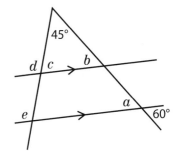

4   Work out the size of angle x.

   Show your working.

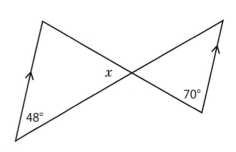

1 How many pairs of parallel sides can a quadrilateral have?

What about a pentagon?

A hexagon?

A heptagon (a seven-sided polygon)?

Sketch diagrams to explain your answers.

Show on your diagrams which angles are equal and which angles add up to 180°.

2 A regular five-pointed star is drawn inside a circle.

The pentagon in the centre is also regular.

Find the angle at each point of the star.

Give reasons for your answer.

3 ABCDE is a regular pentagon.

   a What is the exterior angle x?

   b What is the interior angle w?

   c What is the angle z in triangle ADE?

   d What is angle y?

   e What does this tell you about lines BC and AD?

Give a reason for each answer.

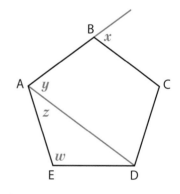

4 The diagram shows a regular decagon with centre O.

   a Prove that angles x and y are equal.

   b What does this tell you about the lines AB and CD?

      Give reasons for each answer.

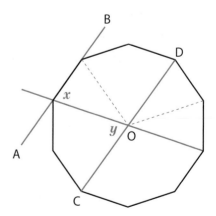

Points to remember

- When a transversal cuts a pair of parallel lines, pairs of **corresponding** and **alternate** angles are formed.

Corresponding angles *Alternate* angles

- When n is even, opposite sides of a regular n-sided polygon are parallel.
- Use alternate and corresponding angles to solve problems involving regular polygons.

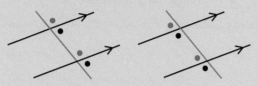

6 Constructions

This lesson will help you to do constructions using compasses and a straight edge.

Exercise 6

Some constructions involve only:

- **compasses** to draw arcs or circles;
- **a straight edge** to join points to form straight line segments.

No measuring is involved.

For other constructions, the length of a line segment or the size of an angle is given. When this is the case, you can use a ruler or protractor to make the measurement.

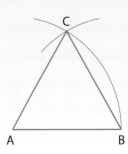

How to construct an equilateral triangle

- Draw an arc, centre A, with radius equal to the length of AB.
- Draw another arc, centre B, with the same radius. The two arcs cross at C.
- Use the straight edge to complete the equilateral triangle ABC.

How to construct the perpendicular bisector of a line AB

◉ Set the compasses with a fixed radius (about $\frac{3}{4}$ the length of AB).

◉ Draw two equal arcs with centres A and B. Make sure that the arcs cross on both sides of AB.

◉ Use a straight edge to draw a line through the points where these arcs cross each other (CD on the diagram).

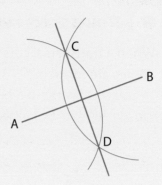

How to construct an angle bisector

◉ Set the compasses with a fixed radius (about $\frac{1}{2}$ the length of the arms of the angle).

◉ Draw an arc with centre A to cut the arms at B and C.

◉ Draw arcs with centres B and C to cross at D.

◉ Use a straight edge to draw the line AD.

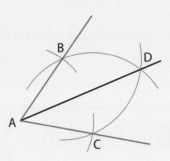

Do this exercise on plain paper. You will need a straight edge, compasses and a sharp pencil.

① **a** Draw a line segment PQ.

Construct an equilateral triangle with PQ as its base.

b Draw a line segment PQ.

Construct the perpendicular bisector of the line PQ.

c Draw an acute angle QPR.

Construct the bisector of angle QPR.

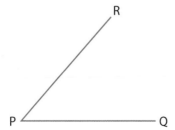

d Draw an obtuse angle QPR.

Construct the bisector of angle QPR.

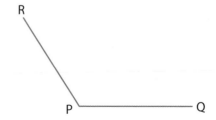

2 Follow the instructions below to construct a square and a regular octagon using only compasses and a straight edge.

> The constructions are based on methods used by the ancient Greeks.
>
> Remember that you must be able to see construction lines, but make them as faint as possible.
>
> In the diagrams below the construction arcs are not shown.
> The red lines are construction lines.

Square 1

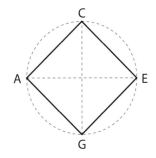

Square 2

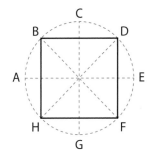

- Draw a circle (make the radius about 4 cm).
- Draw a diameter and label it AE.
- Construct the perpendicular bisector of AE.
- Label the points where it crosses the circumference of the circle C and G.
- Draw the square ACEG.

- Repeat the construction for Square 1 to locate the points A, C, E and G.
- Construct both angle bisectors of the diameters AE and CG.
- Label the points where they cross the circumference of the circle D, F, H and B.
- Draw the square BDFH.

3 You can construct a **regular polygon** by dividing a circle into equal sectors. You will need a protractor.

Follow these instructions to construct a regular pentagon.

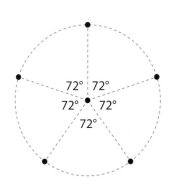

- Draw a circle of radius about 4 cm.
- Calculate the angle at the centre of a regular pentagon (360 ÷ 5 = 72°).
- Place the centre of a protractor at the centre of the circle.
- Mark points on the circumference at 72° intervals.
- Join these points with straight lines.

(4) Use a protractor to construct a regular octagon using a similar procedure to question **3**.

(5) Use a straight edge and compasses to construct a regular octagon using the procedures for squares in question **2**.

Regular octagon

- ◎ Repeat the construction for Square 1 to locate the points A, C, E and G.
- ◎ Repeat the construction for Square 2 to locate the points D, F, H and B.
- ◎ Draw the regular octagon ABCDEFGH.

● Points to remember

- ⊙ Standard constructions are done using only compasses and a straight edge. Always use a sharp pencil.
- ⊙ Equal lengths are constructed by using compasses to draw arcs with the same radius.
- ⊙ Constructions for the perpendicular bisector of a line segment and the angle bisector are based on the properties of the rhombus.
- ⊙ To draw a regular polygon with n sides divide a circle into equal sectors. Each angle at the centre is $360 \div n$ and is measured with a protractor.

7 Constructing triangles

This lesson will help you construct triangles using compasses, ruler and protractor.

Exercise 7

Here are two more constructions.

How to construct the perpendicular from a point P *to* a line

- ◎ Draw an arc from P to cut the line at two points A and B.
- ◎ Construct the perpendicular bisector of AB.

How to construct the perpendicular from a point P *on* a line

- Draw an arc from P to cut the line at two points A and B.

- Construct the perpendicular bisector of AB.

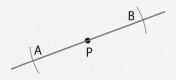

Example

Construct a right-angled triangle, ABC, with a right angle at A.
Make AC equal to 6 cm and AB equal to 4 cm.

This construction requires a ruler because the lines AC and AB must be measured.

- Draw a line 4 cm long; label it AB.

- Extend the line past B about 4 cm.

- Construct the perpendicular to the line AB from B.

- Make the radius on a pair of compasses 6 cm.

- Draw an arc from A to intersect the perpendicular from B.
  Label the point of intersection C.

- Draw the triangle ABC.

You can construct a triangle if any of these sets of three facts is given.

SSS *SSS* *ASA* *RHS*

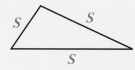 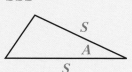 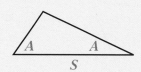 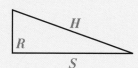

S represents the length of a **side**.
A represents an **angle**.
R represents a **right angle**.
H represents the length of the **hypotenuse**.

Do this exercise on plain paper.
You will need a straight edge, ruler, compasses and protractor, and a sharp pencil.

(1) **a** Draw a line segment PQ.
Mark a point R away from PQ.

Construct the perpendicular from the point R to the line PQ.

b Draw a line segment PQ.
Mark a point R on PQ.

Construct the perpendicular from the point R on the line PQ.

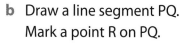

2 Make an accurate drawing of each of these right-angled triangles.

a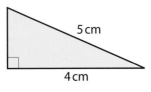
5 cm
4 cm

b
5.2 cm
3.4 cm

c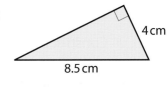
4 cm
8.5 cm

Measure the unmarked length in each triangle.

3 Construct each of these triangles accurately.

All lengths are in centimetres.

a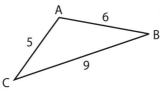
A
6
B
5
9
C

b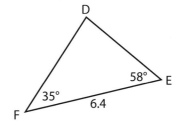
D
58° E
35°
6.4
F

c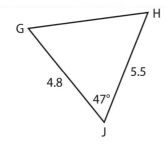
H
G
5.5
4.8
47°
J

d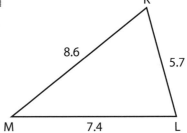
K
8.6
5.7
M   7.4   L

e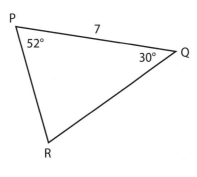
P
52°
7
30° Q
R

f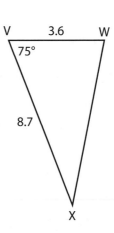
V   3.6   W
75°
8.7
X

Measure the interior angles at these vertices: A, L and X.

Measure these lengths: ED, GH and PR.

4 Mark points A, B, C and D on a straight line as shown.

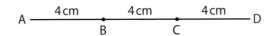

A ———— 4 cm ———— B ———— 4 cm ———— C ———— 4 cm ———— D

a Construct the perpendicular to AD from point B.

Construct the perpendicular to AD from point C.

b Draw these arcs with your compasses fixed at a radius of 4 centimetres.

i With centre B cut the perpendicular from B above AD at E and F.

ii With centre C cut the perpendicular from C below AD at G and H.

c Explain why lines EF and GH are parallel.

d What other lines on the diagram are parallel?

Extension problem

5 Construct accurately each of these quadrilaterals.

a
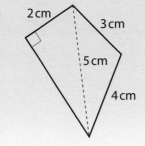
2 cm, 3 cm, 5 cm, 4 cm

b
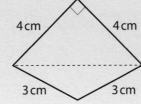
4 cm, 4 cm, 3 cm, 3 cm

c
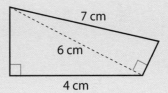
7 cm, 6 cm, 4 cm

⊙ Points to remember

- ⊙ You can construct a triangle if you are given any of these sets of three facts: SSS, SAS, ASA, RHS.

- ⊙ To construct a triangle given RHS, the perpendicular from a point on a line has to be constructed.

- ⊙ To construct a line parallel to a given line AB:
  - construct perpendiculars at points A and B;
  - construct arcs of the same length with centres A and B to cut the perpendiculars at C and D;
  - join CD and extend if necessary.

8 Loci

This lesson will help you to visualise and draw simple loci.

Exercise 8

A **locus** is the path of a point that moves according to a rule.

Example 1

A point moves so that it is always 2 cm from a fixed point A.
Draw its locus.

Here are some points that are 2 cm from A.

Combining all the points that are 2 cm from A gives a circle, centre A, with a radius 2 cm.

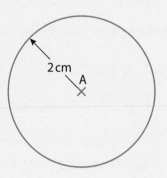

Example 2

A point moves so that it is always 1 cm from a fixed line.
Draw its locus.

Here are some points which are 1 cm from the line AB.

They make two lines parallel to AB and 1 cm away from it.

Here are some points which are 1 cm away from point A and 1 cm away from point B.

They make semicircles, centres A and B, with a radius of 1 cm.

Combining the two parallel lines and the two semicircles gives the complete locus of points that are 1 cm from AB.

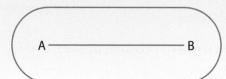

You need plain paper and squared paper, a ruler and compasses.

Use compasses to draw arcs and circles.

(1) A point moves so that it is always 3 cm away from a fixed point P.

Draw its locus.

• A

(2) A point moves so that it is always 2 cm away from a fixed line PQ.

Draw its locus.

P ——————————— Q

(3) Mark a point and label it C.

Mark about 10 points that are 5 cm from C.

Draw the locus of points 5 cm from C.

Shade the region where points are more than 5 cm from C.

(4) Mark a point and label it P.

Mark about 10 points that are 7 cm from P.

Draw the locus of points 7 cm from P.

Shade the region where points are less than 7 cm from P.

(5) Mark a point and label it Z.

Draw the locus of points 4 cm from Z.

Draw the locus of points 6 cm from Z.

Shade the region where points are less than 6 cm from Z and more than 4 cm from Z.

(6) Draw a circle of radius 6 cm.

Mark about 10 points that are 2 cm from the circle.
They can be inside or outside the circle.

Shade the region where points are less than 2 cm from the circumference of the circle.

(7) Mark two points A and B where AB = 8 cm.

A point P is 5 cm from A and 7 cm from B.

A ——————————— B

Find the two possible positions of P.

Mark them with a cross.

8 Mark two points A and B where AB = 8 cm.

    a Draw the locus of points 6 cm from A.

    b Draw the locus of points 4 cm from B.

    c Clearly mark with a cross all points 6 cm from A and 4 cm from B.

    d Shade the region where points are less than 6 cm from A and less than 4 cm from B.

9 Draw a 4 cm by 4 cm square on centimetre squared paper.

Draw the locus of points that are exactly 3 cm from its perimeter.

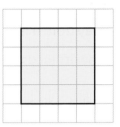

10 **a** Draw a 6 cm by 3 cm rectangle on squared paper.

    b Draw the locus of points exactly 2 cm from the perimeter of the rectangle.

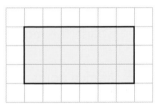

Extension problem

11 **a** Draw this trapezium on a centimetre square grid.

    b Draw the locus of points exactly 2 cm from perimeter of the trapezium.

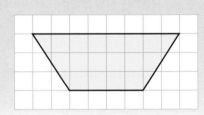

 Points to remember

⊙ A **locus** is the path of a point that moves according to a rule.

⊙ The plural of locus is **loci**.

9 More loci

This lesson will help you to construct loci.

Exercise 9

The locus of points that are **an equal distance from two fixed points A and B** is the perpendicular bisector of AB.

The locus of points that are **an equal distance from two line segments intersecting at A** is the bisector of the angle at A.

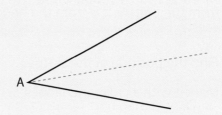

You need plain paper and squared paper, a ruler and compasses.

Use the compasses to draw arcs and circles.

① A point moves so that it is always an equal distance from two fixed points A and B. Draw its locus.

a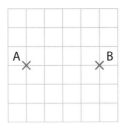

b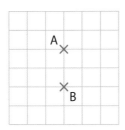

c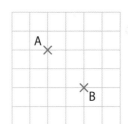

② A point moves so that it is always the same distance from two fixed lines AB and AC.

Draw its locus.

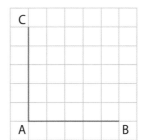

③ Draw an acute angle CAB.

A point moves so that it is always the same distance from AB and AC.

Draw its locus.

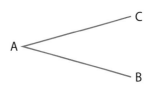

4 A point P is an equal distance from A and B and 2 cm from C.

Find the two possible positions of P.

Mark them with a cross.

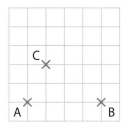

5 This is a plan of a small garden.
It is drawn to a scale of 1 cm to 5 metres.

There is a statue which is the same distance from the path as it is from the hedge.
The tree is also 7.5 m from the wall.

Find the position of the statue.

Mark it with a cross and label it S.

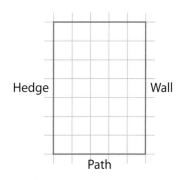

6 A map is drawn to a scale of 1 cm to 10 km.

A, B and C are three ports.

A ship is 75 km from A. It is also the same distance from B as it is from C.

Find the position of the ship.
Mark it with a cross and label it S.

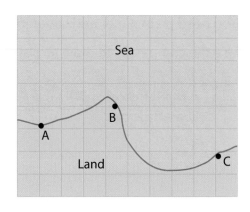

7 The map shows three mobile phone masts, A, B and C.

The scale of the map is 1 cm to 10 km.

Signals from mast A can be received 30 km away, from B 35 km away and from C 20 km away.

Make a sketch of the map.

Shade the region in which signals can be received from all 3 masts.

• B

•
A

•
C

8 The map shows two ports, P and Q.

The scale of the map is 1 cm to 10 km.

A ship is less than 30 km from P and less than 40 km from Q.

Make a sketch of the map.

Shade the region where the ship could be.

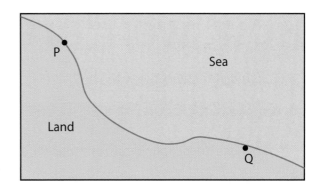

9 Two water sprinklers, 6 m apart, are fitted to a wall, as shown below.

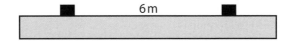

The sprinklers can spray water to a maximum distance of 5 m.

Make a scale drawing to show the region that can be watered by both sprinklers.
Use a scale of 1 cm to 1 m.

> ## ⦿ Points to remember
>
> ⊙ Loci can be constructed accurately using compasses, straight edge, ruler and, if required, protractor.
>
> ⊙ The locus of points that are **a fixed distance from a fixed point** is a circle with centre the fixed point and radius the fixed distance.
>
> ⊙ The locus of points that are **the same distance from a fixed line segment** consists of two parallel lines equidistant from the line segment and two semicircles.
>
> ⊙ The locus of points that are **the same distance from two fixed points** is the perpendicular bisector of the line joining the points.
>
> ⊙ The locus of points that are **the same distance from two fixed lines** is the bisector of the angle between the two lines.

How well are you doing?

Can you:

- prove the interior angle sum of a triangle, a quadrilateral, pentagon or hexagon?
- calculate the exterior angle and interior angle of any regular polygon?
- prove that for a regular polygon the exterior angle equals the angle at the centre?
- use the properties of parallel lines or regular polygons to solve problems?
- construct triangles using compasses, ruler and protractor?
- do standard constructions using compasses and a straight edge?
- construct loci?

1. a The sum of the interior angles of an n-sided polygon is 900°.
   What is the value of n?

   b What is the sum of the interior angles of an octagon?
   Give a reason for your answer.

2. a The diagram shows a pentagon.
   Calculate angle x.

   b The diagram shows a hexagon.
   Calculate angle y.

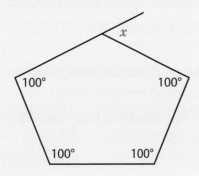

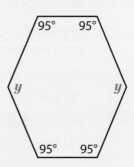

3. *Year 8 Optional Test level 6*
   One angle of a rhombus is 58°. Each side is 6 cm.
   Make an accurate drawing of the rhombus.
   Show your working and leave in your construction lines.

4 *2006 level 6*

Look at the diagram, made from four straight lines.
The lines marked with arrows are parallel.

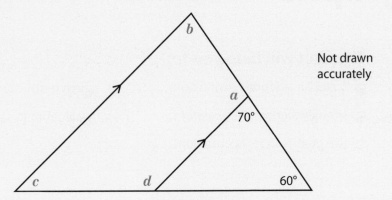

Not drawn accurately

Work out the sizes of the angles marked with letters.

5 *2004 level 6*

The diagram shows the net for a right-pyramid with a regular pentagon as its base.

The net is constructed using five straight lines.

a Without measuring, explain why angle a must be 108°.

b Calculate the size of angle b. Show your working.

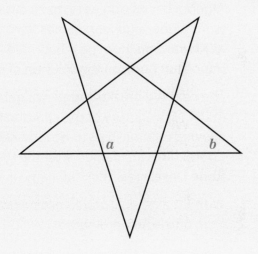

Extension problem

6 *2006 level 7*

In a wildlife park in Africa, wardens want to know the position of an elephant in a certain area. They place a microphone at two adjacent corners of a 4 km by 4 km square.
Each microphone has a range of 3.5 km.

The elephant is out of range of microphones A and B.

Draw the square accurately using a scale of 2 cm to 1 km.
Construct the region where the elephant could be.
Label the region R.

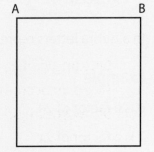

A 5.5 Equations, formulae and graphs

This unit will help you to:

- factorise algebraic expressions;
- simplify algebraic expressions;
- use graphs to solve equations;
- match graphs to real-life situations;
- use algebra to solve problems.

Did you know that...?

Algebra has its origins in many different cultures. The word 'algebra' (*al-jabr*) comes from the work of **al'Khwarizmi**, born near Baghdad in AD 790. He wrote an important book on the solution of equations.

The next big breakthrough in algebra was the invention in the 16th century of the coordinate system, which allowed relationships to be represented as graphs. Coordinates are named after the French mathematician **René Descartes**. Their full name is 'Cartesian coordinates'.

Without algebra it would not be possible to plot this trace from an electrocardiogram.

1 Factorising

This lesson will help you to factorise algebraic expressions.

Exercise 1

In algebra letters represent numbers.

Example 1

6 is a factor of 24   3 is a factor of both 9 and 15

2 is a factor of $2x$ y is a factor of $3y$ $2a$ is a factor of both $6a$ and $8ab$

When you multiply out brackets, remember to multiply everything in the bracket.

Example 2

$5(2a + 3) = 10a + 15$

You can simplify an expression by collecting together like terms.

Example 3

$2(3b + 6) + 4(b - 1) = 6b + 12 + 4b - 4 = 10b + 8$

You can factorise an expression when each term has a common factor.

Example 4

$6c + 15d - 21 = 3(2c + 5d - 7)$

1 Write down all the factors of these numbers.

   a 10   **b** 17

   c 25   **d** 28

   e 48   **f** 70

2 Write down the common factors of these sets of numbers other than 1.

   a 4, 20   **b** 24, 60

   c 15, 35   **d** 16, 20, 32

   e 12, 18, 30   **f** 8, 36, 40, 60

3 Write down the highest common factor (HCF) of these sets of numbers.

   a 15, 30, 45   **b** 34, 85, 102

   c 4, 26, 54, 80   **d** 26, 65, 91, 104, 130

   e 14, 35, 49, 63   **f** 18, 45, 72, 99, 108

4 Multiply out these brackets.

   a $3(2x + 7)$ **b** $9(6x + 5)$

   c $8(x - 6)$ **d** $10(4x - 9y)$

   e $7(3x - 4y)$ **f** $5(2x + 8y - 6z)$

5 Multiply out these brackets and simplify the expressions.

    a $4(3x + 8) + 9(2x - 3)$ **b** $6(7x + 1) - 4(3x + 1)$

    c $5(4x - 2) - 3(3x - 7)$ **d** $7(8x - 3y) - 4(5x - 2y)$

    e $6(6x - 5y) + 5(3x - 7y)$ **f** $8(4x + 3y - z) - 2(x - y)$

6 Factorise these expressions.

    a $6x + 10$ **b** $15t + 25$

    c $16a + 40$ **d** $21y - 56$

    e $9b - 63$ **f** $20w + 36$

    g $34z + 22$ **h** $39d - 15$

7 Factorise these expressions.

    a $10x + 18y$ **b** $24p + 33q$

    c $30a + 45b$ **d** $16m - 28n$

    e $6x - 4y + 14z$ **f** $70w + 100x - 50y$

    g $49a + 21b + 35c$ **h** $27l - 72m + 63n$

8 The two shorter sides of the hexagon have length $(x - 1)$ and the four longer sides have length $(x + 2)$.

    a Write an expression for the perimeter of the hexagon.

    b Factorise the expression.

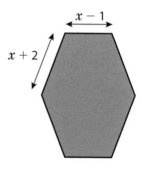

9 **a** Write an expression for the perimeter of the triangle.

    b Factorise the expression.

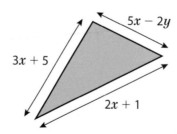

10 This shape consists of a semicircle with radius r and an equilateral triangle.

    a Write an expression for the perimeter of the shape.

    b Factorise the expression.

Extension problems

11 Multiply out these brackets.

    a $\frac{1}{2}(3x + 5)$ **b** $\frac{3}{4}(7x + 3)$

    c $\frac{2}{3}(2x - 4)$ **d** $\frac{\pi}{2}(5x - 3)$

    e $0.2(0.5x + 0.3)$ **f** $-0.1(9x - 7y)$

12 Factorise these expressions.

    a $ax + 9bx$ **b** $28pq + 40pr$

    c $15m^2 + 25m$ **d** $7ax - 21bx^2$

    e $2\pi r^2 - 4\pi r$ **f** $6w^3 + 15w^2$

    g $5z^3 + 7z^2 - 3z$ **h** $4\pi rl - 6\pi r^2$

13 This cylinder has base radius x and perpendicular height $3x + 4$.

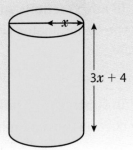

    a Write an expression for the total surface area of the cylinder.

    b Factorise the expression.

Points to remember

- ⊙ Look for common factors in an algebraic expression and take them outside a bracket.
- ⊙ Factors can be whole numbers, fractions, decimals or irrational numbers.
- ⊙ It is good practice to factorise an algebraic expression when presenting answers.

2 Working with algebraic fractions

This lesson will help you to add and subtract algebraic fractions.

 Did you know that...?

The **Egyptians** wrote fractions from as early as 1800 BC.

They used only fractions with the number 1 as the numerator. These are called unit fractions.

They used to express other fractions as the sum of unit fractions. For example, they could write:

$$\frac{5}{6} = \frac{1}{3} + \frac{1}{2}$$

It wasn't until the 17th century that fractions as we know them today came to Europe.

Exercise 2

To **add fractions with the same denominator**, add the numerators but do not change the denominator. For example

$$\frac{6}{a} + \frac{7}{a} = \frac{13}{a}$$

To **subtract fractions with the same denominator**, subtract the numerators but do not change the denominator. For example

$$\frac{7}{b} - \frac{3}{b} = \frac{4}{b}$$

① Solve each equation.

a $\dfrac{3y}{5} = 6$

b $\dfrac{2p}{7} = 6$

c $\dfrac{3x}{5} = 12$

d $\dfrac{7z}{8} = 21$

e $\dfrac{4n}{9} = 32$

2 Solve each equation.

a $\dfrac{p+1}{3} = 8$

b $\dfrac{z+5}{4} = 8$

c $\dfrac{2x+4}{5} = 6$

d $\dfrac{3a-2}{8} = 2$

3 Solve each equation.

a $\dfrac{4(h-1)}{2} = 6$

b $\dfrac{2(b+7)}{9} = 8$

c $\dfrac{3(17z-1)}{6} = 8$

d $\dfrac{6(3q+2)}{10} = 12$

4 Add or subtract these fractions.

a $\dfrac{3}{a} + \dfrac{5}{a}$

b $\dfrac{9}{p} - \dfrac{7}{p}$

c $\dfrac{1}{2z} + \dfrac{7}{2z}$

d $\dfrac{b}{3x} + \dfrac{c}{3x}$

5 The expression or number in each cell is the result of adding the expressions or numbers in the two cells beneath it.

Copy each diagram and fill in the missing expressions.

a

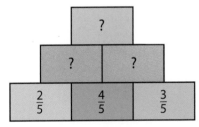

b

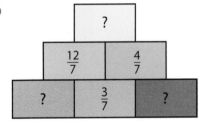

c

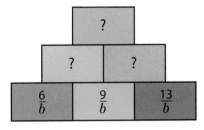

d

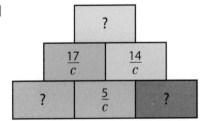

6 In a magic square the sum of the expressions in each row, column and diagonal is the same.

Copy and complete the magic squares.

a

$\dfrac{5}{a}$		$\dfrac{4}{a}$
		$\dfrac{7}{a}$
		$\dfrac{7}{a}$

b

$\dfrac{2}{b}$	$\dfrac{7}{b}$	
	$\dfrac{5}{b}$	
	$\dfrac{3}{b}$	

Extension problem

7 The expression in each cell is the result of adding the expressions or numbers in the two cells beneath it.

Copy the diagram and fill in the missing expressions.

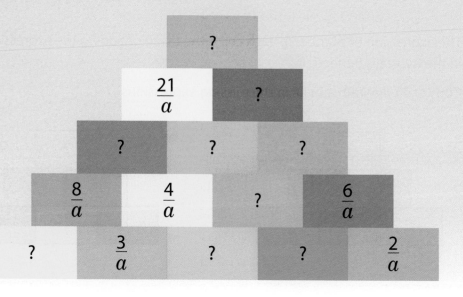

Points to remember

⊙ You can only add or subtract fractions with the same denominator.

⊙ With different denominators, first change the fractions to the same denominator.

3 Working with formulae

This lesson will help you to use formulae to solve problems.

Exercise 3

You can change the subject of a formula by rearranging the equation.

Whatever you do to one side of the equation, you must do to the other.

Example 1

Make r the subject of the formula $q = 3 + r$.

Subtract 3 from both sides: $q - 3 = r$

Turn the equation around: $r = q - 3$

Example 2

Make s the subject of the formula $t = 6s$.

Divide both sides by 6: $\frac{t}{6} = s$

Turn the equation around: $s = \frac{t}{6}$

Example 3

Make x the subject of the formula $y = \frac{x}{3}$.

Multiply both sides by 3: $3y = x$

Turn the equation around: $x = 3y$

① Work with a partner.

Which equations are **not** the same as $27 + 95 = 122$?

A $122 = 27 + 95$

B $122 + 95 - 27 = 0$

C $122 - 27 = 95$

D $122 - 27 - 95 = 0$

E $27 + 95 - 122 = 0$

F $-122 + 27 = -95$

G $122 - 95 = 27$

H $122 + 27 = 95$

I $-27 = 95 - 122$

② Work with a partner.

Which equations are **not** the same as $4x + 5y = 29$?

A $29 = 4x + 5y$ B $5y = 29 - 4x$ C $5y = 29 + 4x$

D $4x = 29 - 5y$ E $29 - 5y = 4x$ F $4x - 29 = -5y$

G $29 = 4x - 5y$ H $5y - 29 + 4x = 0$ I $29 + 5y = 4x$

③ Make p the subject of these formulae.

a $r = 3 + p$ b $m = p - 2$

c $q + p = r$ d $5r = p + 1$

e $v - 5 = 3 + p$ f $q - p = 5$

④ Make w the subject of these formulae.

a $sw = 7$ b $t = 8w$

c $p = qw$ d $V = wxy$

e $t = \dfrac{3w}{7}$ f $5s = 3w$

⑤ The cost of electricity supplied by GoElectric is calculated using the formula:

$$C = 15 + mn$$

C is the total cost in pounds, £15 the quarterly standing charge, m the cost of a unit of electricity in pounds and n the number of units used.

a In one quarter the Lee family used 1800 units of electricity and paid a total of £141. What was the cost of a unit of electricity?

b Two years later the cost of electricity was £0.09 a unit.
The Lee family had a quarterly bill of £150.
How many units of electricity did they use?

Extension problems

⑥ a Make p the subject of this formula: b Make r the subject of this formula:

$$m = pq$$ $$C = 2\pi r$$

c Make R the subject of this formula: d Make S the subject of this formula:

$$P = \dfrac{R}{S}$$ $$P = \dfrac{R}{S}$$

7 **a** Make u the subject of this formula:
$$v = u + at$$

b Make t the subject of this formula:
$$v = u + at$$

c Make l the subject of this formula:
$$V = l^3$$

d Make w the subject of this formula:
$$V = lwh$$

 Points to remember

⊙ When you rearrange formulae, remember to do the same thing to both sides.

⊙ You can use formulae to help solve problems.

4 Forming equations

This lesson will help you to turn a word problem into a maths problem so that you can solve it.

Exercise 4

Read through a problem and decide what you want to find.

Let a letter represent the unknown quantity.

Set up an equation and solve it.

Example

Find two consecutive whole numbers whose sum is 97.

Let n be the smallest number and $n + 1$ the next number.

$$n + n + 1 = 97 \text{ or } 2n + 1 = 97$$
$$2n = 96$$
$$n = 48$$

The two numbers are 48 and 49.

 1 **a** Find two consecutive whole numbers whose sum is 1947.

b Find three consecutive whole numbers whose sum is 267.

c Find two consecutive whole numbers whose sum is 10 more than the cube of 7.

d Find four consecutive whole numbers whose sum is 15 less than 245.

e Find five consecutive whole numbers whose sum is 5 less than 10^2.

2 The sum of the numbers along the red line is equal to the sum of the numbers along the blue line.

   a Write an expression in x for the sum of the numbers along the red line.

   b Write an expression in x for the sum of the numbers along the blue line.

   c Write an equation in x.

   d Solve the equation for x.

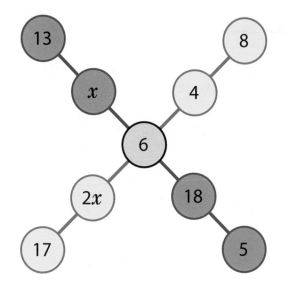

3 The number in each square is found by adding together the numbers in the two adjacent circles.

   a Write the number in A as an expression in x.

   b Write the number in B as an expression in x.

   c Write an equation in x.

   d Solve the equation for x.

   e What are the numbers in A and B?

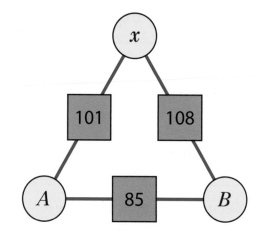

4 Bags of marbles have the same number of marbles in them.

Josh bought four bags of marbles.
He gave away seven marbles to his brother.

Kate already had five marbles.
She bought three more bags of marbles.

Kate now has the same number of marbles as Josh.

How many marbles are there in a bag?

5 Year 9 is going to the theatre at Stratford.

Miss Maple is to order some coaches.
Each coach has the same number of seats.

If she orders five coaches,
there will be 10 empty seats.

If she orders four coaches,
32 people will be left behind.

How many seats does each coach have?

6 Boxes of Chocos have the same number of chocolates in them.

Anil bought three boxes of Chocos.
He gave 35 chocolates to his friends.

Ram bought two boxes of Chocos.
He gave away 17 chocolates to his friends.

Anil and Ram now have the same number of chocolates.

How many chocolates are there in each box of Chocos?

Extension problems

7 Alan and his dad have their birthdays on the same day.
On their birthday in 2007, Alan's dad was five times Alan's age.
On their birthday in 2014, Alan's dad will be three times Alan's age.

How old was Alan on his birthday in 2007?

8 A car travelled from Arden to Bartrum for 3 hours at an average speed of 45 mph.
It then travelled from Bartrum to Corrs for another 2 hours.
The average speed for the whole journey was 50 mph.

What was the car's average speed from Bartrum to Corrs?

⊙ Points to remember

- ⊙ When you use algebra to help you to solve problems, first define any letters you are going to use.
- ⊙ Use the information given in the problem to write an equation, then solve it.

5 Visualising graphs

This lesson will help you to visualise the graphs of linear and quadratic equations.

Exercise 5

An equation in x and y gives you information that can help you sketch a graph.

Example 1

Look at the linear equation $y = 2x + 1$.

The graph of the equation has a gradient of 2.
It intersects the y-axis at (0, 1).

You can use a ruler to draw the straight-line graph.

Mark the point (0, 1).

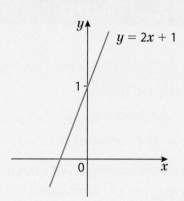

Example 2

Look at the linear equation $y - 3x = 6$.

Rearrange the equation into its normal form,
$y = 3x + 6$.

The graph of the equation has a gradient of 3 and it intersects the y-axis at (0, 6).

You can use a ruler to draw the straight-line graph.

Mark the point (0, 6).

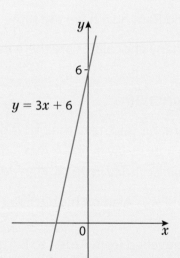

Example 3

Look at the quadratic equation $y = x^2 + 2$.

The graph of this equation (the blue curve) is a U-shaped curve.

It has the same shape as $y = x^2$ (the red curve) but has been moved two units up.

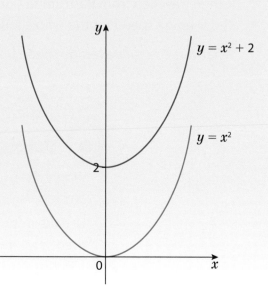

Example 4

Look at the quadratic equation $y = 3x^2$.

The graph of this equation (the blue curve)
is a U-shaped curve.

It has a similar shape to $y = x^2$ (the red curve)
but is steeper.

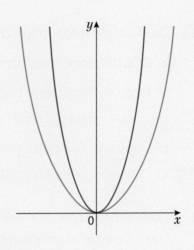

You will need squared paper.

1 On the right is the graph of the linear equation $y = 4x - 3$.

   a What is the gradient of the graph?

   b At what point does the graph intercept the y-axis?

   c Copy and complete the sentence:

       As x increases, y ……

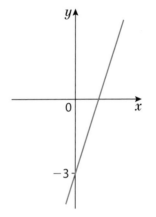

2 Sketch the graphs of these equations.
Use a new set of axes for each graph.

   a $y = x + 1$ **b** $y = x + 3$

   c $y = x - 1$ **d** $y = x - 5$

   e $y = 2x$ **f** $y = 0.5x$

   g $y = 3x + 2$ **h** $y = 4x - 1$

3 Sketch the graphs of these equations.
Use a new set of axes for each graph.

   a $y = -x$ **b** $y = -x + 2$

   c $y = -x - 3$ **d** $y = -x + 4$

   e $y = -2x$ **f** $y = -0.5x$

   g $y = -3x + 1$ **h** $y = -4x + 5$

4 Rearrange these equations into their normal form and sketch their graphs.
Use a new set of axes for each graph.

   a $y - x = 5$ **b** $y - 4x = 2$

   c $y + x = 7$ **d** $y - 2x - 8 = 0$

   e $3x + y = 9$ **f** $y - 4x + 5 = 0$

   g $7 + y = 2x$ **h** $y - 11 = x$

⑤ On the right is the graph of $y = x^2 + 3$.

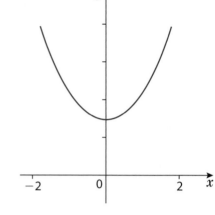

  a At what point does the graph intersect the y-axis?

  b Copy and complete the sentence:

    As x increases from -2 to 0, y ......

  c Copy and complete the sentence:

    As x increases from 0 to 2, y ......

⑥ Sketch the graphs of these equations.
Use a new set of axes for each graph.

  a $y = x^2$ b $y = x^2 + 4$

  c $y = x^2 - 1$ d $y = x^2 + 7$

  e $y = x^2 - 3$ f $y = x^2 - 8$

  g $y = x^2 + 0.5$ h $y = x^2 - 1.5$

⑦ Sketch the graphs of these equations.
Use a new set of axes for each graph.

  a $y = -x^2$ b $y = -x^2 + 1$

  c $y = -x^2 - 1$ d $y = -x^2 + 3$

  e $y = -x^2 - 2$ f $y = -x^2 - 0.5$

  g $y = -x^2 + 5$ h $y = -x^2 + 6$

Extension problem

⑧ Sketch the graphs of these equations on the same set of axes.
Label the graphs.

  a $y = x^2$ b $y = 2x^2$

  c $y = 3x^2$ d $y = 0.5x^2$

◉ Points to remember

⊙ The normal form of a **linear equation** is $y = ax + b$.
The graph of $y = ax + b$ is a straight line.
a gives the **gradient** of the line and b the **intercept** on the y-axis.

⊙ The graph of a **quadratic equation** $y = ax^2 + b$ is a U-shaped curve.
a changes the gradient of the curve and b moves the curve up or down.

6 Interpreting graphs

This lesson will help you to interpret graphs.

Exercise 6

When you see a real-life graph, first study the axes and decide what the scales represent.

Try to make sense of a graph before you answer any questions about it.

The graph below shows the temperature of water of the South Atlantic ocean as the water gets deeper.

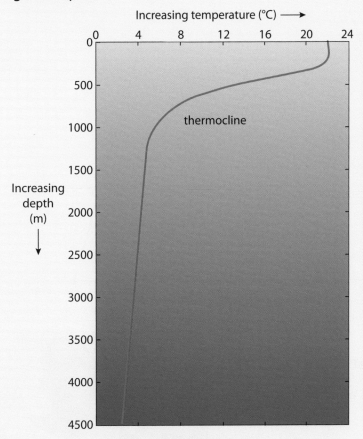

The horizontal scale shows temperature and the vertical scale shows the depth of the water.

It is easy to see from the graph where the water is warmer and where it is colder.

We could describe the 'story' of the graph like this.

For the first 250 metres, the water is a constant temperature of about 22°C.

After 250 metres, the water rapidly gets colder.

The temperature falls from about 22 °C at 250 metres to about 6 °C at 1000 metres.

At greater depths, the temperature drops steadily but more slowly to about 4 °C at 4500 metres.

1 This is a graph of William taking a day out on his bike.

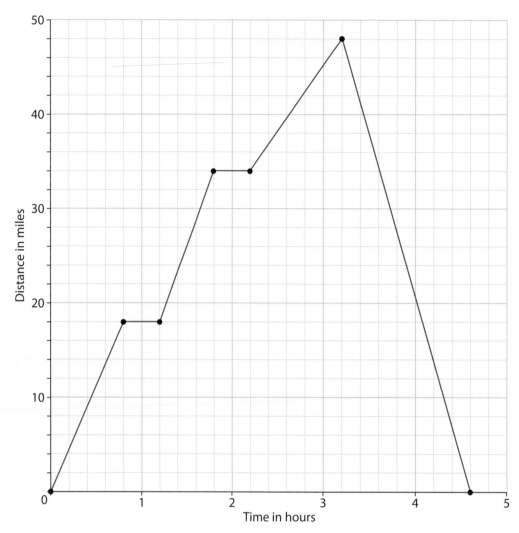

Distance in miles (y-axis: 0 to 50)
Time in hours (x-axis: 0 to 5)

a William left home at 09:30.
At what time did he arrive at his first stop?

b How far had William cycled when he first stopped?

c How long was William's first rest stop?

d How far had William cycled from home at 12:42?

e Which was William's fastest leg of the journey?

f Write a short story about William and his day out on a bike.

Make sure that you use the correct mathematical information from the graph.

2 This is a distance–time graph

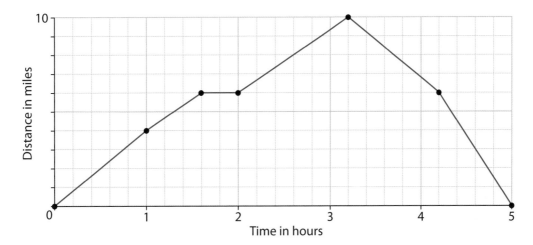

a Write a brief story, using all the information in this graph.

b Write five questions about the graph to ask a partner.

3 This graph shows how the volume of water in a tank, in litres, changes with time.

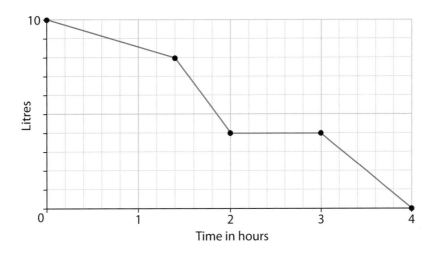

a Write a brief story, using all the information in this graph.

b Write five questions to ask a partner.

⊙ Points to remember

⊙ Before you interpret a graph, inspect the axes and work out the scales.

⊙ One graph can represent a number of different stories provided that the mathematical facts are correct.

7 Matching graphs to real-life situations

This lesson will help you to explore linear graphs of real-life contexts.

Exercise 7

When you read information from a graph of a real-life context, the first thing to do is to study the axes and decide what the scales represent.

Try to make sense of a graph before you answer any questions about it.

The graph below shows the percentage of salt in the water of the South Atlantic ocean as the water gets deeper.

The graph on the right shows that the water between 500 and 1000 metres is less salty than at other depths.

Why do you think the water is saltier at the surface?

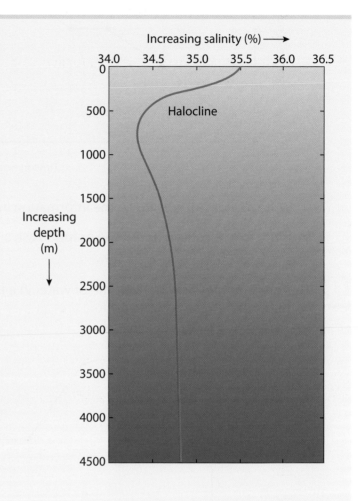

① For each of these, say which graph below has a shape that most accurately describes it.

a The distance travelled by an accelerating car, plotted against time.

b The number of litres of water left in a tank as it empties at constant speed, plotted against time.

c The distance travelled by a car as it applies its brakes, plotted against time.

d The distance travelled by a bicycle as it travels at constant speed, plotted against time.

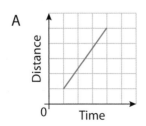
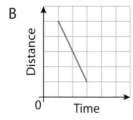
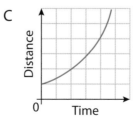
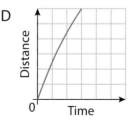

(2) Jessica's granddad gives her two pence on 1st January.

He says that he will give her double this on the first of the next month, and will keep on doubling the money for the next 12 months.

a   How much will Jessica's granddad give her on 1st June?

b   The graph shows how the amount of money increases over the twelve months.

Estimate from the graph how much Jessica's granddad gives her on 1st December.

c   Describe the shape of the graph.

d   Would it be sensible for Jessica's granddad to continue to double the money he gives her each month? Give reasons.

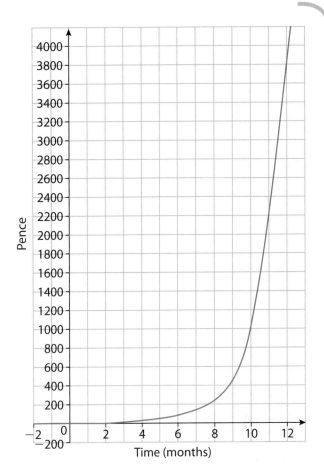

(3) Sketch graphs to show the depth of water against time when water runs steadily from a tap to fill each of these containers.

a

b

c

d

e

f

4 Sketch a graph to show the depth of water against time when water runs steadily from a tap to fill this vase.

5 A train starts off slowly from a station and accelerates until it reaches a speed of 120 mph.

It travels at this speed for an hour then gradually slows down until it stops at the next station.

Sketch a distance–time graph to show this journey.

Points to remember

⊙ Look at what is happening to a graph as the x-values increase by equal amounts.

⊙ Decide on the relationship between x and y before you try to fit a graph to a real-life situation.

8 Using graphs to solve problems

This lesson will help you see how you can use graphs to solve problems.

Exercise 8

When a linear equation is in the form $y = ax + b$,
then a is the gradient of the straight-line graph and $(0, b)$ is the intercept on the y-axis.

Example 1

$y = 3x + 1$

The gradient of the line is 3 and the intercept is $(0, 1)$.

Example 2

$y - 5x = 9$

First put the equation in its normal form.

$y = 5x + 9$

The gradient of the line is 5 and the intercept is (0, 9).

Example 3

Let x pence be the cost of a glass of cola and y pence the cost of a cake in a café.

Write an expression for the total cost of one order of six colas and five cakes and another order of four colas and three cakes.

Simplify your expression.

The first order is $6x + 5y$ and the second order is $4x + 3y$.

The total is $10x + 8y$.

For questions **9** and **10**, work with a partner.

You will need a **computer with graph-plotting software**, or a **graphics calculator**.

1 Write down the gradient and intercept on the y-axis for the graphs of these equations.

a $y = 7x + 5$
b $y = 4x - 3$
c $y - 2x = 9$
d $y + 5x = 1$
e $y - x - 10 = 0$
f $y + 3x + 9 = 0$
g $2y = 6x + 4$
h $3y + 9x - 12 = 0$

2 Sketch the graphs of these equations.

a $y = 2x + 1$
b $y = 3x - 2$
c $y - 3x = 5$
d $y + x = 10$
e $y - 2x - 7 = 0$
f $y + 5x + 1 = 0$
g $2y = 4x + 6$
h $5y + 15x - 25 = 0$

3 Which point lies on the graphs of both $y = 3x - 7$ and $y = 2x - 4$?

A $(2, -1)$ **B** $(1, -2)$ **C** $(5, 6)$ **D** $(3, 2)$

4 Which point lies on the graphs of both $y = 2x - 3$ and $y = -2x + 5$?

A $(3, 3)$ **B** $(2, 1)$ **C** $(1, 3)$ **D** $(4, 5)$

(5) Which point lies on the graphs of both $y = 3x + 2$ and $y = -x + 6$?

A (1, 5) **B** (3, 11) **C** (3, 3) **D** (2, 8)

(6) Let the mass of a tin of tomatoes be x grams and the mass of a packet of pasta be y grams.

Write expressions for the mass of these combinations.

a Four tins of tomatoes and two packets of pasta

b Nine tins of tomatoes and five packets of pasta

c Seven tins of tomatoes and three packets of pasta

(7) Let x pence be the cost of a glass of lemonade and y pence the cost of a sandwich in a café.

Write expressions for the total cost of each pair of orders.

Simplify your expressions.

a One order of four lemonades and three sandwiches and another order of three lemonades and six sandwiches

b One order of seven lemonades and four sandwiches and another order of five lemonades and five sandwiches

c One order of three lemonades and one sandwich and another order of eight lemonades and four sandwiches

(8) **a** Find two numbers whose difference is 24 and whose quotient is 4.

b Find two numbers whose sum is 63 and whose quotient is 8.

c Find two numbers x and y such that $3x + 2y = 22$ and $2x + 3y = 23$.

For the rest of the questions, work with a partner. Read the questions carefully.
Set up two equations. Use a **computer** or **graphics calculator** to draw the graphs.
Use the graphs to help solve the problem.

(9) Paul spends £51 on three CDs and two DVDs.
Sally spends £66 on two CDs and four DVDs.

What is the cost of five CDs and three DVDs?

(10) The junior Frisbee league awards points for winning or drawing a game.

Winston scores a total of 42 for six wins and four draws.
Chris scores a total of 27 for three wins and four draws.

How many points are awarded for a win?

11 A school shop sells fresh fruit.

8 apples and 9 bananas cost £3.35.
5 apples and 12 bananas cost £3.05.

What is the cost of one apple and one banana?

Extension problem

12 Work with a partner.

Use a **computer** or **graphics calculator** to help you find the values for x and y that satisfy these pairs of equations.

a $4x + y = 8$ and $3x + y = 10$

b $x + 2y = 8$ and $x + 5y = 17$

c $7x + 2y = 26$ and $3x - 2y = 14$

d $5x + 3y = 27$ and $2x + y = 10$

e $5x + 3y = 14$ and $8x + 2y = 14$

f $4x + 3y = 23$ and $2x + 5y = 29$

Points to remember

- For an equation in the form $y = ax + b$:
  - a is the gradient of its graph;
  - $(0, b)$ is the intercept on the y-axis.
- When you know two facts about two unknowns, you can form two equations.
- You can solve two linear equations by finding out where the graphs of the two equations cross.

How well are you doing?

Can you:

- factorise algebraic expressions?
- use graphs to solve equations?
- match graphs to real-life situations?
- use algebra to solve problems?

① Factorise the expression $20x - 28$.

② *2007 level 6*

Solve the equation $2(2n + 5) = 12$.

③ *2004 level 6*

Rearrange this equation to make t the subject.

$$5(2 + t) = w$$

④ *1997 level 6*

a The points $(-5, -2)$ and $(4, 7)$ lie on the same line.

If the line were extended, would it pass through point $(-100, -103)$?

Write **Yes** or **No**.
Explain how you know.

b Use x and y to write the equation of the line.

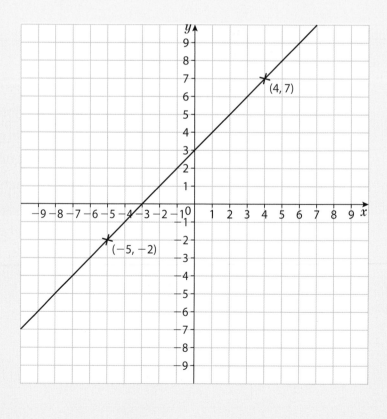

5 *2005 level 6*

I think of a number.

I multiply this number by 8, then subtract 66.

The result is twice the number that I was thinking of.

What is the number I was thinking of?

6 *2007 level 6*

Here are two equations.

$$k = a + b$$

$$a + b + k = 30$$

What is the value of k?

7 *1998 level 6*

Here are five containers:

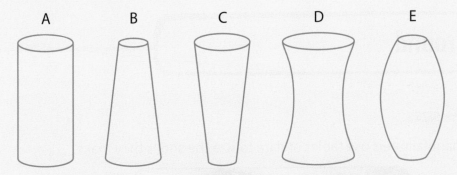

Water is poured at a constant rate into three of the containers.

The graphs show the depth of water as the containers fill up.

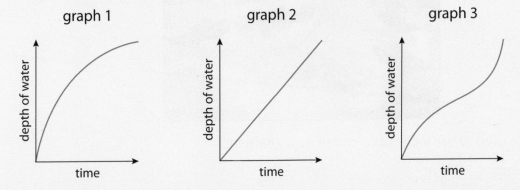

Copy and complete these sentences to show which container matches each graph.

Graph 1 matches container ....

Graph 2 matches container ....

Graph 3 matches container ....

Functional skills 4

Shoe sizes

This group activity will help you to:

- make an initial model of a situation using suitable forms of representation;
- decide on the methods, operations and tools to use, including ICT;
- consider how appropriate and accurate your results and conclusions are.

Background

UK shoe sizes

Shoe manufacturers use tables of data to size the shoes they make.

We used to use inches as a unit of measurement.

1 inch = 2.54 cm.

This table shows the length in inches of some shoe sizes.

Shoe size	2	$3\frac{1}{2}$	5	$6\frac{1}{2}$	8	$9\frac{1}{2}$	11
Length (inches)	9	$9\frac{1}{2}$	10	$10\frac{1}{2}$	11	$11\frac{1}{2}$	12

Is there a formula connecting a shoe's size to its length in inches?

Would it help to draw a graph? It might be helpful to use a spreadsheet.

Can you find a simple way to express the relationship?

Background

Continental shoe sizes

Sometimes shoes are sold with continental shoes sizes.

This table shows the length in millimetres of some continental shoe sizes.

Shoe size	33	34	35	36	37	38	39	40	41
Length (mm)	220	227	233	240	247	253	260	267	273

Problem 2

a Draw a graph and construct a formula relating continental shoe size and shoe length in centimetres.

b Make a table relating UK shoe sizes 2, $3\frac{1}{2}$, 5, …, 11 to the closest continental shoe size.

Be prepared to discuss your findings and their accuracy with other groups.

Probability 2

This unit will help you to:

- identify all the mutually exclusive outcomes of an experiment (outcomes that cannot occur at the same time);
- use lists and tables to record these outcomes in a systematic way;
- know that the sum of probabilities of these outcomes is 1;
- know that, if the probability of an event occurring is p, then the probability of it not occurring is $1 - p$;
- compare theoretical probabilities with estimated probabilities from experimental data.

1 Theoretical and experimental probability

This lesson will help you to work with experimental and theoretical probabilities.

Did you know that...?

Girolamo Cardano (1501–1576) was an Italian doctor and mathematician famous for his work on algebra.

He also wrote some of the earliest work on probability.

He is said to have made this statement about rolling a fair dice in a game of chance.

'Rolling a 3 is a 'natural occurrence' even when it occurs twice in two rolls but if a 3 is rolled for a third or fourth time a prudent man should treat it with suspicion'.

Exercise 1

Example 1

Two coins are spun at the same time.

a Write a list of all the possible outcomes. HH, HT, TH, TT

b What is the probability that one coin will show heads and the other tails?

There are 2 chances out of 4 of getting one head and one tail.

This is a probability of $\frac{2}{4} = \frac{1}{2}$.

Example 2

- Players choose three numbers from 1 to 6.

- Two dice are rolled.
  The numbers are added to give a total.

- If the dice total is one of a player's chosen numbers,
  they add it to their score.

- The winner is the player with the highest score after 12 turns.

Tom and Terri play the game.

Tom chooses 10, 11 and 12.
Terri chooses 6, 7 and 8.

The 12 dice totals in the game are 9, 7, 9, 12, 8, 10, 4, 6, 3, 4, 5 and 10.

a Give a possible reason for Tom's choice of
numbers.

They are the highest possible scores.

b Give a possible reason for Terri's choice of
numbers.

Terri made a table of all the possible scores
that could occur. She chose numbers that
are likely to occur more often.

First dice

+	1	2	3	4	5	6
1	2	3	4	5	6	7
2	3	4	5	6	7	8
3	4	5	6	7	8	9
4	5	6	7	8	9	10
5	6	7	8	9	10	11
6	7	8	9	10	11	12

Second dice

c Who won the game?

Tom's total score = 12 + 10 + 10 = 32

Terri's total score = 8 + 6 = 14

Tom won.

d What is the theoretical probability of getting a dice total of 9?

The table shows that there are 4 chances out of 36 of getting 9.

This is a probability of $\frac{9}{36} = \frac{1}{4}$.

e What is the experimental probability of getting a dice total of 9?

The 12 dice totals in the game were 9, 7, 9, 12, 8, 10, 4, 6, 3, 4, 5 and 10.

9 occurred twice.

This is a probability of $\frac{2}{12} = \frac{1}{6}$.

1 George is flying to Disney World on a jumbo jet.
A game on his personal TV screen has two windows.

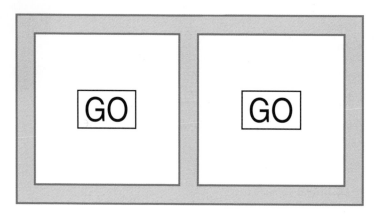

When George clicks on 'Go', in each window one of three pictures is equally likely to appear.

1 lemon

2 strawberries

3 cherries

When both windows show the same picture, this counts as a win, and he scores a point.

Estimate the probability of getting a win by simulating the game.

◉ Take three digit cards 1, 2 or 3. Put them face down and shuffle them.

◉ Pick a card. This represents the picture that appears in window 1.

◉ Replace the card, face down. Shuffle the cards again.

◉ Pick a card. This represents the picture that appears in window 2.

Decide how to record this result.

Decide how many times you are going to repeat the simulation.

Use your results to estimate the probability of getting a win of two matching pictures.

2 **a** Jamie played the game in question **1**. He clicked on 'Go' 75 times.
He scored 30 points.
Estimate the probability of getting two matching pictures from Jamie's score.

3 Tony has two bags of shopping.
One bag contains red apples and green apples.
The other bag contains white bread and brown bread.

One item is picked at random from each bag.
List all the possible combinations that could be chosen.

4 A basket of fruit contains apples, oranges and bananas.
Two fruits are chosen at random. List the possible outcomes.

5 Jacket potatoes are sold with cheese, beans or tomatoes.
Harry and Joe each buy a jacket potato.

a Copy and complete the table.

Harry	Joe
cheese	cheese
cheese	beans

b Work out the probability of:

  i Harry choosing beans

  ii Joe choosing beans

  iii Joe choosing not beans

  iv Harry choosing tomatoes and Joe choosing cheese

  v both choosing beans

  vi both choosing the same

  vii both choosing different

  viii both choosing not cheese.

6 Scoops of ice cream are strawberry, vanilla or chocolate.

Zita has a two-scoop ice cream.
Each flavour is picked at random.

a Record all the possible outcomes for the two scoops of Zita's ice cream.

b Find the probability that

  i the two scoops will be the same flavour

  ii one scoop will be strawberry and the other scoop will be vanilla.

7 This two-way table gives information about the hair colour of students in a school.

	Fair hair	Brown hair	Black hair	Total
Boys	96		35	
Girls		275		444
Total		500	100	

a Copy and complete the table.

b One of the students is to be picked at random.

  i Find the probability that the student picked will have brown hair.

  ii Find the probability that the student picked will be a boy who has fair hair.

Give your answers in their simplest forms.

Extension problem

8 Three fair coins are spun.

a Write a list of all eight possible outcomes.

b Find the probability that the three coins will land on the same side.

c Find the probability that the coins will show two heads and a tail.

d Write down the number of possible outcomes when:

  i four coins are spun   ii five coins are spun.

◉ Points to remember

⊙ For equally likely outcomes, the **theoretical probability** of an event is:

$$\frac{\text{number of favourable outcomes}}{\text{total number of possible outcomes}}$$

⊙ The **experimental probability** of an event is:

$$\frac{\text{number of successful trials}}{\text{total number of trials}}$$

⊙ Record all the outcomes of an experiment in a systematic way.

⊙ Different experiments can give different values of experimental probability.

⊙ Increasing the number of times an experiment is repeated generally leads to better estimates of probability.

2 Mutually exclusive events

This lesson will help you to understand when outcomes and events are mutually exclusive, and to find all the mutually exclusive outcomes of an experiment.

Exercise 2

Outcomes or events that cannot occur at the same time are called **mutually exclusive**.

Example 1

In a pack of playing cards there are 52 cards.

There are four suits: hearts, diamonds, spades and clubs.

Each suit contains 13 different cards:
ace, 2, 3, 4, 5, 6, 7, 8, 9, 10, jack, queen and king.

a   List the outcomes of the event 'picking a heart'.

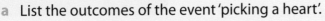

A♥   2♥   3♥   4♥   5♥   6♥   7♥   8♥   9♥   10♥   J♥   Q♥   K♥

b   Explain why 'picking a heart' and 'picking a club' are mutually exclusive.

A heart cannot be picked at the same time as a club.
The events have no outcomes in common.

c   List the outcomes of the event 'picking a king'.

K♣   K♠   K♦   K♥

d   Explain why the events of 'picking a king' and 'picking a heart' are *not* mutually exclusive.

The K♥ is an outcome common to both events, so the events can occur at the same time.

The sum of the probabilities of all mutually exclusive outcomes of an experiment is 1.

The probability of an event occurring and of the event **not** occurring add up to 1.

When two events are mutually exclusive, you can add their probabilities to find the probability of one event **or** the other occurring.

Example 2

A card is picked at random from a pack of cards.
What is the probability of picking an ace **or** a king?

The probability of picking a king is $\frac{4}{52}$.

The probability of picking an ace is $\frac{4}{52}$.

Since $\frac{4}{52} + \frac{4}{52} = \frac{8}{52}$, the probability of picking an ace or a king is $\frac{8}{52}$.

1   For each trial write whether or not the pairs of events are mutually exclusive.
Give a reason for each answer.

    a   Trial: Rolling a fair 1 to 6 dice
       Event 1:   Rolling a 6
       Event 2:   Rolling an odd number

    b   Trial: Rolling two fair dice
       Event 3:   Rolling a total of 10
       Event 4:   Rolling the same score on both dice

    c   Trial: Selecting a pupil at random
       Event 5:   Selecting a left-handed pupil
       Event 6:   Selecting a right-handed pupil

    d   Trial: Selecting a pupil at random
       Event 7:   Selecting a left-handed pupil
       Event 8:   Selecting a blue-eyed pupil

2   Kirsty spins the arrow on this fair spinner twice.
She writes down the letters that the arrow lands
on in order.

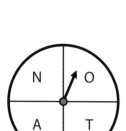

    a   Copy and complete this two-way table
to show all the outcomes.

First spin

		N	O	T	A
Second spin	**N**	NN	ON	TN	
	O	NO			
	T				
	A				

    b   What is the total number of possible outcomes?
Explain why they are mutually exclusive.

c Kirsty looks at these events:

Event 1: One of the two letters is a vowel.
Event 2: The two letters make a word.

List all the possible outcomes.
Explain why the two events are **not** mutually exclusive.

d Explain why the events 'both of the letters are vowels' and 'none of the letters are vowels' are mutually exclusive.

3 A fruit machine has two windows. In each window one of three different fruits – strawberry, apple and banana – is equally likely to appear.

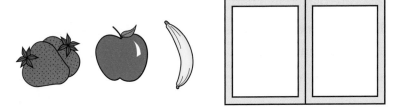

a Copy and complete this two-way table to show all the possible outcomes. Use S for 'strawberry', A for 'apple' and B for 'banana'.

Left window

Right window		S	A	B
	S			
	A			
	B			

b Show that the sum of the probabilities of all the outcomes is 1.

c Work out the probabilities of each of these events.

A An apple in the right-hand window

B A banana in the right-hand window

C The same fruit in both windows

D At least one banana

E No bananas

d Work out the probability of event A **or** event B occurring.

e Explain why the sum of the probabilities of events D and E is 1.

4 The outcomes for the trial rolling a fair dice are shown in this table.

Outcome	1	2	3	4	5	6
Probability	$\frac{1}{6}$					

a Copy and complete the table.

b Show that the sum of the probabilities of all the outcomes is 1.

c Show that the sum of the probabilities of 'rolling a 1' and 'not rolling a 1' is 1.

d What is the probability of rolling a 1 **or** a 2?

5 A number of discs are placed in a bag.

Some of the discs are marked with the numbers 1, 2, 3 or 4.
The rest of the discs are unmarked.

A disc is taken at random from the bag.

The probabilities of drawing each numbered disc are shown in the table.

Outcome	1	2	3	4
Probability	0.15	0.2	0.05	0.35

a What is the probability of taking a disc marked:

  i 1 **or** 2? ii 2, 3 **or** 4? iii with an even number?

b What is the probability of taking a disc *not* marked with a number?

Extension problem

6 In a school project on temperature a group of pupils classify each day as:

  'very cold', 'cold', 'warm', 'hot' or 'very hot'.

Using weather records they work out that in October:

The probability that a day is very cold **or** cold is 0.3.
The probability that a day is very cold is 0.05.
The probability that a day is warm is 0.4.

a What is the probability that a day in October is warm **or** cold?

b In October, the probability that a day is hot is twice the probability that it is very hot.

  Approximately how many days in October are likely to be very hot?

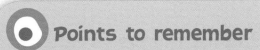

Points to remember

⊙ Outcomes that cannot occur at the same time are **mutually exclusive**.

⊙ The sum of the probabilities of all mutually exclusive outcomes of an experiment is 1.

⊙ If the probability of an event occurring is p, then the probability of it not occurring is $1 - p$.

⊙ If A and B are mutually exclusive events then:

probability of A **or** B = probability of A + probability of B

3 Using experimental probability

This lesson will help you to use probabilities to make informed choices.

Exercise 3

To work out the **experimental probability** of an event, record the outcomes of a repeated trial, then work out

$$\frac{\text{number of successful trials}}{\text{total number of trials}}$$

Use experimental probability:

☺ to work out probabilities when outcomes are not equally likely;

☺ to test whether the outcomes of an experiment are equally likely.

Example

Aliyah threw two coins 100 times. The results are shown in the table.

Outcome	HH	HT	TH	TT
Frequency	27	23	29	21

a Work out the experimental probabilities for each outcome.

The experimental probabilities are shown in the table.

Outcome	HH	HT	TH	TT
Probability	0.27	0.23	0.29	0.21

b Are the coins fair?

If the coins are fair the theoretical probability of each outcome is 0.25.

The experimental probabilities are close to this theoretical probability, so it is likely that the coins are fair.

Increasing the number of trials in an experiment generally leads to better estimates of probability, so more trials might confirm that the coins are fair.

Work with a partner.

1. You will need **a dice**.

A dice is rolled three times and the number of sixes thrown is recorded.

a **Experiment 1**

The trial is repeated 100 times.
The results are shown in this table.

Number of sixes	0	1	2	3
Frequency	57	30	11	2

Work out the experimental probability of each outcome.

b **Experiment 2**

Repeat the trial 50 times. Record your results in a tally chart.

Work out the experimental probability of each outcome.

c **Experiment 3**

Combine the results of experiment 1, experiment 2 and the outcomes from experiment 2 for one other pair to give a set of results for 200 trials.

Work out the experimental probability of each outcome.

d Which experiment is most likely to give the most reliable estimate of the probabilities? Explain your answer.

Extension problem

2. You will need **two sets of four cards**.
Each set should contain one card of each suit: ♣, ♠, ♦, ♥.

Select a card from each set at random. Record the results in a copy of this table.

Event	Tally	Frequency
Same suit		
Different suit		

a Repeat this trial 20 times.
Work out the experimental probability of each outcome.

b Repeat for a further 20 trials.
Work out the experimental probability for the combined set of 40 trials.

c Continue with more sets of 20 trials until you can complete this table.

Event	Experimental probability after …				
	20 trials	40 trials	60 trials	80 trials	100 trials
Same suit					
Different suit					

d Copy and complete this table to show all the equally likely outcomes of the experiment.

First card

e Work out the probability of each of these events.

A The two cards are from the same suit.

B The two cards are from different suits.

f Compare the theoretical and experimental probabilities of each event.
What do you notice?

Points to remember

⊙ **Experimental probability** is used when the outcomes of an experiment are not equally likely. It is:

$$\frac{\text{number of successful trials}}{\text{total number of trials}}$$

⊙ Experimental probability can also be used to test whether outcomes are equally likely.

⊙ Better estimates of probability are usually obtained by carrying out more trials.

⊙ When experiments are repeated, there are often different results.

4 Choice or chance?

This lesson will help you use probabilities to make informed choices when you play games of chance.

Did you know that...?

The more you know about probability, the better chance you have at winning some games.

The **Monty Hall Game** is an American TV game show. The host's name is Monty Hall.

In the game contestants try to win a car.

They are faced with three doors.

Behind one of the doors is the car but behind each of the other doors is a goat.

Initially, the contestant chooses one of the doors, without opening it.

Monty Hall knows where the car is.
He opens one of the other two doors to reveal a goat.

Contestants now have a choice.
They can stick with their original choice or change doors.
If they know the right strategy they can double their chance of winning.

1 Use cards from **S5.4 Resource sheet 4.1** (one car and two goats).

Simulate the Monty Hall game.
Play a number of times with a partner.

One of you should take the part of the contestant.
The other should be Monty Hall and set out the cards face down each time.

Design a tally chart to use to record the result of each game.
You will need to record whether you decided to Stick or Change,
and whether you won the car or lost the game.

○ Does sticking with the original door give a better chance of winning the car?

○ Does changing doors give a better chance of winning?

○ Does it make no difference?

Use your results to decide on the best strategy – to stick or to change.

Describe your strategy in your book.
Give a reason based on probability to support your decision.

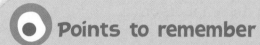

○ **Points to remember**

⊙ A knowledge of probability can be used to help make informed
choices when you play games of chance.

How well are you doing?

1. *1997 level 5*

   Karen and Huw each have three cards,
   numbered 2, 3 and 4.

   They each take any one of their own cards.
   They then add together the numbers on
   the two cards.

   The table shows all the possible answers.

   Karen

+	2	3	4
2	4	5	6
3	5	6	7
4	6	7	8

   (Huw — left vertical label)

   a What is the probability that their answer is an
     even number?

   b What is the probability that their answer is a
     number greater than 6?

   c Both Karen and Huw still have their three cards, numbered 2, 3 and 4.

     They each take any one of their own cards.
     They then multiply together the numbers on the two cards.

     Draw a table to show all possible answers.

   d Use your table to copy and complete these sentences:

     The probability that their answer is a number that is less than … is $\frac{8}{9}$.
     The probability that their answer is a number that is less than … is zero.

② *2000 level 6*

Here is a spinner with five equal sections.

Jane and Sam play a game.
They spin the pointer many times.

If it stops on an odd number, Jane gets 2 points.
If it stops on an even number, Sam gets 3 points.

Is this a fair game? Write **Yes** or **No**.
Explain your answer.

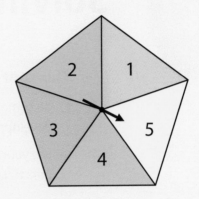

③ *1999 level 6*

A special dice has the numbers 1 to 6 on it.

It is in the shape of a cuboid so that a 6 or a 1
is less likely to come up than a 2, 3, 4 or 5.

- ⊙ The probability of rolling a 6 is 0.1.

- ⊙ The probability of rolling a 1 is 0.1.

- ⊙ The numbers 2, 3, 4 or 5 each have an equal
  probability of coming up.

Calculate the probability of rolling a 5 with this dice.

④ *1997 level 6*

A charity raffle sells red tickets, blue tickets and green tickets.

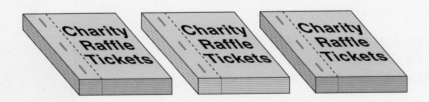

These tickets are sold:

- ⊙ Red ticket numbers 1 to 50

- ⊙ Blue ticket numbers 1 to 70

- ⊙ Green ticket numbers 1 to 80

a Calculate the probability that the ticket for the first prize has the number 63
  on it.

b Calculate the probability that the ticket for the first prize is blue.

Solving problems

This unit will help you to:

- ◉ do some research to find out how different cultures have influenced the development and history of mathematics;
- ◉ use your mathematical knowledge of calculations or algebra to solve unfamiliar problems;
- ◉ work logically and use mathematical reasoning;
- ◉ solve problems by breaking them into parts;
- ◉ find counter-examples to prove that a statement is not true.

1 History of our number system and zero

This lesson will help you to appreciate how different cultures have influenced the development and history of mathematics.

Did you know that...?

Many different mathematicians were connected with the development of the number system that we use today.

Here are the names of some of them:

Pythagoras, Brahmagupta, Al-Khwarizmi, Cardano, Fibonacci, Al-Uqlidisi, Xu Yue, Ch'in Chiu-Shao, Zhu Shijie.

The image on the right is of Fibonacci.

Exercise 1

① A magazine for Key Stage 3 pupils intends to publish a series of articles about these mathematicians.

Do some Internet research to find out more information about one of them. Make notes while you do this. Your teacher will suggest some useful websites.

For homework, you are to write an article for the magazine based on your notes.

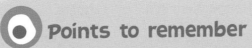
2 Number puzzles based on 3 by 3 grids

This unit will help you to use mathematical reasoning to solve problems, and to suggest extensions to problems.

Exercise 2

Use a set of 1–9 digit cards to help you.

1 In this 3 by 3 square, each of the digits 1 to 9 has been used.

- ⊙ The three-digit number in the middle row is double the number in the top row.

- ⊙ The three-digit number in the bottom row is three times the number in the top row.

Investigate other ways of doing it.
Record your results in your book.

1	9	2
3	8	4
5	7	6

2 Use all the digits 1 to 9.
Arrange them in a 3 by 3 square.

Make the three rows add up to 999.

Investigate different ways of doing it.
Record your results in your book.

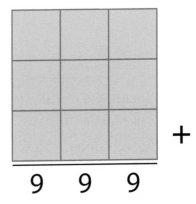

(3) Use all the digits 1 to 9. Arrange them in a 3 by 3 square.

Make the top row minus the middle row
equal the bottom row.

Investigate different ways of doing it.
Draw your results in your book.

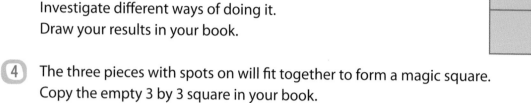

(4) The three pieces with spots on will fit together to form a magic square.
Copy the empty 3 by 3 square in your book.
Write where the numbers 2 to 10 should go.

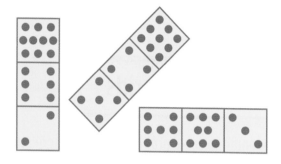

(5) The magic number of this magic square is 30.

Work out the value of a.

Draw an empty 3 by 3 square in your book.

Complete it to show the number in each cell.

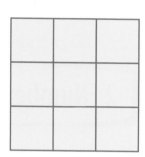

$a - 1$		$a + 3$
	a	
		$a + 1$

Extension problem

(6) This is a magic square.
Copy and complete it.

Yes! It can be done!

7		14
	11	

Points to remember

⊙ Decide which information could be useful.

⊙ Look for patterns and relationships.

⊙ Use reasoning to establish what might be possible in the context of the
problem and to help you to explain and justify your solution.

3 Exploring fractions

This lesson will help you to use mathematical reasoning to solve problems involving fractions, and to solve harder problems by breaking them into parts.

Exercise 3

Example

One fifth of a 10 metre by 10 metre vegetable plot is used for growing peas.
One quarter of the plot is used for growing carrots.
The rest is used for growing potatoes.

What is the size of the area that is used for growing potatoes?

The area of the vegetable plot is $10\,m \times 10\,m = 100\,m^2$.

The fraction of the plot that is used for growing potatoes is:

$$1 - \frac{1}{4} - \frac{1}{5} = \frac{20}{20} - \frac{5}{20} - \frac{4}{20} = \frac{11}{20}$$

So the area used for growing potatoes is $\frac{11}{20}$ of $100\,m^2 = 55\,m^2$.

You can solve the problems in this exercise by using fractions.
Explain and justify your answers by showing the calculations that you do with fractions.

1   The shapes in the diagrams below have been created by joining vertices or midpoints of the sides of a square. What fraction of the whole square is each lettered shape?

a
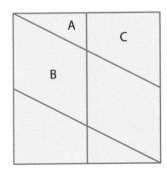

b
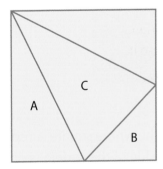

c
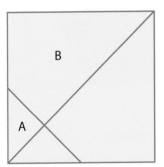

d

2 These diagrams are drawn on a square grid.
For each diagram, state what fraction is shaded and explain how you know.

a
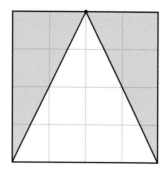

b
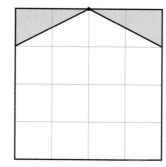

3 Copy this diagram.

Mark off and then shade three quarters of the whole square by drawing two straight lines, both starting at point X.

Find two different ways to do it.

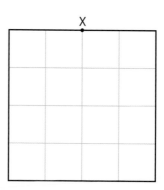

4 The shapes in the diagrams below have been formed by joining vertices or midpoints of the sides. What fraction of the whole shape is each lettered shape?

a
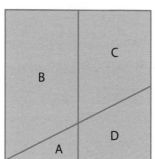

b
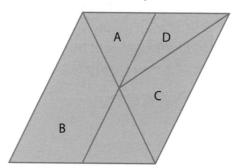

5 What fraction of the whole square is represented by each lettered shape?
In part **a**, the top side of the square is divided into one quarter and three quarters.

a
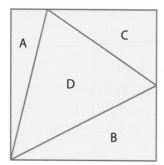

b
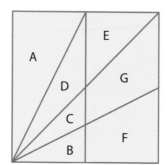

6 Draw more squares.
Join midpoints and corners to create other fractions.
Label each part of your shapes with the correct fraction.

> **⊙ Points to remember**
> - ⊙ Fractions can be used to describe and compare the size of areas of shapes.
> - ⊙ Showing how calculations with fractions are worked out can help to explain and justify solutions to problems.

4 Problems involving properties of numbers

This lesson will help you to solve harder problems by breaking them into parts and to use mathematical reasoning.

Exercise 4

1 You need a copy of **N5.4 Resource sheet 4.1**.
Complete the cross-number puzzle on the resource sheet.

2 Solve each of these problems. Explain clearly how you found your solution.

a Halve me, then add 10.
Find the square root.
The answer is 7.

Who am I?

b I am a two-digit number.
I am three less than a multiple of 7.
I am one less than a multiple of 8.
I am not divisible by 13.

Who am I?

c I have two digits.
I am a multiple of 4.
I am 27 less than my digits reversed.

Who am I?

d My three digits add up to 18.
Their product is a square number.
My first and last digits are the same.

Who am I?

e I have three digits.
The first and last are the same.
The product of my digits is a cube.
The sum of my digits is a square.

Who am I?

f I have three digits.
Each of my digits is a different prime.
I am the product of four primes.
The sum of these four primes is 30.

Who am I?

Did you know that...?

G. H. Hardy was an English mathematician who studied properties of numbers in the late 19th and early 20th centuries.

Hardy recognised the genius of an Indian mathematician, **Srinavasa Ramanujan**, and invited him to visit Cambridge.

While he was there, Ramanujan got TB (tuberculosis). Hardy took a taxi to visit him. He told Ramanujan that the taxi's number 1729 was 'not a very interesting number'.

'On the contrary,' said Ramanujan, 'it's very interesting. It's the smallest number that can be written as the sum of two cubes in *two different ways*.'

Ramanujan (1887–1920)

Ramanujan died from TB at the early age of 33.

It took until 1957 to find the smallest number that can be written as the sum of two cubes in *three different ways*. The number was discovered by the British mathematician **John Leech** (1926–1992) after a long computer search.

$$87\,539\,319 = 167^3 + 436^3 = 228^3 + 423^3 = 255^3 + 414^3$$

Nowadays, mathematicians define the smallest number that can be written as the sum of two cubes in n different ways as the nth **taxicab number**, or Taxicab(n).

So Taxicab(2) = 1729 and Taxicab(3) = 87 539 319.

Extension problems

 One way to write 1729 as the sum of two cubes is

$$1729 = 12^3 + 1^3$$

What is the other way?
Hint: Make a table of cube numbers from 1^3 to 12^3 to help you.

 1729 can also be written as the product of three prime numbers each less than 20. What are the three prime numbers?

Points to remember

⊙ Breaking problems into parts can help to find a suitable starting point.

⊙ Solutions to problems should be supported by examples, and by clear, written explanations that are easy to understand.

5 Using algebra and counter-examples

This lesson will help you to find an example to prove that a statement is not true, and to use algebra to solve problems.

Exercise 5A

Some number problems can be solved by writing an equation.

Example 1

96 kg of potatoes are divided between two sacks.
One sack has 14 kg of potatoes more than the other sack.
What is the mass of potatoes in each sack?

Let the mass of potatoes in one sack be x kg.
The mass in the other sack is $(x + 14)$ kg.

So $x + x + 14 = 96$
$$2x + 14 = 96$$
$$2x = 96 - 14$$
$$2x = 82$$
$$x = 41$$

So one sack contains 41 kg of potatoes and the other $41 + 14 = 55$ kg of potatoes.

Check $41 + 55 = 96$

To prove a statement is **not true**, you can find just one example where the result does not work. This is called finding a **counter-example**.

Example 2

Nasreen says that when you square a number the answer is the same as or bigger than the original number.

Show that Nasreen is wrong.

Try 1 $1^2 = 1$, which is the same as 1
Try 2 $2^2 = 4$, which is bigger than 2
Try 3 $3^2 = 9$, which is bigger than 3

Try -2 $(-2)^2 = 4$, which is bigger than -2
Try -3 $(-3)^2 = 9$, which is bigger than -3

Try some decimal numbers smaller than 1.
Try 0.5 $(0.5)^2 = 0.25$, which is smaller than 0.5

This is a **counter-example**, so Nasreen is wrong.

Showing that a statement is true in certain cases doesn't prove that it is always true.

It **verifies** that the statement is true in only those particular cases.

You can use step-by-step reasoning to **prove** that a statement is true.

Example 3

Prove that the sum of any three consecutive numbers is always a multiple of 3.

We can verify the result for some particular cases like this.

Try 1, 2, 3 $1 + 2 + 3 = 6 = 3 \times 2$
Try 8, 9, 10 $8 + 9 + 10 = 27 = 3 \times 9$
Try 50, 51 and 52 $50 + 51 + 52 = 153 = 3 \times 51$

We can prove the result like this.

Let the smallest of the consecutive numbers be n.
So the next two numbers are $n + 1$ and $n + 2$.
$n + (n + 1) + (n + 2) = 3n + 3 = 3(n + 1)$

So 3 is a factor of the sum of the numbers and the sum is a multiple of 3.

1. The sum of two consecutive numbers is 57. What are the numbers?

2. I think of a number, add 2 to it, and multiply the result by 5.
   The answer is 45.
   What is my number?

3. I think of a number, double it, and add 12.
   The answer is 28.
   What is my number?

4. The sum of three consecutive numbers is 9 more than the smallest number.
   What are the numbers?

5. Peter walked 4 miles.
   He then took a bus for a certain distance.
   He then went on a train for twice
   the distance he went by bus.

   Altogether, Peter travelled 70 miles.
   How far did he travel on the train?

(6) In a rugby match, the difference in the scores of two teams was 15 points.
The winning team scored four times as many points as the losing team.
What was the score in the match?

(7) In rugby, a try is 5 points and a goal is 3 points.
A team scored the same number of tries and goals.
Their total score was 40 points.
How many goals did the team score?

(8) In a rugby match, Patrick and Sean scored 37 points between them.
Patrick scored 15 points more than Sean.
How many points did Sean score?

Extension problems

(9) Wendy is four times older than Sarah.
In 24 years' time, she will be twice as old as Sarah.
How old is Sarah now?

(10) Ann, Bob and Tom shared £35 between them.
Ann had £10 more than Bob and twice as much as Tom.
How much did each of them get?

Exercise 5B

(1) Work with a partner to identify a counter-example to each statement.

   a All fruits have their seeds on the inside.

   b All birds can fly.

   c All metals are solids at normal temperatures.

   d Every word in the English language has a vowel.

   e No number words have the letter 'a' in them.

   f Years that have dates that are divisible by 4 are always leap years.

A clue!

(2) **a** Sharifa says that every prime number is odd.
Explain why Sharifa is wrong.

b Steve says that the sum of any two prime numbers is even.
Explain why Steve is wrong.

c Robert says the sum of any two multiples of 7 is always a multiple of 14.
Show that Robert is wrong.

(3) n stands for any positive integer.

a Kylie says that $2n^2$ is never a multiple of 3.
Prove that Kylie is wrong.

b Bashir says that $n^2 + n + 1$ is always a prime number.
Explain why Bashir is wrong.

(4) n is an odd number.
Explain why $n^2 + 1$ is always an even number.

(5) b is an even number.
Explain why $3b - 1$ is always an odd number.

Extension problems

(6) a is an odd number.
Explain why $(a + 1)(a + 2)$ is always an even number.

(7) n is an odd number and m is an even number.

a Explain why $m + n + 1$ is always an even number.

b Explain why $mn - 1$ is always an odd number.

◉ Points to remember

- When you solve a problem by writing an equation:
  - say what the letter you are using represents;
  - check that your answer fits the information in the question.
- Showing that a statement is true in particular cases doesn't prove that it is always true.
- To **prove** that a statement is true, use reasoning, with one statement following from another.
- Finding just one **counter-example** is enough to show that a statement is not true.

How well are you doing?

Solving problems (no calculator)

1. Amit says: 'When you add three odd numbers the answer is always even.'
   Is he correct?
   Write **Yes** or **No**.
   Explain how you know.

2. *2004 Key Stage 2 level 5*
   Liam thinks of a number.
   He multiplies the number by 5 and then subtracts 60 from the result.
   His answer equals the number he started with.
   What was the number Liam started with?

3. *2001 level 6*
   Write two decimals, each less than 1, which multiply to make 0.1.

   $\square \times \square = 0.1$

4. *2006 level 6*

   a Give an example to show the statement below is **not** correct.

When you multiply a number by 2, the answer is always greater than 2.

   b Now give an example to show the statement below is **not** correct.

When you subtract a number from 2, the answer is always less than 2.

   c Is the statement below correct for all numbers?

The square of a number is greater than the number itself.

   Write **Yes** or **No**. Explain how you know.

5 *2005 level 7*

A three-digit number is multiplied by a two-digit number.

How many digits could the answer have?

Write the minimum number of digits and the maximum number of digits that the answer could have.

Show your working.

Solving problems (calculator allowed)

6 *2005 level 6*

I think of a number.

I multiply this number by 8, then subtract 66.

The result is twice the number that I was thinking of.

What is the number I was thinking of?

Revision unit 1

This unit will help you to:

⊙ revise the work you have done so far during the year;

⊙ answer test questions.

Many of the questions are from National Curriculum test papers (SATs).

1 Using a calculator

This lesson will remind you how to estimate and calculate efficiently.

Exercise 1

Use rounding to estimate results of calculations.

In general, round numbers as follows.

Numbers between:	Round to the nearest:	Example:
100 and 1000	multiple of 100	$642.78 \approx 600$
10 and 100	multiple of 10	$52.3 \approx 50$
1 and 10	whole number	$8.573 \approx 9$
0.1 and 1	tenth	$0.427 \approx 0.4$
0.01 and 0.1	hundredth	$0.0871 \approx 0.09$

The sign $\approx$ means 'is approximately equal to'.

It is important that you know how to use your calculator efficiently.

You should be able to use the four basic function keys $+, -, \times, \div$, the square and square-root keys and the key for powers.

Besides these, you should be able to use the sign-change key, the fraction key, bracket keys and the memory.

Calculators vary. The way that calculations are keyed in may be different on your calculator.

Example 1

Calculate $\sqrt{18.5^2 - 3.5^2}$.

Here are two different ways to key in this calculation using the square-root, bracket and square keys.

√ (1 8 . 5 x^2 − 3 . 5 x^2) =

(1 8 . 5 x^2 − 3 . 5 x^2) √ =

The display should show: 18.16590212

Give your answer to a sensible number of decimal places.

Answer: 18.17 to 2 d.p.

Example 2

Calculate $(1\frac{3}{10} - \frac{4}{5}) \times \frac{3}{4}$.

Using the fraction button $a^b/_c$ key in:

(1 $a^b/_c$ 3 $a^b/_c$ 1 0 − 4 $a^b/_c$ 5) × 3 $a^b/_c$ 4 =

The display should show: 3/8 which represents $\frac{3}{8}$.

Answer: $\frac{3}{8}$

---

1   Estimate the answer. Show your working.

a 49^2

b $\sqrt{79}$

c 4.2^3

d $\sqrt{390.6}$

e $(0.032)^2$

f 6.85×4.6

g $48.6 \div 1.9$

h 0.042×0.61

i $0.85 \div 0.091$

j $\dfrac{21.3 - 1.1}{30.6 - 10.7}$

k $\left(\dfrac{2.89 \times 1.9}{1.7}\right)^2$

l $\sqrt{\dfrac{4.87 \times 18.7}{0.9 \times 3.8}}$

Use your calculator. Round answers to a suitable number of decimal places where appropriate.

2   Use the bracket and/or memory keys to work out:

a $\dfrac{48.7 - 33.1}{4.32 + 0.88}$

b $\sqrt{0.41^2 - 0.09^2}$

c $9.75 \div (13.1 - 11.6)$

3   Use the fraction key to work out:

a $\frac{1}{8} + \frac{3}{16} + \frac{2}{5}$

b $1\frac{2}{5} + 2\frac{2}{9} - \frac{2}{3}$

c $\frac{3}{8} \times \frac{4}{15} \div \frac{2}{9}$

4   Use the power and root keys to work out:

a $\sqrt{3^5 + 5^3}$

b $\sqrt[3]{1331}$

c 5.2×2.17^3

(5) Solve these problems.

a A crate holds 315 apples.
66 000 apples are to be packed in crates.

How many crates can be packed with apples?
How many apples will be left over?

b A factory uses a 50 kg sack of flour to make cakes.
Each cake needs 127 g of flour.

How many cakes can be made from the flour?
How many grams of flour will be left over?

(6) *2005 level 5*

Use your calculator to work out the answers.

a $(48 + 57) \times (61 - 19) =$

b $\dfrac{48 + 57}{61 - 19} =$

(7) **a** Find the area A of a trapezium, given that
$A = \frac{1}{2}(a + b) \times h$, and $a = 2.1$ m, $b = 3.8$ m and $h = 2.7$ m.

b Find the circumference C of a circle, given that
$C = 2\pi r$, and $r = 6.25$ cm.

c Find the volume V of a cylinder, given that
$V = \pi r^2 h$, and $r = 7.2$ cm and $h = 9.15$ cm.

d *2005 level 6*

About 2000 years ago, a Greek mathematician
worked out this formula to find the area of
any triangle.

A triangle has sides, in cm, of 3, 5 and 6.
Use $a = 3$, $b = 5$ and $c = 6$ to work out the
area of this triangle.

> For a triangle with sides a, b and c
>
> Area $= \sqrt{s(s - a)(s - b)(s - c)}$
>
> where $s = \dfrac{a + b + c}{2}$

 Points to remember

⊙ Estimate the answer to a calculation before you use a calculator. Check
your calculator answer against your estimate.

⊙ Add brackets, if needed, before you enter calculations in a calculator.

⊙ Make sure that you can use your calculator keys for fractions, powers and
roots, brackets and the memory.

⊙ Make sure that you know how to deal with remainders on a calculator.

⊙ Include units in answers to problems where necessary.

2 Using percentages to compare proportions

This lesson will remind you how to use percentages to compare proportions.

Exercise 2

A **proportion** is usually given as a fraction or percentage.

Take account of the totals when you compare proportions.

Example

A school has 1800 pupils. 860 of these pupils are girls.

75% of the girls like swimming. 70% of the boys like swimming.

Do more girls or more boys like swimming?

There are 860 girls. 75% of them like swimming.

75% of $860 = \frac{75}{100} \times 860 = 645$

There are 940 boys. 65% of them like swimming.

70% of $940 = \frac{75}{100} \times 940 = 658$

Answer: More boys like swimming.

① **Without using a calculator**, work out what percentage the first number is of the second.

   a 13, 25   **b** 17, 20   **c** 22, 40   **d** 8, 200

   Use a calculator to work out what percentage the first number is of the second.

   e 27, 60   **f** 66, 120   **g** 133, 190   **h** 81, 180

② There are about 60 million people in the UK.
The table shows roughly what percentage of people in the UK are in different age groups.

Under 15	15–39	40–59	Over 59
19%	35%	25%	21%

How many of the 60 million people are there in each age group?

3 The answer to each calculation is 60. Find the value represented by each letter.

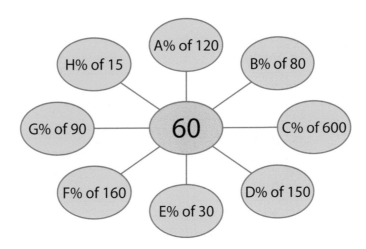

4 *1997 level 6*

The cost of an old toy vehicle depends on its condition and on whether it is in its original box.

Condition	Value
excellent, and in its box	100%
good, and in its box	85%
poor, and in its box	50%
excellent, but not in its box	65%
good, but not in its box	32%
poor, but not in its box	15%

A Mail Van in excellent condition, and in its original box, costs £125.

a How much is a Mail Van in good condition, and in its box?

b How much is a Mail Van in good condition, but not in its box?

c A Petrol Tanker in excellent condition, and in its box, costs £152.

Another Petrol Tanker should be sold for £98.80.
Using the chart above, what is its condition and does it have a box?

5 This is the nutritional information for a 60 g serving of Goldflakes, and a 40 g serving of Brancrunch breakfast cereal.

Goldflakes: 60 g provides	
Energy	256 kcal
Protein	14 g
Carbohydrate	45 g
Fat	6 g
Fibre	7.5 g
Salt	2 g

Brancrunch: 40 g provides	
Energy	169 kcal
Protein	10 g
Carbohydrate	25 g
Fat	3 g
Fibre	11 g
Salt	1.5 g

a Which serving of cereal has a higher proportion of protein?

b Which serving of cereal has a higher proportion of carbohydrate?

c Which serving of cereal has a higher proportion of fat?

d Which serving of cereal has a higher proportion of fibre?

e Which serving of cereal has a higher proportion of salt?

6 *1998 level 5*

These pie charts show the ages of people in Ireland and in Greece.

There are about 3.5 million people in Ireland, and about 10 million people in Greece.

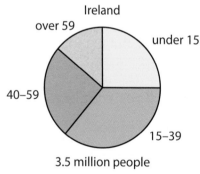

3.5 million people

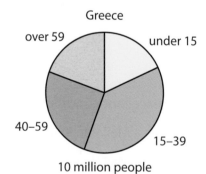

10 million people

a Roughly what percentage of people in Greece are aged 40−59?

b There are about 10 million people in Greece.
Roughly how many of the 10 million people in Greece are aged 40−59?

c Dewi says: 'The charts show that there are more people under 15 in Ireland than in Greece.'

Dewi is wrong. Explain why the charts do not show this.

7 All the children at two primary schools chose their favourite soup.

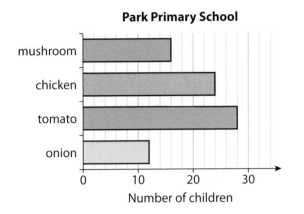

Park Primary School

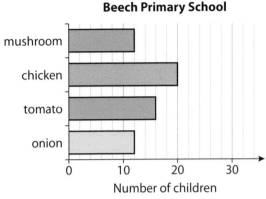

Beech Primary School

a How many children attend Park Primary School?

b How many children attend Beech Primary School?

c What percentage of children at Park Primary School prefer mushroom soup?

d What percentage of children at Beech Primary School prefer mushroom soup?

e Joe says: 'The charts show that the school with a higher proportion of children who prefer chicken soup is Park Primary School.'

Explain why Joe is wrong.

f Which school has a higher proportion of children who prefer tomato soup?

Explain your answer.

g Which school has a higher proportion of children who prefer onion soup?

Explain your answer.

 Points to remember

⊙ A proportion is a fraction or percentage.

⊙ When you use percentages to compare proportions in two sets of data, take account of the whole total in each data set.

When you solve problems:

⊙ always write down the calculation that you need to do;

⊙ check that the answer is reasonable;

⊙ interpret your answer to fit the question.

3 Sequences, equations and graphs

This lesson will remind you how to find the nth term of a linear sequence, solve linear equations and plot the graphs of simple linear functions.

Exercise 3A

You can work out an expression for the nth term of a linear sequence if you know the difference between consecutive terms.

Example 1

Write an expression for the nth term of the sequence 3, 7, 11, 15, 19, …

Sequence   3   7   11   15   19   …

Difference   4   4   4   4   …

The nth term is $4n - 1$.

Check your answer using substitution. For example, to find the 5th term, substitute $n = 5$.

The 5th term: $4 \times 5 - 1 = 19$, which is correct.

You can use the formula for the nth term of a sequence to work out any term.

Example 2

The nth term of a sequence is $4n - 3$. What is the 25th term?

Substituting $n = 25$ into the expression $4n - 3$ gives $4 \times 25 - 3 = 97$.

① *2006 level 5*

Look at this sequence of patterns made with hexagons.

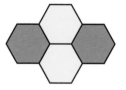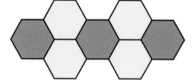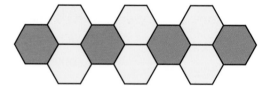

Pattern number 1   Pattern number 2   Pattern number 3

To find the number of hexagons in pattern number n you can use these rules:

> Number of blue hexagons $= n + 1$
>
> Number of cream hexagons $= 2n$

Altogether, what is the total number of hexagons in pattern number 20?

2 *2001 level 6*

Here is a sequence of patterns made from octagons and squares.

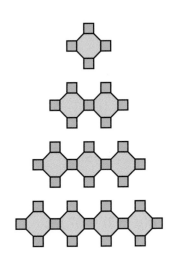

Number of octagons (n)	Number of squares (q)
1	4
2	7
3	10
4	13

The sequence continues.

a q represents the number of squares.

n represents the number of octagons.

What is the rule connecting q and n?

b How many squares will there be in the pattern that has 40 octagons?

3 *2006 level 5*

Look at the three expressions below.

$$8 + k \qquad\qquad 3k \qquad\qquad k^2$$

When $k = 10$, what is the value of each expression?

a $8 + k$

b $3k$

c k^2

4 *Year 8 Optional Test level 6*

Work out the value of $(a + b)(a - b)$ when $a = 6.5$ and $b = 3.5$.

1999 level 6

a Copy the rectangles.

Write an expression for each missing length.
Write each expression as simply as possible.

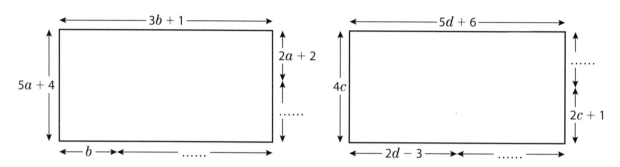

b The length of one side of a different rectangle is y.

This equation shows the area of the rectangle: $y(y + 2) = 67.89$.

Find the value of y and show your working.
You may find it helpful to make a table starting like this.

y	$y + 2$	$y(y + 2)$	
8	10	80	too large

Exercise 3B

Did you know that...?

The first algebra book written in English was *The Whetstone of Witte* by **Robert Recorde** in 1557.

The equals sign '=' was used for the first time in this book. Before this, people used to write 'eq.' which was short for the Latin for 'is equal to'.

On the right is the page where the equals sign is used. The writing is hard to read but the last paragraph says:

'And to avoid tedious repetition of the words "is equal to", I will use a pair of parallels of one length, thus =====, because no two things can be more equal.'

The **equals sign** in an equation is like a balance.

When you rearrange an equation you must keep it in balance.

What you do to one side you must do to the other side.

Example 1

Solve $3x + 5 = 17$.

To solve the equation you can use the inverse function.

$$3x + 5 = 17 \qquad x \rightarrow \boxed{\times 3} \rightarrow \boxed{+5} \rightarrow x$$

Subtract 5 from both sides: $\qquad 3x = 12 \qquad 4 \leftarrow \boxed{\div 3} \leftarrow \boxed{-5} \leftarrow 17$

Divide both sides by 3: $\qquad\qquad x = 4$

The equation $y = ax + b$ is a **linear equation**.

The coefficient of x is a. This gives the gradient of the graph of the equation.

The number b gives the point $(0, b)$ where the line intercepts the y-axis.

Example 2

What is the gradient of the line $y = 5x - 4$?

What is the intercept of the y-axis?

The equation $y = 5x - 4$ is in the form $y = ax + b$.

The gradient of its straight-line graph is 5 and the intercept on the y-axis is $(0, -4)$.

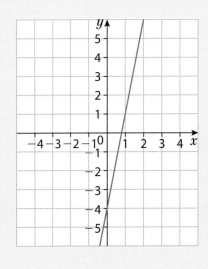

---

1 *2006 level 5*

Solve these equations.

a $2k + 3 = 11$ **b** $2t + 3 = -11$

2 *2006 level 6*

Look at this equation: $3a + 20 = 4a + k$.

a If $a = 15$, find the value of k.   **b** If $a = -15$, find the value of k.

3 *2006 level 6*

Solve this equation.

$3y + 14 = 5y + 1$

4 *2003 level 6*

The diagram shows a square drawn on a square grid.

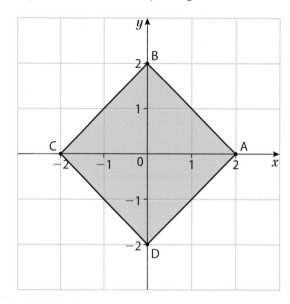

Points A, B, C and D are at the vertices of the square.

The line $y = 0$ passes through the vertices A and C.

Which two vertices of the square do these lines pass through?

a $x = 0$ **b** $x + y = 2$ **c** $x + y = -2$

Extension problem

5 *2003 level 5*

Find the values of t and r.

a $\dfrac{2}{3} = \dfrac{t}{6}$ **b** $\dfrac{2}{3} = \dfrac{5}{r}$

⦿ **Points to remember**

- The difference between consecutive terms of a linear sequence can help you to find the nth term.

- In algebra, letters represent numbers.

- When you solve an equation, what you do to one side you must do to the other side.

- For a graph, the x-axis is the line $y = 0$ and the y-axis is the line $x = 0$.

4 Angles and polygons

This lesson will remind you how to calculate angle sums of polygons and solve problems using properties of angles, triangles and other polygons.

Exercise 4

The diagrams show pairs of parallel lines cut by a transversal.

Equal angles are formed.

The diagram on the left shows a pair of **corresponding angles.**

The diagram on the right shows a pair of alternate angles.

a
b

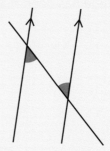

You can use what you know about angles to solve problems. Always give reasons for the statements that you make.

Example 1

Calculate the missing angles in this diagram.
Give reasons for your answers.

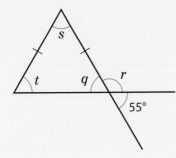

$r = 180° - 55° = 125°$ (angles on a straight line)

$q = 55°$ (angles on a straight line)

$t = 55°$ (base angle of an isosceles triangle)

$s = 180° - 55° - 55° = 70°$ (angle sum of triangle is 180°)

Example 2

Calculate the angle sum of a nine-sided polygon (a nonagon).

The angle sum of a polygon with n sides is $180° \times (n - 2)$.

Substituting $n = 9$, gives the angle sum as:

$180 \times (9 - 2) = 180 \times 7 = 1260°$.

1 *2004 level 5*

   a A pupil measured the angles in a triangle.

       She said: 'The angles are 30°, 60° and 100°.'

       Could she be correct? Write **Yes** or **No**.
Explain your answer.

   b This diagram is not drawn accurately.

       Calculate the size of angle *m*.

       Show your working.

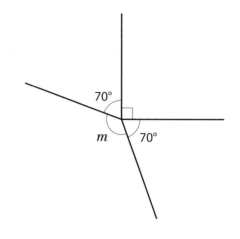

2 *2005 level 6*

This shape has been made from two congruent isosceles triangles.

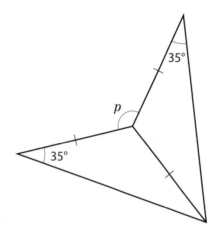

What is the size of angle *p*?

3 *2004 Mental Test level 6*

The diagram shows a pair of parallel lines.

The angle marked is 140°.

Copy the diagram.

Mark two different angles that are 40°.

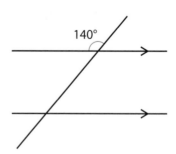

4 *2003 Mental Test level 6*

The diagram shows a rhombus.
The angle marked *x* is 75°.

What is the size of the angle marked *y*?

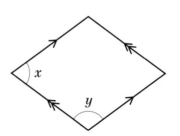

5 *2000 level 6*

a Any quadrilateral can be split into 2 triangles.

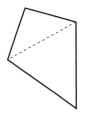

Explain how you know that the angles inside a quadrilateral add up to 360°.

b What do the angles inside a pentagon add up to?

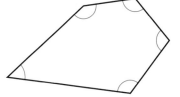

c What do the angles inside a heptagon (7-sided shape) add up to?

Show your working.

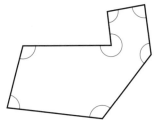

6 *2006 level 6*

Look at the diagram, made from four straight lines.

The lines marked with arrows are parallel.

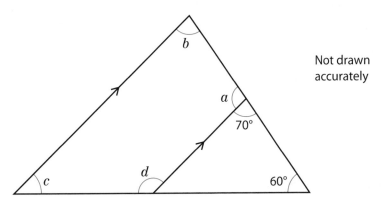

Not drawn accurately

Work out the size of angle *a*, angle *b*, angle *c* and angle *d*.

7 *2002 level 6*

The diagram shows a right-angled triangle and three parallel lines.

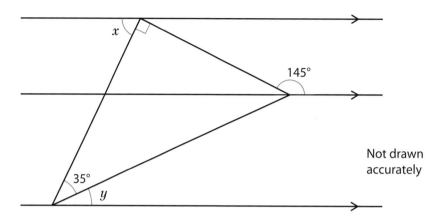

Not drawn accurately

Work out the size of angle x and angle y.

8 *2003 level 6*

The drawing shows how shapes A and B fit together to make a right-angled triangle.

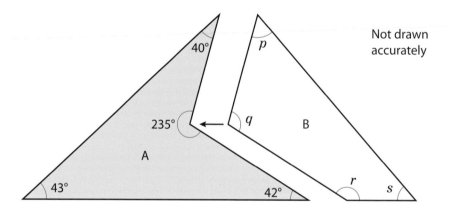

Not drawn accurately

Work out the size of each of the angles p, q, r and s in shape B.

5 Charts and diagrams

This lesson will remind you how to draw and interpret frequency diagrams, pie charts and stem-and-leaf diagrams, and to compare sets of data.

Exercise 5

Data can be shown in a **stem-and-leaf diagram**.

From this, the mode, median and range can be found easily.

Example 1

The ages, in years, of eleven people are:

12   9   20   24   15   17   31   4   15   17   28.

Draw a stem-and-leaf diagram to show these ages.

Stem	Leaves
0	4 9
1	2 5 5 7 7
2	0 4 8
3	1

Key: 1 | 2 means age 12

The key is part of the diagram. The stem shows the tens and the leaves show the units.

A **frequency diagram** can be drawn from continuous data.

It is similar to a bar chart but represents continuous data so there is no gap between the bars.

There is a scale on the horizontal axis rather than a label under each bar.

Example 2

The grouped frequency table shows information about the heights of 42 pupils.

a   Write down the modal class interval.

The modal class interval is $165 \leqslant h < 170$.
This has the highest frequency of 14.

Height (h cm)	Frequency
$160 \leqslant h < 165$	10
$165 \leqslant h < 170$	14
$170 \leqslant h < 175$	8
$175 \leqslant h < 180$	5
$180 \leqslant h < 185$	3
$185 \leqslant h < 190$	2

b Draw a frequency diagram to represent this information.

The frequency is on the vertical axis.
There are no gaps between the bars.

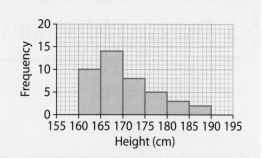

To draw a **pie chart** you must work out the size of the angle for each sector.

Example 3

The table shows the favourite colour of each of 30 pupils.

Draw a pie chart to represent this information.

Colour	Red	Blue	Yellow	Green
Frequency	9	14	4	3

$360 \div 30 = 12$, so $12°$ represents 1 pupil.

Red	$9 \times 12 = 108°$
Blue	$14 \times 12 = 168°$
Yellow	$4 \times 12 = 48°$
Green	$3 \times 12 = 36°$

To draw the pie chart, draw a circle and mark the centre.

Draw a radius and from this line, use a protractor to measure the angle of the sector for the colour red.

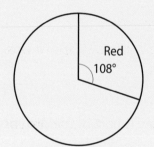

Use a protractor to measure the angles for all the other sectors.

Remember to label each sector of the pie chart.

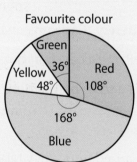

Favourite colour

---

① A company records the number of emails it receives each day.

Here are its results for the last 20 days.

178	189	147	147	166	167	153	171	164	158
189	166	165	155	152	147	158	148	151	172

a Draw a stem-and-leaf diagram to show this information.

b Use your stem-and-leaf diagram to find the median number of emails.

2 *2005 level 6*

Bumps are built on a road to slow cars down.

The stem-and-leaf diagrams show the speed of 15 cars before and after the bumps were built.

	Before				
2					
2	7	8			
3	0	2	4		
3	5	6	8	9	
4	1	3	4	4	4
4	6				

	After					
2	3	4	4			
2	6	6	7	8	8	9
3	0	0	0	1	2	
3	5					
4						
4						

Key: 2 | 3 means 23 mph

Use the diagrams to complete these sentences. Write the sentences in full.

a Before the bumps:

The maximum speed was …… mph, and …… cars went at more than 30 mph.

b After the bumps:

The maximum speed was …… mph, and …… cars went at more than 30 mph.

3 *1996 level 6*

A school has five year groups.

80 pupils took part in a sponsored swim.

Lara drew this graph.

a Did Year 10 have fewer pupils taking part in the swim than Year 7?

Choose an answer from **Yes**, **No**, **Cannot tell**. Explain your answer.

b Use the graph to work out the mean number of lengths swum by each of the 80 pupils.

Show your working.

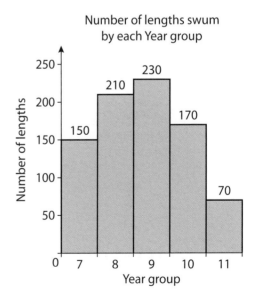

Number of lengths swum by each Year group

The two diagrams show the heights of some girls and boys.

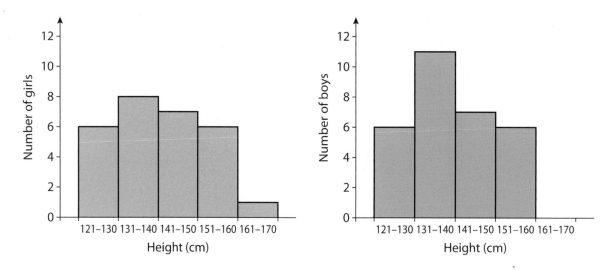

a Use the diagrams to decide whether these statements are true or false.

   i 'There are more girls than boys.'
   Show calculations to explain how you know.

   ii 'The modal class for girls is the same as the modal class for boys.'
   Explain how you know.

b The height of the shortest girl is the same as the height of the shortest boy.

   Is the range of girls' heights greater than the range of boys' heights?
   Explain how you know.

The pie charts show how pupils answered three questions about teachers.

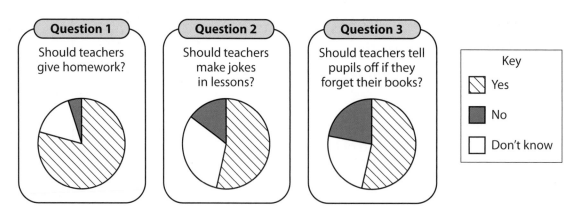

a What was the least common answer to question 2?

b What was the modal answer to question 3?

c About what proportion of pupils answered 'Yes' to question 1?

6 *2003 level 6*

Two beaches are very similar.

A survey compared the number of animals found in one square metre on each beach.

One beach had not been cleaned. The other beach had been cleaned.

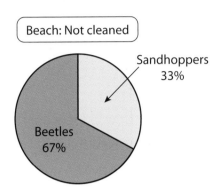

Beach: Not cleaned
Sandhoppers 33%
Beetles 67%

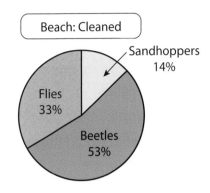

Beach: Cleaned
Sandhoppers 14%
Flies 33%
Beetles 53%

a The data for the beach that had not been cleaned represent 1620 animals.

Copy and complete the table to show how many of each animal were found.

Beach: Not cleaned

	Number found
Sandhoppers	
Beetles	
Flies	

b The data for the beach that had been cleaned represent 15 animals.

Complete the table to show how many of each animal were found on the cleaned beach.

Beach: Cleaned

	Number found
Sandhoppers	
Beetles	
Flies	

c Cleaning the beach changes the numbers of animals and the proportions of animals.

Write a sentence to describe both these changes.

(7) *2004 level 6*

   a A teacher asked her pupils if they recycled newspapers and glass.

    The pie chart shows the results.

    5 pupils answered 'Neither'.
How many pupils answered 'Newspapers only'?
Show your working.

   b The teacher asked a different class if they recycled newspapers and glass.

    There were 24 pupils in the class. 9 pupils answered 'Newspapers only'.

    On a pie chart, what would the angle be for the sector 'Newspapers only'?
Show your working.

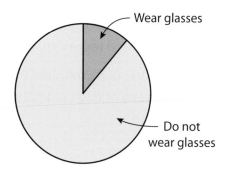

(8) *2001 level 6*

   There are 60 pupils in a school.
6 of these pupils wear glasses.

   a The pie chart is not drawn accurately.
What should the angles be?

    Show your working.

   b Exactly half of the 60 pupils in the school are boys.

    What percentage of boys in this school wear glasses?

    Choose your answer from the following:

    5%   6%   10%   20%   50%   Not possible to tell

◉ Points to remember

⊙ In a **pie chart**:

  – the angle at the centre of the circle is proportional to the frequency
for that category;

  – the number of degrees for one item is 360° ÷ total number of items.

⊙ A **stem-and-leaf diagram** shows data in order from lowest to highest.
You can use it to work out the mode, median and range.

Revision unit 2

This unit will help you to:

- ⊙ revise the work you have done so far during the year;
- ⊙ answer test questions.

Many of the questions are from National Curriculum test papers (SATs).

1 Ratio and proportion

This lesson will remind you how to solve problems involving ratio and proportion.

Exercise 1

A **ratio** compares two quantities in the same units.

The ratio 50p : £1 is 1 : 2; 200 : 50 = 4 : 1.

Example 1

Divide £28 in the ratio 1 : 2 : 4.

Since $1 + 2 + 4 = 7$, the three parts are $\frac{1}{7}$, $\frac{2}{7}$ and $\frac{4}{7}$ of £28.

The first part is $\frac{1}{7}$ of £28 = £4.

The second part is $\frac{2}{7}$ of £28 = £8.

The third part is $\frac{4}{7}$ of £28 = £16.

Two quantities are **directly proportional** if their ratio is always the same.

Example 2

For 80 g of jam you need 50 g of sugar. How much sugar do you need for 400 g jam?

Unitary method

First find how much sugar is needed for 1 g of jam.

	jam (g)	sugar (g)
	80	50
÷80	1	$50 \div 80 = 0.625$
×400	400	$0.625 \times 400 = 250$

Answer: 250 g of sugar will make 400 g of jam.

1 *2005 level 6*

The screens of widescreen and standard televisions look different.
They have different proportions.

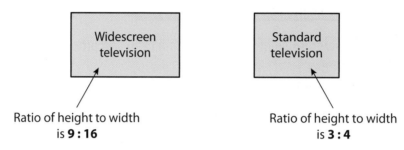

Ratio of height to width is **9 : 16**

Ratio of height to width is **3 : 4**

Keri starts to draw scale drawings of the televisions.
For each, the height is 4.5 cm.

a What should the width of the scale drawing for the widescreen television be?

b What should the width of the scale drawing for the standard television be?

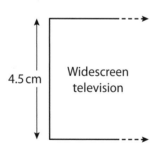

4.5 cm — Widescreen television

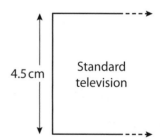

4.5 cm — Standard television

2 *1999 level 6*

a Use £1 = 9.6 Swiss francs to work out how much 45p is in Swiss francs.
Show your working.

b Use 240 Japanese yen = £1 to work out how much 408 yen is in pounds.
Show your working.

c Use £1 = 9.6 Swiss francs and £1 = 240 Japanese yen to work out how much
1 Swiss franc is in Japanese yen. Show your working.

3 *1995 level 6*

a Last summer, Ravi carried out a survey of the birds in the school garden.

He saw 5 pigeons, 20 crows, 25 seagulls and 45 sparrows.

Copy and complete the line below to show the ratios.

Pigeons	:	Crows	:	Seagulls	:	Sparrows
1	:	………	:	………	:	………

b What percentage of all the birds Ravi saw were sparrows?

c This spring Ravi carried out a second survey. This time he saw:

the same number of pigeons

25% fewer crows

60% more seagulls

two thirds of the number of sparrows.

Copy and complete the line below to show the ratios for the second survey.

Pigeons	:	Crows	:	Seagulls	:	Sparrows
1	:	………	:	………	:	………

4 *Year 7 Optional Test level 6*

The arrow on the speedometer of my car turns through 90° when the speed increases from 20 mph to 70 mph.

Through how many degrees does the arrow turn when the speed increases from 30 mph to 50 mph?

Show your working.

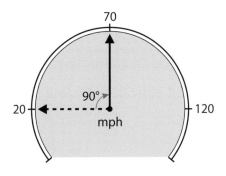

5 *1996 level 6*

a What is the volume of this standard size box of salt?

b What is the volume of a special offer box of salt that is 20% bigger?

c The standard size box contains enough salt to fill up 10 identical salt pots.

How many salt pots may be filled up from the special offer box of salt?

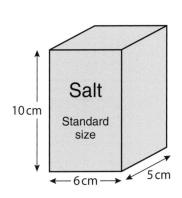

6 *2001 level 6*

a The label on yoghurt A shows this information.

How many grams of protein does 100 g of yoghurt provide?

Show your working.

Yoghurt A	**125 g**
Each 125 g provides	
Energy	430 kJ
Protein	4.5 g
Carbohydrate	11.1 g
Fat	4.5 g

b The label on yoghurt B shows different information.

A boy eats the same amount of yoghurt A and yoghurt B.

Which yoghurt provides him with more carbohydrate?

Show your working.

Yoghurt B	**150 g**
Each 150 g provides	
Energy	339 kJ
Protein	6.6 g
Carbohydrate	13.1 g
Fat	0.2 g

7 *2000 level 6*

Shortcrust pastry is made using flour, margarine and lard in the ratio

8 : 3 : 2 by weight.

How many grams of margarine and lard are needed to mix with 200 grams of flour?

Extension problem

8 *2006 level 7*

The diagram shows a shaded rectangle.

It is divided into four smaller rectangles, labelled A, B, C and D.

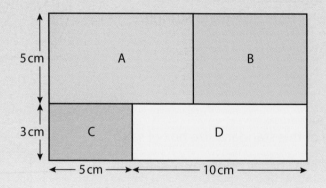

Not drawn accurately

The ratio of area C to area B is 1 : 2. Calculate area A.

Points to remember

⊙ A ratio compares two quantities in the same units,
e.g. 50p : £1 is 1 : 2, 200 : 50 = 4 : 1.

⊙ Two sets of numbers are **directly proportional** if the ratio of
corresponding pairs is always the same.

⊙ Pairs of numbers that are directly proportional lie on a straight-line graph.

⊙ When you solve direct proportion problems you can:
  – use equivalent ratios and a scaling method;
  – use the unitary method to reduce the value of one of the variables to 1.

2 Solving number problems

This lesson will remind you how to solve number problems in different contexts, present and explain
your methods and solutions and check your results.

ⓘ Did you know that...?

Problem solving has always been at the heart
of mathematics.

The oldest mathematical text in the world
discovered so far is the **Moscow papyrus**. It is a
tattered Ancient Egyptian scroll, housed in the
Pushkin Museum of Fine Arts in Moscow, and
has been dated as about 1850 BC.

It consists mainly of what are today called
'word problems' or 'story problems', which were
apparently intended as entertainment.

Pushkin Museum of Fine Arts, Moscow

Exercise 2A

① *2001 level 6*

The population of the world is approximately 6200 million people.
It is increasing by approximately 93 million people each year.

Rob says: 'An increase of 93 million people each year is more than 170 people
each minute.'

Show that he is correct.

② 1998 *level 6*

The table shows the land area of each continent.

a Which continent is approximately 12% of the world's land area?

b What percentage of the world's land area is Antarctica?

Show your working.

c About 30% of the world's area is land.
The amount of land is about 150 million km².
The rest of the land is water.

Work out the approximate total area (land and water) of the world.

Show your working.

Continent	Land area (in 1000 km²)
Africa	30 264
Antarctica	13 209
Asia	44 250
Europe	9 907
North America	24 398
Oceania	8 534
South America	17 793
World	148 355

③ 1996 *level 6*

Emlyn has found some data about the population of the regions of the world in 1950 and 1990.

a In 1950, what percentage of the world's population lived in Asia?

Show each step in your working.

b In 1990, for every person who lived in North America how many people lived in Asia?

Show your working.

Regions of the world	Population (in millions) in 1950	Population (in millions) in 1990
Africa	222	642
Asia	1558	3402
Europe	393	498
Latin America	166	448
North America	166	276
Oceania	13	26
World	2518	5292

c For every person who lived in Africa in 1950 how many people lived in Africa in 1990?

Show your working

d Emlyn thinks that from 1950 to 1990 the population of Oceania went up by 100%.
Is Emlyn right? Write **Yes** or **No** or **Cannot tell**.
Explain your answer.

4 *1999 level 6*

A report on the number of police officers in 1995 said:

'There were 119 000 police officers.
Almost 15% of them were women.'

The percentage was rounded to the nearest
whole number, 15.

a Which of these is the smallest value the percentage
could have been, to one decimal place?

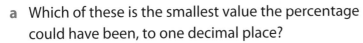

14.1%   14.2%   14.3%   14.4%   14.5%   14.6%   14.7%   14.8%   14.9%

b What is the smallest number of women police officers that there might have been in
1995?

Use your answer to part **a** to help you. Show your working.

c A different report gives exact figures:

Number of women police officers	
1988	12 540
1995	17 468

Calculate the percentage increase in the number of women police officers from 1988 to
1995. Show your working.

d The table below shows the percentage of police officers in 1995 and 1996 who were
women.

1995	14.7%
1996	14.6%

Use the information in the table to decide which one of the three statements below is the
true statement.

⦿ In 1996 there were more women police officers than in 1995.

⦿ In 1996 there were fewer women police officers than in 1995.

⦿ There is not enough information to tell.

Explain your answer.

1 *2002 level 5*

Here are five number cards. A and B stand for two **different** whole numbers.

The sum of all the numbers on all five cards is 30.

What could be the values of A and B?

2 *2002 level 6*

Paulo makes a sequence of numbers.
He chooses a starting number and then subtracts equal amounts each time.

The third number in his sequence is 45. The tenth number is −32.

What is the first number in the sequence?

3 *2003 level 6*

Here are six number cards.

| 1 | 2 | 3 | 4 | 5 | 6 |

a Arrange the six cards to make the calculations below. The first one is done for you.

939 = | 4 | 2 | 3 | + | 5 | 1 | 6 |

1164 = | | | | + | | | |

750 = | | | | + | | | |

b Now arrange the six cards to make a difference of 115.

115 = | | | | − | | | |

4 *1997 level 6*

Look at these number cards.

| +3 | 0 | −5 | +9 |

| +2 | −8 | +7 | −2 |

a Choose a card to give the answer 4.
Write the equation.

$$\boxed{+2} + \boxed{-5} + \boxed{} = 4$$

b Choose a card to give the lowest possible answer.
Write the equation, including the answer.

$$\boxed{-2} + \boxed{} =$$

c Choose a card to give the lowest possible answer.
Write the equation, including the answer.

$$\boxed{-2} - \boxed{} =$$

d Now choose a card to give the highest possible answer.
Write the equation, including the answer.

$$\boxed{-2} - \boxed{} =$$

5 *2004 level 6*

> There are **20 questions** in a quiz.
>
> A correct answer scores **2 points**. An **incorrect** answer **loses 1 point**.
> A question not answered scores 0 points. A negative total is possible.

a What are the maximum and minimum points you could get on the quiz?

b A pupil answers 10 of the 20 questions. 8 are correct.
How many points does he score?

c Copy and complete the table to show three different ways to score 24 points.

Number of correct answers	Number of incorrect answers	Number of questions not answered
12	0	8

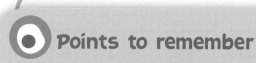

Points to remember

When you are solving problems:

- read the problem and identify key information;
- write down the calculation that you need to do;
- choose a suitable calculation method and, if you use a written method, show your working;
- check your answer for accuracy and make sure that it fits the question.

3 Expressions, equations and formulae

This lesson will remind you how to manipulate expressions, use formulae and solve equations.

Exercise 3

Algebra can be used to help with calculations that you have to make again and again.

First you decide what letter you are going to use and then you make a formula.

Example 1

An exercise book costs x pence and a pencil costs y pence.
How much will 7 exercise books and 8 pencils cost?

The total cost will be $7x + 8y$.

When you write an equation or formula with one letter on the left-hand side like this: $a = b + 5$, then a is called the 'subject' of the equation.

You can rearrange the equation to make a different letter the subject of the equation.

Example 2

Make b the subject of the equation $a = b + 5$.

Subtract 5 from both sides: $a - 5 = b$

Turn the equation around: $b = a - 5$

Example 3

Make b the subject of the equation $a = 5(b + c)$.

First multiply out the brackets: $\qquad\qquad\qquad a = 5b + 5c$

Next, subtract $5c$ from both sides: $\qquad a - 5c = 5b$

Next, divide both sides by 5: $\qquad\qquad \dfrac{a - 5c}{5} = b$

You can solve simple problems with unknown quantities by using letters and setting up equations.

Example 4

Two numbers multiply together to make 24. They add together to make 10. What are the numbers?

Let one number be a and the other b.

$ab = 24$ and $a + b = 10$

Try the different factor pairs of 24 until you find a pair that satisfies both equations:

$a = 6$ and $b = 4$

① *2006 level 5*

A ruler costs k pence.

A pen costs m pence.

Write an expression for each of these for the correct amount in pence.

a   The total cost of 5 rulers.

b   The total cost of 5 rulers and 5 pens.

c   How much more 5 pens cost than 5 rulers.

d   The change from £5, in pence, when you buy 5 pens.

② *2004 level 6*

Make the letter in brackets the subject of the formula.

a $q = p + 4$ $\qquad (p)$

b $s = 4r$ $\qquad\quad (r)$

c $4k = m - 3$ $\quad (m)$

③ *2006 level 6*

Multiply out this expression. Write your answer as simply as possible.

$5(x + 2) + 3(7 + x)$

2006 level 6

The graph below shows information about the diameters and heights of a sample of three types of tomato.

The dotted lines on the graph can be used to decide which type of tomato each point is likely to represent.

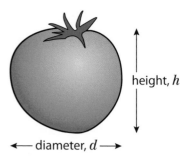

height, h

← diameter, d →

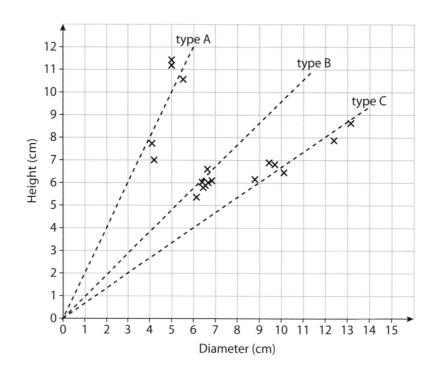

a   The diameter of a tomato of type C is 11 cm.

What would you expect its height to be?

b   The diameter of a different tomato is 3.2 cm. Its height is 5.8 cm.

Which of the three types of tomato is it most likely to be?
Explain your answer.

c   Which type of tomato is most nearly spherical in shape?
Explain your answer.

d   You can find the approximate volume of a tomato by using this formula:

$$V = \tfrac{1}{6}\pi d^2 h$$

V is the volume

d is the diameter

h is the height

If the diameter and the height of a tomato are both 3.5 cm, what is the approximate volume of this tomato?

5 *2005 level 6 and 2000 level 6*

Write each expression in its simplest form.

a $9 - 3k + 5k$

b $k^2 + 2k + 4k$

c $(3d + 5) + (d - 2)$

d $3m - (-m)$

6 *2000 level 6*

a Two numbers multiply together to make -15.

They add together to make 2.

What are the two numbers?

b Two numbers multiply together to make -15.

They add together to make -2.

What are the two numbers?

c Two numbers multiply together to make 8.

They add together to make -6.

What are the two numbers?

d The square of 5 is 25.

The square of another number is also 25.

What is that other number?

Extension problem

7 *2002 level 7*

a The subject of the equation below is p.

$p = 2(e + f)$

Rearrange the equation to make e the subject.

b Rearrange the equation below to make d the subject.

$r = \frac{1}{2}(c - d)$

Show your working.

Points to remember

⊙ When you use algebra to solve problems, first decide what letters you are going to use and then set up an equation or formula.

⊙ When a formula is written as $y = \ldots$, y is the subject of the formula.

⊙ You can rearrange a formula to make another letter the subject.

⊙ When you rearrange a formula or equation, you must do the same thing to both sides.

4 Circles and enlargements

This lesson will remind you how to find the circumference and area of a circle and how to enlarge 2D shapes.

Exercise 4A

This triangle can help you to use the formula for the circumference of a circle:

circumference of a circle = $\pi \times$ diameter

Cover up C to give: $C = \pi \times d$

Cover up π to give: $\pi = C \div d$

Cover up d to give $d = C \div \pi$

The **formula for the area of a circle** is:

area of circle = $\pi \times$ (radius)^2

Example 1

Calculate the circumference of a circle diameter 5 mm.
Write your answer to one decimal place.

Circumference = $\pi \times$ diameter

Circumference = $\pi \times 5 = 15.70796\ldots$ mm

Circumference = 15.7 mm to 1 d.p.

Example 2

Using 3 as an approximation for π, find the area of a circle with diameter 14 m.

Diameter = 14 m, so the radius is $14 \div 2 = 7$ m

Area = $\pi \times$ (radius)^2

Area = $3 \times 7^2 = 3 \times 49 = 147$ m^2

Example 3

A model car is built to a scale of 1 : 32.

The model car is 48 mm wide.

How wide is the real car?

A scale of 1 : 32 means that for every
1 unit of length on the model there
are 32 units of length on the real car.

This is the same as an enlargement with scale factor 32.

The model is 48 mm wide so the real car is 48 × 32 = 1536 mm wide.

Example 4

Two towns are 37 cm apart on a map. The scale of the map is 2 cm to 5 km.

What is the actual distance between the two towns?

Every 2 cm on the map represents 5 km on the ground.

Every 1 cm represents 5 ÷ 2 = 2.5 km.

So 37 cm represents 37 × 2.5 = 92.5 km.

The actual distance between the two towns is 92.5 km.

Example 5

Enlarge this shape by a scale factor of 3.

The centre of enlargement is marked with a dot.

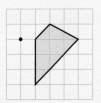

All the points on the enlarged shape must be three
times further from the centre of enlargement than the
corresponding point in the original shape.

All the lengths of the enlarged shape are three times
bigger than the corresponding lengths of the original
shape but all the angles remain the same.

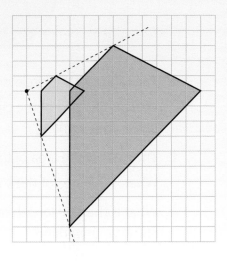

① *2005 Mental Test level 6*

A circle has a radius of 6 centimetres.

Give an approximate value for the circumference of the circle.

② *2003 Mental Test level 6*

Using 3 as an approximation for π, what is the area of a circle with radius 5 cm?

③ *1999 level 6*

a A circle has a radius of 15 cm.

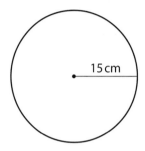

15 cm

Calculate the area of the circle. Show your working.

b A different circle has a circumference of 120 cm.

What is the radius of the circle? Show your working.

④ *2000 level 6*

The diagram shows a circle and a square.

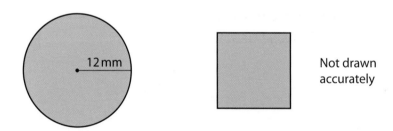

12 mm

Not drawn
accurately

a The radius of the circle is 12 mm.

What is the area of the circle to the nearest mm²?
Show your working.

b The ratio of the area of the circle to the area of the square is 2 : 1.

What is the area of the square to the nearest mm²?

c What is the side length of the square?
Show your working.

You will need squared paper.

1 *2003 Mental Test level 5*

The scale on my map is 4 cm to 1 km.

On the map the distance to the rail station is 20 cm.

How many kilometres is it to the rail station?

2 *2006 Mental Test level 6*

This rectangle has been enlarged by a scale factor of 2.

Write down the dimensions of the rectangle before the enlargement.

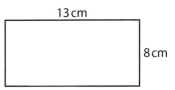

13 cm

8 cm

3 *2006 level 6*

Look at the square grids.

Each diagram shows an enlargement of scale factor 2.

The centre of this enlargement is marked with a cross.

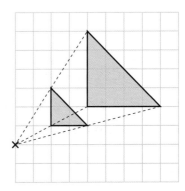

Where is the centre of enlargement in these diagrams?

Copy each diagram on squared paper.
Mark each centre of enlargement with a cross.

a

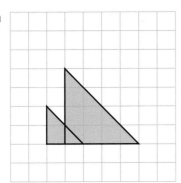

b

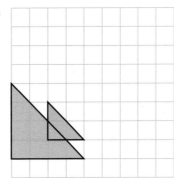

4 *2002 level 6*

The grid shows an arrow.

Copy the grid on squared paper.
Draw an enlargement of scale factor 2 of the arrow.
Use point C as the centre of enlargement.

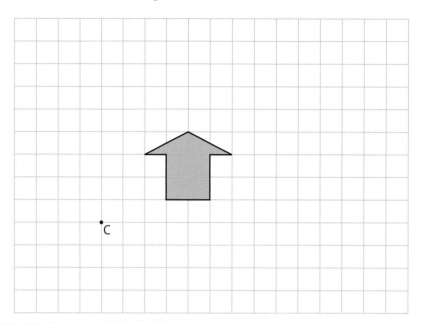

5 *Year 8 Optional Test level 6*

The grid shows two L-shapes.
The bigger L-shape is an enlargement of the smaller L-shape.

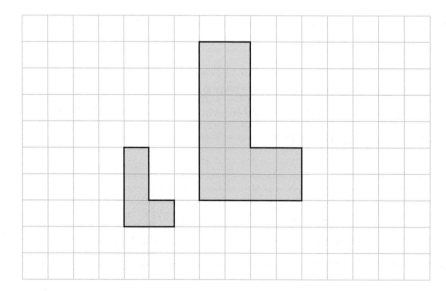

a What is the scale factor of the enlargement?

b Copy the grid on squared paper.

Show where the centre of enlargement is by marking the correct place with a cross.

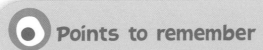

Points to remember

- This triangle can help you to work out the circumference (C) or diameter (d) of a circle.
- The area of a circle $= \pi \times$ (radius)^2.
- When a shape is enlarged:
  - each length is multiplied by the scale factor;
  - the area is multiplied by (scale factor)^2;
  - angles remain the same.

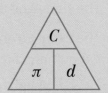

5 Probability

This lesson will remind you how to identify mutually exclusive outcomes, know that the sum of their probabilities is 1, and list all the outcomes for two successive events.

Exercise 5A

When outcomes are equally likely, the **theoretical probability** of an event is:

$$\frac{\text{number of favourable outcomes}}{\text{total number of possible outcomes}}$$

When outcomes are not equally likely, the **experimental probability** of an event is:

$$\frac{\text{number of successful trials}}{\text{total number of trials}}$$

Theoretical and experimental probabilities are closer when the number of trials is large.

Example 1

Seema does an experiment on this fair spinner.
She spins the arrow on this spinner 200 times.

Her results are shown in this table.

Number	1	2	3	4
Frequency	46	48	49	57

The **theoretical probability** of the arrow landing on each number is $\frac{1}{4}$ or 0.25.

The **experimental probabilities** from Seema's experiment are shown in this table.

Number	1	2	3	4
Seema's experiment	$\frac{46}{200} = 0.23$	$\frac{48}{200} = 0.24$	$\frac{49}{20} = 0.245$	$\frac{57}{200} = 0.285$

Seema's experimental probabilities are close to the theoretical probability.

Events that cannot occur at the same time are called **mutually exclusive.**

The sum of all the mutually exclusive outcomes of an experiment is 1.

The events A and **not** A are mutually exclusive and include all the outcomes in an experiment. So:

probability of A + probability of **not** A = 1

If A and B are mutually exclusive events

probability of A **or** B = probability of A + probability of B

Example 2

The arrow on the spinner on the right is spun.

The numbers obtained are added to give a score.

This table shows all the possible outcomes.

+	1	2	3	4
1	2	3	4	5
2	3	4	5	6
3	4	5	6	7
4	5	6	7	8

The probability of each score is shown in this table.

Score	2	3	4	5	6	7	8
Probability	$\frac{1}{16}$	$\frac{2}{16}$	$\frac{3}{16}$	$\frac{4}{16}$	$\frac{3}{16}$	$\frac{2}{16}$	$\frac{1}{16}$

① A counter is taken at random from a bag.
The table shows the number of different coloured counters in the bag.

Colour	Red	Blue	Green	White
Number	7	5	9	4

a What is the probability that the counter will be green?

b What is the probability that the counter will be blue **or** green?

c What is the probability that the counter is not white?

② Tom and Angie are doing an experiment to test whether or not a dice is fair.

In his experiment Tom rolls the dice for 60 trials and records the scores.
In her experiment Angie rolls the dice for 300 trials and records the scores.

a Tom says: 'I think that my results show that the dice is biased.'

Copy and complete this table to show a possible set of results for Tom's experiment.

Score	1	2	3	4	5	6
Frequency						

b Angie says: 'From my results the dice is fair.'

Copy and complete this table to show a possible set of results for Angie's experiment.

Score	1	2	3	4	5	6
Frequency						

c Whose conclusion is more likely to be reliable? Give a reason for your answer.

③ Ajit has two sets of cards, set A and set B.

Ajit picks a card at random from set A.
He then picks a card at random from set B.

Set A   Set B

Ajit adds the numbers on the cards to get a score.

a Make a table showing all the possible scores.

b What is the probability that the score is an even number?

c What is the probability that the score is **not** an even number?

④ A ball is picked at random from a bag containing different coloured balls.
The table shows the probabilities of picking different colours.

Colour	Red	Blue	Green	White
Number	0.4	0.2	0.3	0.1

a Explain how you know that there are only red, blue, green and white balls in the bag.

b Work out the probability of picking a red or white ball from the bag.

c There are a total of 20 balls in the bag. How many of each colour are there?

1 *Year 8 Optional Test level 6*

Anita is going to play a game.

> The probability that she will win the game is 0.7.

Is she more likely to win the game or lose the game? Explain how you know.

2 *2001 level 6*

There are some cubes in a bag. The cubes are either red (R) or black (B).

The teacher says:

> If you take a cube at random out of the bag, the
> probability that it will be red is $\frac{1}{5}$.

a What is the probability that the cube will be black?

b A pupil takes one cube out of the bag. It is red.
What is the smallest number of black cubes there
could be in the bag?

c Then the pupil takes another cube out of the bag.
It is also red.

From this new information, what is the smallest number
of black cubes there could be in the bag?

d A different bag has blue (B), green (G) and yellow (Y) cubes in it.
There is at least one of each of the three colours.

The teacher says:

> If you take a cube at random out of the bag, the
> probability that it will be green is $\frac{3}{5}$.

There are 20 cubes in the bag.

What is the greatest number of yellow cubes there could be in the bag?
Show your working.

(3) *1998 level 6*

I have two fair dice.
Each of the dice is numbered 1 to 6.

a The probability that I will throw double 6 (both dice showing number 6) is $\frac{1}{36}$.

What is the probability that I will not throw double 6?

b I throw both dice and get double 6.

Then I throw the dice again.

Is the probability that I will throw double 6 this time less than $\frac{1}{36}$, $\frac{1}{36}$ or more than $\frac{1}{36}$?

Explain your answer.

c I start again and throw both dice.

What is the probability that I will throw double 3 (both dice showing 3)?

d What is the probability that I will throw a double?

(It could be double 1 or double 2 or any other double.)

(4) *2005 level 6*

A spinner has the numbers 1 to 4 on it.

> The probability of spinning a number 4 is 0.1.
>
> The probability of spinning a number 1 is 0.6.
>
> The probability of spinning a number 2 is the same as the probability of spinning a number 3.

a Calculate the probability of spinning the number 3.

b Calculate the probability of not spinning the number 3.

c Calculate the probability of spinning the numbers 3 or 4.

This dice with four faces has one blue, one green, one red and one yellow face.

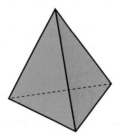

Five pupils did an experiment to investigate whether the dice was biased or not.

The data they collected is shown in this table.

Pupil's name	Number of throws	Face landed on			
		Red	Blue	Green	Yellow
Peter	20	9	7	2	2
Caryl	60	23	20	8	9
Shana	250	85	90	36	39
Keith	40	15	15	6	4
Paul	150	47	54	23	26

a   Which pupil's data is most likely to give the best estimate of the probability of getting each colour on the dice?

Explain your answer.

The pupils collected all the data together.

Number of throws	Face landed on			
	Red	Blue	Green	Yellow
520	179	186	75	80

b   Consider the data.

Write whether you think the dice is biased or unbiased, and explain your answer.

c   From the data work out the probability of the dice landing on the blue face.

d   From the data work out the probability of the dice landing on the green face.

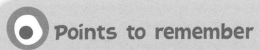 Points to remember

- For equally likely outcomes, the **theoretical probability** of an event is:

$$\frac{\text{number of favourable outcomes}}{\text{total number of possible outcomes}}$$

- When two events occur at the same time or one after the other, you can record the equally likely outcomes in a list or table.

- When events A and B are **mutually exclusive**:
  - the probability of **not** A = 1 − probability of A;
  - probability of A **or** B = probability of A + probability of B.

- The **experimental probability** of an event is:

$$\frac{\text{number of successful trials}}{\text{total number of trials}}$$

- Experimental probability tends to get closer in value to theoretical probability as the number of trials increases.

Answers to
How well are you doing?

N5.1

1. a. $3^2, 2^4, 5^2, 3^3$ or 9, 16, 25, 27
   b. $5^7 = 5^5 \times 5^2 = 3125 \times 25 = 78\,125$
2. a. $3^4 = 81$ is the largest. $3^4 = 9^2$
   b. 2^5 and 2^7 are not square numbers.
3. a. $3^2 = 9$ b. $2^7 = 128$
   c. $3^2 \times 2 = 18$
4. a. $a = 3$ b. $b = 2$
5. a. HCF is 12   b. LCM is 144
6. Suzy's number is 4.9.
7. $5 \times 11 \times 19 = 1045$

A5.1

1. $T_n = 2n + 3$
2. a. $4n + 2$
   b. $3n + 3$
   c. $10n - 6$
3. $T_n = 5n + 3$
4. a. $y = 4 - n\sqrt{b}$
   b. Gradient -1, intercept $(0, 6)$
5. a. $x = 8$ b. $y = x + 7$
   c. $y = x - 1$
6. a.

Age (months)	Height at start (cm)	Height at end (cm)	Growth (cm)
12 to 24	74	86	12
24 to 36	86	**about 94**	**8**
36 to 48	**about 94**	**about 102**	**8**

   b. 198 cm

G5.1

1. a. 2.5 cm   b. 10 cm
   c. Pupils' answers
      e.g. $a = 6, b = 4, h = 2$
2. a. 706.9 cm² (to 1 d.p.)
   b. 19.1 cm (to 1 d.p.)

3. a. 452 mm²   b. 226 mm²
   c. 15 mm
4. a. 188.5 cm   b. 5.8 times
5. 64
6. a. Surface area of A: 38 sq. units
      Surface area of B: 32 sq. units
   b. Volume of A: 12 cubic units
      Volume of B: 12 cubic units

N5.2

1. 9 oranges
2. a. £2.45   b. 600 grams
3. $\frac{7}{16}$
4. a. 2   b. 6
5. 5519 miles to the nearest mile
6. 223 grams
7. a. 3.6 g   b. Yoghurt A

S5.1

1. a. Before the bumps, the maximum speed was **46** mph, and **12** cars went at more than 30 mph.
      After the bumps, the maximum speed was **35** mph, and **3** cars went at more than 30 mph.
   b. Before the bumps median = 38 mph
      After the bumps median = 28 mph
      $38 - 28 = 10$ mph
2. a. For example, 'Bumps will slow down traffic.'
   b. The average speed after the bumps is reduced.
   c. The speeds are more consistent after the bumps.
   d. True
3. a. 'There are more boys than girls' — False; there are 30 boys and 28 girls.
      'The modal class for girls is the same as the modal class for boys' — True; the modal class is 131-140 for girls and boys.
   b. Yes, because the height of the tallest girl is between 161 and 170 cm, whereas the height of the tallest boy is between 151 and 160 cm.

A5.2

1. $3(2a + 1) = 6a + 3$

2. $8x + 31$

3. 7.48 (to 2 d.p.)

4. a. $k = 2$ b. $y = \frac{1}{2}$ c. $y = 1\frac{5}{6}$

5. a. $b = a - 4$
   $d = \frac{c}{4}$
   $m = 4k + 3$
   b. $2 + t = \frac{w}{5}$
   $t = \frac{w}{5} - 2$

6. $y = 7.3$

G5.2

1. a. A, B, C, D

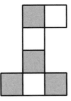

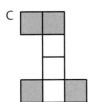

b. c.

2. 5 cm

3. a. 10.625 cm² b. 37.1875 cm³

4. 34°

5. a. 360 ÷ 5 b. 28°

N5.3

1. 0.001

2. 300 000 litres

3. 9

4. 100

5. 1.84 m

6. 120.33

7. a. 4410 b. 2.5

8. a. Films of 24 photos would cost £56.10
   Films of 36 photos would cost £61.40
   The films of 24 photos are cheaper.
   b. £5.30

9. a. 3.1416 b. D

S5.2

1. a.

Colour of counters	Number of counters	Probability
Red	6	$\frac{2}{5}$
Blue	3	$\frac{1}{5}$
Green	6	$\frac{2}{5}$

b. B

2. a. 30%, $\frac{3}{10}$, $\frac{6}{20}$, 0.3
   b. $\frac{9}{20}$ and 45%

3. a.

	1	2	3	4	5
6	7	8	9	10	11
7	8	9	10	11	12
8	9	10	11	12	13
9	10	11	12	13	14
10	11	12	13	14	15

b. 9

c. $\frac{1}{5}$

d. For example, scoring a 1 and a 6, or a 5 and a 10.

e. Scoring below 11 and scoring 11 or above.

A5.3

1. Yes. $25 \times 3 = 75$

2. Pupils' graphs

3. Gradient 4, intercept (0, 7)

4. a. B and D
   b. B and A
   c. C and D

5. a. C and E b. $y = x + 2$

6. Yes

G5.3

1. a. 7 b. 4
   c. 2 d. 4

2.

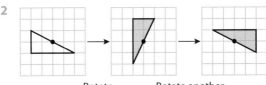

Rotate 90° clockwise   Rotate another 90° clockwise

3 a

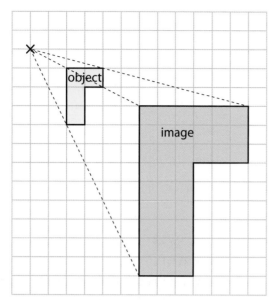

b 3   **c** 4 square units

d 36 square units   **e** 9

4

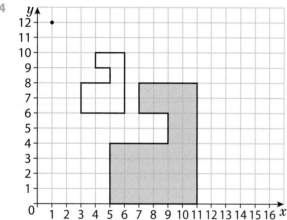

5 a

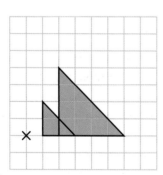

b

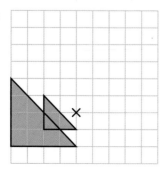

6 34 000 cm or 340 m

7 a 167°   **b** 350 km

c

A5.4

1 a Area = $15ab$

Perimeter = $6a + 10b$

b Length $4a$, width $3a$

2 a 98

b $T = 2R - 2$

3 a $n^2 - 1$ **b** 82

c

First number in row n	$n^2 - 2n + 2$
Second number in row n	$n^2 - 2n + 3$

4 5 cm

S5.3

1 For example:

How many brothers have you got? Include step- and half-brothers if they usually live in the same house as you.

How many sisters have you got? Include step- and half-sisters if they usually live in the same house as you.

2 a The bean germinated.

b 12.5 cm

c The bean plant germinated on day 4 and grew rapidly. Some days it grew faster than others and grew more slowly between days 8 and 11.

d We can't tell because the graph stops at day 14.

3 a Games A and B: positive relationship

    Games A and C: no relationship

  b Games B and C: no relationship

  c 65

  d 30 and 50

G5.4

1 a 7   b $1080°$ (6×180 or $8 \times 180 - 360$)

2 a $40°$ b $170°$

3 Accurately drawn rhombus with sides of 6 cm, and one pair of opposite angles of $58°$ and another pair of opposite angles of $122°$

4 Angle a is $110°$ ($\angle$s on straight line sum to $180°$)

  Angle b is $70°$ (corresponding $\angle$s)

  Angle c is $50°$ ($\angle$s in triangle sum to $180°$)

  Angle d is $130°$ ($\angle$s in quadrilateral sum to $360°$)

5 a The external angle of a pentagon is $360° \div 5 = 72°$. The internal angle and external angle lie on a straight line so they sum to $180°$. So the internal angle is $180 - 72 = 108°$.

  b Angle b is $180 - (72 + 72) = 180 - 144 = 36°$ ($\angle$s in a triangle)

6 The scale drawing should look similar to this.

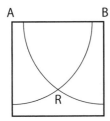

Each side of the square should be 8 cm.

The arcs should be drawn with radius 7 cm, centres A and B.

A5.5

1 $4(5x - 7)$

2 $n = 0.5$ or $\frac{1}{2}$

3 $t = \frac{w}{5} - 2$

4 a No. The line goes through $(-100, -97)$.

  b $y = x + 3$

5 11

6 $k = 15$

7 Graph 1 matches container C

  Graph 2 matches container A

  Graph 3 matches container E

S5.4

1 a $\frac{5}{9}$

  b $\frac{3}{9} = \frac{1}{3}$

  c

Karen

×	2	3	4
2	4	6	8
3	6	9	12
4	8	12	16

Huw

  d The probability that their answer is a number that is less than 16 is $\frac{8}{9}$.

    The probability that their answer is a number that is less than 4 is zero.

2 Yes, this is a fair game.

  P(odd number) = 0.6. 0.6×2 points = 1.2

  P(even number) = 0.4. 0.4×3 points = 1.2

3 0.2

4 a 0.01

  b 0.35

N5.4

1 No. Amit is not correct.

  1, 3 and 5 are odd numbers, and their sum is 9, which is odd, not even. This is a counter-example. So the sum of three odd numbers cannot always be even.

2 Liam's number is 15.

3 e.g. $0.5 \times 0.2 = 0.1$

4 a $2 \times 0.5 = 1$, which is less than 2

  b $2 - (-3) = 5$, which is more than 2

  c No. For example, $(0.2)^2 = 0.04$, which is less than 0.2. This counter-example shows that the statement is not correct.

5 The maximum number of digits is from 999×99, which is just less than $1000 \times 100 = 100\,000$, so it has five digits.

  The minimum number of digits is four digits from $100 \times 10 = 1000$.

6 11

Index

continuous data 79, 83, 87, 90, 93, 345

conversion 33, 51, 69

conversion graph 27

coordinate axes 20

coordinates 19–20, 172, 176, 181, 272

correlation 227–30, 239

corresponding angles 116–17, 121, 195–6, 202, 254–5, 257, 341

cost 54–5, 143, 151, 178, 280

counter-examples 316, 323, 325–7

cross-number puzzle 2, 321

cross-section 45–7, 49–50, 128, 133, 151, 188, 190, 208

cube root 5

cube-root key 3

cubes 3, 49, 52, 58, 123, 125, 127–9, 134, 158, 163, 169, 188, 190, 204, 281, 321–2, 372

cubic units 47, 50, 129, 131

cuboids 45–50, 53, 102–3, 108–9, 127, 129, 131–5, 190, 204, 206, 219, 315

currency 71

curves 184, 284–6

cylinder 275

data 224, 229–35, 300, 335, 345, 349, 374

data collection 83–7

data-handling cycle 75

De Moivre, Abraham 155

decagon 120, 190, 247–8, 251, 256

Decimal game 144

decimals 145, 147, 150, 153, 275, 327, 330

degrees 100, 350, 353

denominator 56–60, 276, 278

depreciation 54–5

Descartes, Rene 20, 227, 272

diagrams 211, 218, 233, 256, 345

diameter 37–41, 43–4, 52, 138–9, 150–2, 259, 362, 364, 369

dice 160, 164, 166–7, 300–1, 306–7, 310, 315, 371, 373–4

dimensions 122, 132, 200, 204–6, 218, 221, 367

direct proportion 56, 69, 72–3, 177, 180, 351, 355

discrete data 79, 87, 90, 93

distance 39, 41, 83, 99, 102, 139, 141, 151, 180, 199–200, 210, 212, 268, 290, 324, 365, 367

distance-time graph 289, 292

division 6

divisor 146–7

dollar 71

Egyptians 37, 56, 214, 276

elevations 114, 122–6, 134

enlargement 187, 195–9, 201, 203–4, 206–9, 364–5, 367–8

equal probabilities 169

equally likely outcomes 157–60, 168

equals sign 24, 338–9

equations 4–5, 10, 21–31, 95, 104–8, 111, 171–4, 176, 180–2, 185–6, 211, 213–15, 272, 276–86, 293–4, 296–7, 323, 326, 336, 338–40, 359–60, 363

equilateral triangle 190, 205, 208, 255, 257

equivalent 62

estimated probabilities 300

estimation 4, 33, 80, 82, 88–9, 91, 137, 150–1, 153, 178, 291, 302, 304, 310, 329, 374

Euclid 6, 65, 107, 242

Euler, Leonhard 101–3

evaluation 82, 235

even numbers 14, 156, 166, 315, 326–7, 371

events 155–6, 159–61, 164–5, 305–7, 309, 311, 314, 369–70

evidence 81

exchange rate 71

experiment 167–8, 300, 304–5, 308, 314, 370–1

experimental probability 155, 163–8, 301, 304, 309–11, 314, 369, 375

expressions 2, 4, 10, 13, 31, 95–6, 131, 147–8, 218–19, 273–5, 277–8, 282, 293–4, 336–8, 360, 363

exterior angles 117, 242–50, 252–3, 256, 270, 344

factorise expressions 97–8, 272–5, 296

factors 97, 324, 361

Fahrenheit 100

Fahrenheit, Gabriel Daniel 100

fairness 213

Farr, William 224

Fibonacci 316

finite 14

foreign exchange 71

formula 11, 13–17, 19–20, 30, 32–3, 40, 45–7, 50–1, 95, 99–104, 110, 132, 148, 177, 211–15, 218, 272, 274–5, 279–81, 299, 331, 336, 360, 362–4

fraction equivalent 58

fraction key 329–31

fractions 56–62, 66, 68, 73, 169, 275–8, 319–21, 330, 332, 335

frequency 167, 345, 350

frequency diagrams 75, 164, 345–6

Frogs and toads puzzle 216–17

Published and distributed by Pearson Education Limited, Edinburgh Gate, Harlow, Essex, CM20 2JE, England
www.longman.co.uk

First published 2008
ISBN-13 978-1-405-84418-5

Freelance development editor: Sue Glover

Typeset by Tech-Set, Gateshead

Printed and bound in Great Britain at Scotprint, Haddington

The publisher's policy is to use paper manufactured from sustainable forests.

Picture Credits

The publisher would like to thank the following for their kind permission to reproduce their photographs:
(Key: b-bottom; c-centre; l-left; r-right; t-top)

www.dreamstime.com: 298; akg-images Ltd: 101b, 227; **Alamy Images:** Alex Segre 112, 234l; Andrew Holt 233; Bill Bachman 113b; Colin Palmer Photography 78; Corbis 288; Dennis Hallinan 287; Andrew Fox 62r, 257; Jeff Greenberg 170; Jim West 16; Kari Marttila 5b; Kuttig - People 73; Libby Welch 60l; Paul Doyle 177; Petr Svarc 194r; Photofusion Picture Library 87; Robert Harding Picture Library Ltd 56, 199l; Ron Buskirk 279; Travelshots.com 18tr; Wayne Linden 83; Wildscape 109; **Alex Gough:** 129, 131; **Amy Vander Veer:** 242; **Art Directors and TRIP photo Library:** 34; **Bibliothèque nationale de France:** Miniature of Nicole Oresmes Traité de l'espere, Bibliothèque Nationale, Paris, France, fonds français 565, fol. 1r. 20; **Bridgeman Art Library Ltd:** Or.Ms.27 Tahir Uqlidus (ink on paper), Nasir al-Din al-Tusi / Edinburgh University Library, Scotland, With kind permission of the University of Edinburgh 107; Rhind Mathematical Papyrus, treatise claiming to be a copy of a 12th dynasty work, Thebes, Hyksos period, 15th dynasty, c.1550 BC (papyrus) (see also 116092), Egyptian, Second Intermediate Period (c.1750-c.1650 BC) / British Museum, London, UK, 214r; **Corbis:** 6; Anders Ryman 77; Daniel Hambury / epa 29; Don Mason 222; Jacques Langevin 200r, 200l; Kim Eriksen / zefa 28; Rob Lewine 55; Roy Morsch 205; Rune Hellestad 67; The Art Archive 218l; Tom Stewart 68; Yann Arthus-Bertrand 124; **Courtesy of Trinity College, Cambridge:** 322t; DK Images: 37t, 70b, 156, 283, 305, 355; Cecile Treal and Jean-Michel Ruiz 194l; Clive Streeter and Patrick McLeavy 247l; Andy Crawford 207, 294l; Dave King 5t; John Heseltine 8; Judith Miller / Lyon and Turnbull Ltd. 292; Lin White 276; Matthew Ward 199; Max Alexander 149l; NASA 41t; Rob Reichenfeld 119tr, 247r; Tony Souter 149r; **Mary Evans Picture Library:** 100; **Getty Images:** Duomo Photography Inc. 41b; **www.granger.com:** 300; **iStockphoto:** 24, 46l, 61, 71t, 102, 113t, 146, 212r, 247c, 302c, 331, 365; Adrian Beesley 324; Alberto Pomares 114; Alexander Sakhatovsky 101t; Andrea Reh 91; Andy Watson 74; Bojan Pavlukovic 232l; Bruce Lonngren 282; Christine Balderas 272; David Cannings-Bushell 195r, 195l; David Kneafsey 357; Dawn Hudson 133; Don Bayley 299; Doug Cannell 302l; Eliza Snow 150; Fatih Kilic 295; Florin Tirlea 119br; Frank ven Haalen 253; Geoffrey Hammond 187tr; Gerville Hall 166br; Graeme Purdy 325t; Hedda Gjerpen 333; James Steidl 119bc; Jan Rihak 187bl; Jarek Szymanski 114r; Jim Jurica 76, 220; Kelly Cline 294; Laurie Knight 119bl; Linda Steward 166tr; Lisa F. Young 11; Liz McCorkle 283r; Luke Daniek 71b; Mark Bond 88; Mike Bentley 70t; Mohsen Mohamed Hafez 194c; Niels Quist 213; Paul Vasarhelyi 17; Pavel Losevsky 151; Per Øyvind Mathisen 301; Peter Mlekuž 302r; Petrea Alexandru 199c; Robert Byron 232r; Sam Sefton 231l; Scott Leigh 141; Skip ODonnell 212l; Stefan Klein 65t; Thomas Perkins 303; Tim McCaig 231r; Trista Weibell 39t; **Jupiter Unlimited:** 62, 63; Bananastock 322l, 325b; Brand X Pictures 2; PhotoObjects.net 119tc; Photos.com 44; Polka Dot Images 99; © **British Library Board:** © British Library Board, shelfmark 530.g.37, folio P109v 338; **Nature Picture Library:** Richard Du Toit 114l; **No Trace:** 155; **PA Photos:** 1783686 46r; Paul Sakuma 137; **Pearson Education Ltd:** 160, 166l, 246l, 310; Anita Straker 164; © Ellen B. Senisi 24; Jonathan Longstaffe 190; Pearson Education 58, 221t, 221b; Sue Glover 329; Sue Jennings 183; **Photo Edit Inc:** Bill Aron 72; **Photolibrary.com:** Ron Bill Swartz 138; **PunchStock:** 18tl; Digital Vision 119tl, 235; Photodisc 178; Uppercut 182; **Rex Features:** Alisdair Macdonald 39b; Andre Jenny / Stock Connection 187br; Beverley Goodway 37b; **Science & Society Picture Library:** 65b; **Science Photo Library Ltd:** 316; Victor De Schwanberg 246; **STILL Pictures The Whole Earth Photo Library:** Jochen Tack / Das Fotoarchiv 234r; TopFoto: 224

Cover image: iStockphoto: **Yusuf Anil Akduygu**

All other images © Pearson Education

Picture Research by: Kevin Brown

Acknowledgements

We are grateful to the following for permission to reproduce copyright material:

Cambridgeshire County Council for the graphs "Number of times that the respondent has used an HWRC in the past twelve months (users of household waste recycling centres in the past 12 months)"; "Types of material recycled at HWRO's - prompted unless states (users of household waste recycling centres in the past 12 months)"; "Barriers to using a household waste recycling centre - prompted (non-users of household waste recycling centres in the past 12 months)" and the table "Proportion of households that recycle specified materials or goods, by district (all respondents)" published on www.cambridgeshire.gov.uk, reproduced with permission; Rob J. Hyndman (n.d.) for the data "Number of polio cases in 1970 in the USA"; "Reported monthly cases of measles, New York City 1931-1971"; "Reported monthly cases of mumps, New York City 1931-1971"; and "Reported monthly cases of chickenpox, New York City 1931-1971" *Time Series Data Library*, http://www.robhyndman.info/TSDL. Accessed in 2008; KCP Technologies for screenshots from *Geometer's Sketchpad*. The Geometer's Sketchpad® name and images are used with permission of Key Curriculum Press, 1150 65th Street, Emeryville, CA 94608, 1-800-995-MATH, www.keypress.com/sketchpad; Planet Ark for the graph "the 2004 results of the 'Recycling Olympics' from www.planetark.com, reproduced with permission; and WorldClimate for a table showing the average temperature and average rainfall for each month in Toronto, Canada www.worldclimate.com.

Every effort has been made to trace the copyright holders and we apologise in advance for any unintentional omissions. We would be pleased to insert the appropriate acknowledgement in any subsequent edition of this publication.